D0956086

# DANGEROUS TO MAN

## WILD ANIMALS
### *A Definitive Study of Their Reputed Dangers to Man*

*By the same author:*
ANTARCTICA: LAND OF FROZEN TIME

WILD ANIMALS · *A Definitive Study of Their Reputed Dangers to Man*

# DANGEROUS TO MAN

FULLY ILLUSTRATED AND WITH SEVEN TECHNICAL APPENDICES

*By* ROGER A. CARAS

## CHILTON BOOKS

A DIVISION OF CHILTON COMPANY
*Publishers*
Philadelphia          New York

Copyright © 1964 by Roger A. Caras

First Edition

*All Rights Reserved*

Published in Philadelphia by Chilton Company,
and simultaneously in Toronto, Canada,
by Ambassador Books, Ltd.

Library of Congress Catalog Card Number 64-16521

Designed by William E. Lickfield

Manufactured in the United States of America by
Quinn & Boden Company, Inc., Rahway, N. J.

To whom else could an author dedicate a book entitled "Dangerous to Man," but to his wife?

For Jill . . .

ACKNOWLEDGMENTS

I have endeavored to thank all those who have personally aided me in the preparation of this book. For these acknowledgments, see page 378.

# *Foreword*

It is always a pleasure to know that a book is badly needed and then to hear it will be written. Being asked to assist in its preparation as well, makes the pleasure exquisite.

Roger Caras has written a book which will have to be a staple in every scientific and sporting library the world over. The amount of painstaking documentation which buttresses this work, he alone can appreciate. No facts were accepted, however eminent the source, without systematized cross-checking. And in that fact lies the book's value to science.

As an editor in the field of natural history, I have digested thousands of pages of hearsay "true adventure," "white hunters'" tales and the like. Even men of science are not above adding to the folklore of dangerous (alleged) animals, particularly when tempted to write of animals they have never personally studied!

In a methodical and remorseless manner, the author has destroyed two thousand years of legend, rumor, and pure inventive baloney. For that, he deserves the thanks of every scientist connected with zoology.

But there is more. This book could have been a dry, dull, and purely academic series of lists and charts. To the author's ability we owe the fact that it is not: instead, it is a fascinating narrative, one of exploration as well as explanation. Any literate child (or adult) can understand, appreciate, and be taught from this story.

For that is what it is, a story; and, like all the finest stories, it is, as well as being entertaining, true!

STERLING E. LANIER

*Philadelphia, Pa.*

# Contents

## PART I · *The Mammals*

The cats of Africa · Lions that run and lions that kill · The mystery of the Tsavo River bridge · India and the tiger · The leopard of Africa and India · North America, The Mountain Lion · Some that aren't cowards · South America and the Jaguar.

Conflicting opinions · Gentle soul or mad killer? · The wolves found in India, Europe, and the New World · What are the differences? · Winter vs. summer · Wolf, friend or foe?

The greatest terrestial carnivores left on our planet · The bears of India more feared than tigers · The bears of North America · The grizzlies · The black bears · The Polar Bear · Bears in National Parks.

Stories from old tars · Claims unsubstantiated · No danger to anyone who isn't looking for it.

# Part V · *The Fishes*

# Part VI · *The Invertebrates*

PART VII · *Epilogue*

# List of Illustrations

# Introduction

A scanning review of all "written" records—from cave paintings to encyclopedias—reveals Man's eternal interest in the animal life with which he shares this planet. If this panorama of scratches and scrawls has recorded a true measure of our curiosity about the animal kingdom, we must assume that, for much of our history on earth, the subject has been our prime concern.

This concern has taken many forms and has arisen from a multitude of factors. First, and foremost, mankind has been concerned with animal life because we are omnivorous, and need clothing, and require the flesh and hides of animals to survive. Secondly, as agriculturists and travelers, we have needed certain animals to help with our labors and to transport us and our goods. Also, agricultural man has had to protect his crops from other animal forms all too ready to enjoy the fruits of human labor.

There is also the factor of mysticism. Animals as totem devices, as legendary heirs of both despised and sacred qualities, and even as gods, were important ingredients, in one form or another, in all early cultures. Many such human complexes survive to this day and embrace the hearts and souls of millions. Last, but perhaps not least, we have feared, not without justification in some cases, our fellow creatures. It is this last consideration that is the subject of this book.

The need to protect ourselves against certain animal forms has been a very real one for most of our history, and over a wide area. There can be no doubt that we once lived very close to a competition level with at least the larger animals; if a man killed a Cave Bear, he was warm for the winter and, if he didn't, the cave bear very well might have killed and eaten him. Something like that certainly was the case not so very long ago. It is only very recently that the need for self defense has been reduced to the practically non-existant in most areas. Those areas where the concern still exists in reality are isolated and ever-shrinking. The tribal memory of this need for defense, however, has lingered on and apparently will not die as long as there are wild animals left on our planet to remind us that we once lived on intimate terms, and in intimate combat, with them. The product of this tribal memory has been an incredible rash of masquerading fiction about dangers real and supposed. In this book we shall attempt to make a distinction.

The first point we should establish is that there is no such thing as a *dangerous animal*, only animals *potentially dangerous*. This seemingly elementary point is really very significant. In most circumstances involving man and a wild animal form, man, as certainly the superior mentality, has control over how close they come to each other and the terms on which they meet. Rarely, this is not the case, but we shall discuss the exceptions in good time. If man chooses to get close to a wild animal without a real understanding of the animal's capabilities and response patterns, and has not the means at hand to defend himself, then he with his keenly developed intelligence is to blame for what might ensue. Virtually all accidents with reputedly dangerous animals are avoidable; those few that are *not*, will be stressed in the chapters that follow.

Ideally, I would like to offer finite answers to the many questions that exist about reputedly dangerous animals. This is not possible, and we will time and again be frustrated by our inability to establish hard and fast rules. Animals, although they often function within readily defined boundaries of response, are not totally predictable. Man, certainly, is totally *un*predictable, and a combination of the two cannot help but create unanswerable questions.

We will discover two things in this book, though, and they are almost as valuable as definitive answers. First, there *are* certain facts to be found, and we shall seek them out. Second, we will come to recognize a standard of truth in the discussion of reputedly dangerous animal behavior. In discussing danger to man, truth has apparently been of little concern to a great many writers. Peculiarly, untruths, if repeated often enough, become truths to many people not particularly interested in the refinements of the subject matter or in a scientific approach to natural wonders in general. We will have to upset a few rather well-established apple carts.

Our approach to the animal kingdom will be essentially along the lines of structure. We will begin with the highest animals of all, the mammals, and move on down through the lesser creatures, discussing each in turn. We will not discuss domestic animals, or those too small to be seen with the naked eye. In the first of these two categories, man is totally responsible for whatever happens and, in the second, we can barely touch on the subject without exploding out of the necessary confines of this book. We will touch on it for just a passing moment in an appendix on rabies, and only there because some knowledge of the disease is essential to an understanding of mammalian behavior.

I have tried to avoid the cardinal zoological sin of anthropomorphism (roughly—treating animals as if they were human) in the pages that follow. It is sometimes very difficult, however, for an animal lover to avoid the personal "he" and "she" when writing or speaking of species of which he is particularly fond, but it must not be done. There is more than semantics involved. When we speak of animals in human terms, we think of them in that way and are immediately crippled in our efforts to understand their behavior. Animals are *not* human and *never* have human emotions or qualities. No single consideration is more important in the proper delineation of this book's subject. The minute we think or speak of an animal as "cruel," or "cowardly," or "noble," we have lost our way and will be helpless in our attempt to understand our topic. An animal is none of these. This point will come up from time to time as we examine some of the writings of the past. In virtually every case discussed in this volume, I will be speaking of danger, or potential danger, in the "first person." I will refer to damage the animal can *itself* do with fang, claw, brute weight, or venom.

Then, to take up another point: again and again we will find confusion as to how an animal should be classified, or identified. Zoology suffers from an endless series of contradictions, differences of opinion, and out-right controversy. It is still a young science and must be permitted these natural growing pains. I do not attempt to resolve these differences and will, in fact, avoid taking sides as much as possible. It is not the task of this work to refine the taxonomy of the animal kingdom.

Actually, the theme of this book is conservation. The wildlife of the world is disappearing at an alarming rate, and unless very positive and elaborate steps are taken in the immediate future, most of the world will be without wild forms a few generations from now. Unfortunately, a number of forms have been pushed to the verge of extinction because they have been labeled "dangerous to man." Some individual animals must be destroyed, of course. We will discuss their depredations and point out the necessity for their pursuit and destruction. I am referring to individual specimens, however, and not to whole species. Although it may be difficult to demonstrate the "value" of a stonefish, let us say, there is no species of animal represented in this book whose extinction is justified. The final "murdering" of any species is a horrible thing, for it can but remove us one more step from our natural heritage.

Certain species must nonetheless be brought under control in defense of man's welfare; but control is not destruction, and, what is more, the control itself should be justified on much firmer and more realistic grounds than in the past. Too often control is nothing more than a catch-word justifying endless slaughter. The North American Puma or Moun-tain Lion, wolves, and the Grizzly Bear are examples of animals pushed to the very edge of extinction in the name of control. Actually, we should admit, man loves to kill. Something exciting happens to man when he kills a beast more magnificent than himself. I leave the discussion of that aberration to authors who enjoy discussing men more than animals.

# PART I

## The Mammals

# CHAPTER 1

# *The Great Cats*

THERE are about a hundred distinct kinds of cats known to inhabit the earth today. They range in size from the mighty Siberian tiger (up to twelve feet in length from nose tip to tail tip) to a neat little hunched, spotted species about half the size of the average domestic cat found in South America, and apparently called Hensel's cat. The cats (*Felidae*) are divided into half a dozen genera, though two of these are currently believed by some specialists to warrant uniting. These genera are:

I. *Panthera*   the great cats that *can* roar due to the conformation of their hyoid bones: the Lion, Tiger, Jaguar, Leopard, and Snow Leopard.

II. *Profelis*   the great cats that *cannot* roar: the Puma, Clouded Leopard, and the golden cats.

III. *Felis*   the lesser cats: the Ocelot, related splotched coats, the spotted cats, tabbies, etc.

IV. *Lynx*   the lynxes, jungle cats, Bobcat, and Caracal.

V. *Leptailurus*   the Serval (*possibly* southern forms of the lynxes).

VI. *Herpailurus*   the Jaguarondi and Eyra of the Americas.

The big cats are the most efficient land predators left on earth. They combine power, speed, "intelligence,"[1] patience, camouflage, and considerable individual skill, all assets of a true hunter. All swim well, most climb with great agility and, at least for short bursts, most can move with amazing swiftness. Bruce Wright, who studied the African lion in its natural habitat, reports hearing that this animal "can reach 40 m.p.h. inside of a couple of seconds from a standing start when it charges."

Most cats are nocturnal and can make night-time travel within their range a hazardous practice. The surprising thing about cats is that relatively so few become man-eaters. There is really no reason why the great cats should not hunt man as a normal practice. The number that have taken to man-eating demonstrates that human flesh is palatable to them, that they are better able to take man than their normal fleet prey, and that, in many parts of their range, man is in good supply. For-

---

[1] "Intelligence" not to be related to or compared with human faculties. Strictly "animal intelligence" which, when compared to that of other animals *is* very high indeed. In this sense it can be measured as the capacity to make choice as opposed to responding strictly according to instinct. It also refers, of course, to the ability to learn.

3

tunately, however, though man-eating is not as rare as is generally believed, most great cats avoid man whenever possible. Man, in fact, is
more often the aggressor, for cats have long been major trophies for
the hunter. It may very well be that the great cats were natural man-
eaters before man developed his skill with weapons. The intelligence of
these fascinating animals may have resulted in their aversion for man as a
defensive measure. The cases of man-eating that occur each year arise
from a number of factors, and may provide insight into what was once
normal behavior.

So distinct are the several kinds of great cats that they warrant individual attention in some detail. What is true of one is quite likely not true
of the others, so that the great cats cannot be discussed as a group.

The Leopard (*Panthera pardus*) is, in the author's opinion, the most
beautiful of cats. In the opinion of most hunters, it is the most lethal.
Small by comparison—it rarely exceeds 175 pounds—it is, nonetheless,
pound-for-pound, probably the strongest of the big predators. It can
negotiate rocky ledges that no other cat would attempt, and surpasses
most animals in arboreal agility. It is capable of 40-foot leaps, and can
climb a tree carrying a load twice its own weight. Its gray to gold coat,
with its dark spots and rings, varies markedly from place to place, but
always provides near perfect camouflage. Its ability to freeze on the
ground, or on a tree limb overhanging a trail, contributes to its success
as a hunter, and to the legends of the ghost-like quality that surrounds its
stealth. It walks on its toes, and its hind feet meet the earth in the exact
spot vacated by its large, muscular forefeet. It is a silent, nocturnal
hunter, as "clever" as any animal we know, and as dangerous a man-
killer as there is on land.

The names Panther and Leopard have caused endless confusion. No
matter how often the explanation has been given, writers still confuse the
issue in their efforts to differentiate between the two. Quite simply, and,
one would like to feel, quite finally, panther and leopard *are interchangeable names for one animal throughout the Old World*. In the
New World the mountain lion, or puma, is sometimes misleadingly
called *panther* or *painter*. The leopard is very prone to melanism (i.e.,
having a pure black pelt), especially in some areas, and further mistaken
notions about this have arisen. For instance, many people believe the
name *panther* is reserved for these specimens; but this is not so. The
terms *leopard* and *panther* are interchangeable for both the spotted and
black forms. The two color phases can come from the same litter (and
often do), and can reproduce each other. If you look at a black leopard
in slanting sun rays, you will see its spots. Why so many people have
fought this demonstrable fact is as confusing as why the leopard or

South African Leopard (*Panthera pardus*) with freshly killed baboon.

South African Tourist Corp.

panther so readily tends to melanism. The jaguar of South and Central America is similarly inclined. In both animals, jaguar and leopard, albinism is very much more rare. Indeed, in the leopard it may not occur at all.

Leopards are not only skillful hunters, whether stalking monkeys, peacocks, hoofed prey, dogs, or men, they also tend to be scavengers. It is believed that this characteristic has led to some particularly devastating waves of man-eating in India. Raging epidemics have swept whole districts, leaving dead numbered in the thousands for the leopard to feast upon. Smallpox and cholera, particularly, have been great scourges. Very often, these brush-fire epidemics have been followed by months of terror as leopards indulged their new taste for human flesh and started killing.

Not all cases of man-eating by leopards result from epidemics. Leopards become excited with little provocation, and it is almost certain that many initial attacks are made when the animal is in this state, and not in an attempt to get food. Once a leopard has killed, however, and tastes or smells fresh blood, it is likely to eat unless it is very well-fed at the time of the incident. Even a medium-sized leopard can carry an adult man off into the bushes, or even up a tree, to eat at its leisure.

The following is the text in full of a clipping from the Madras *Mail* of May 24, 1962:

## LEOPARD MENACE
## IN BHAGALPUR

### 350 Persons Killed
### in 3 Years

BHAGALPUR, May 23: The district authorities of Bhagalpur have launched an all-out drive to rid Banka sub-division of the menace of man-eating leopards which, according to local estimates, have claimed about 350 human lives in the last three years.

The District Magistrate, Mr. Srivatsava, told pressmen on Saturday that 82 persons were officially known to have been killed by leopards since 1959 in Karoria, Belhar, Bankan and Chanda in Banka sub-division. He said the number of victims might be higher.

He said eight batches of shikaris and hundreds of beaters had been deployed in a 20-square-mile area to liquidate the leopards. Provision had been made to use tear gas and also to dynamite caves, which were suspected to be the lairs of the man-eaters. A Deputy Magistrate was camping in the jungles of Banka, supervising the drive.

The late Colonel Jim Corbett became world-famous for his one-man war on man-eating tigers and leopards. His book *The Man-Eating Leopard of Rudraprayag* is a treasure store of leopard data and impressions. According to Corbett, leopards have a poor sense of smell and are the most easily stalked of all jungle animals in India. Once turned man-eater, however, they become wary to an incredible degree, and often require months of hazardous effort to exterminate. For one wave of man-eating, 1918–1926, Corbett lists 125 victims. Only one victim was claimed in the first year, three in the second, and six in the third. But the sixth year, twenty-six known victims were claimed. Corbett felt that man-eating leopards are rare, but extremely difficult to deal with. Opinions vary as to how often they do occur, and there doesn't seem to be any way to establish what percentage of these cats do take to man-eating. Problems occur because leopards favor dog flesh. They will often enter villages at night to take dogs, and more than one rural villager in Africa and India has stumbled across a leopard in the middle of the night and been badly mauled.

The range of the leopard, although still vast, is but a fraction of what it formerly was. Known once from the British Isles to Japan, south to Indonesia and Ceylon, and through all of Africa, they are now restricted, in Africa, to below the Sahara. They are no longer found in Europe proper, although they still occur in the Caucasus, northern Persia, and along the Himalayas and the Chinese western escarpment to Manchuria. The Indochinese and Malayan regions, and India, still have large populations. Leopards adapt well, and hang on in agricultural, and even industrial, areas. Their great stealth leads people to believe they are rare or absent when, in fact, they abound. Their pre-disposition to man-eating doesn't appear to be geographically delimited, although reports from India are better known.

The breathtakingly beautiful Snow Leopard (*Panthera uncia*) is a mountain animal of Asia and is anatomically quite distinct. It is a rare and valuable animal. The author does not know of cases of man-eating by this animal, but its reaches are so remote that reports would be unlikely at best. The snow leopard, it should be noted in passing, does move down into inhabited valleys and is not restricted to mountain fastnesses.

Strangely, the great jungle cat of India, the Tiger (*Panthera tigris*), almost certainly began its career in the far north, possibly even in the Arctic. Its migrations carried it to the southern tips of Asia and west to the Elburz Mountains of northern Iran where it reportedly still lives. In southern and southeastern Asia it never reached Ceylon and Borneo. Today, it still ranges from eastern Siberia, through Amuria and Man-churia, Korea, and China to Burma and India, Indochina, Malaya, Su-matra, Java, and Bali. It is still found in Afghanistan, an area seldom thought of as the home of so great a predator. It is in Siberia that the great, heavy-coated tigers are found. Like the snow leopard, the Siberian tiger is a very handsome, relatively rare, and extremely valuable zoo specimen.

The tiger's ground color varies from bright reddish-orange to white. Blue-gray specimens of great rarity are known from parts of China, and a strange, mottled "Clouded Tiger" has been reported on occasion. The black stripes are characteristically different on the two sides of the animal. Pure albinos (i.e., all white) are known, and semi-albinism (black striped white) is evidently fairly common. It is interesting that tigers tend to albinism, leopards and jaguars to melanism, and lions to neither.

Tigers grow to lengths of ten feet or more and can be bigger than the largest lion. They have immense strength. They do not generally strike with their great paws as lions are known to do, but prefer the total contact of the hug. They clutch their prey to them, holding on with their claws, and depend on the crushing bite of their powerful jaws to end the struggle. They swim very well and have often been seen splash-ing about in water on very hot days, since they apparently suffer from the heat. When the air is chill, however, they hate to get their feet wet and avoid wet or damp vegetation. They can climb, but do not approach the leopard's ability in this. They can negotiate treacherous rocky areas, but generally prefer to stay on level ground. They are not as well equipped with senses as one might expect. They apparently depend on their hearing while hunting. Their eyesight is not particularly good and they don't seem to be able to spot prey until it moves. Their sense of

Indian Tiger (*Panthera tigris*).

U.S. National Zoological Park.

smell is reportedly no better than that of the leopard. They can consume an amazing quantity of food and will stay with a kill for days until it has been consumed. They will eat flesh even when it is very "high." They tend to be nocturnal and generally lie up during the heat of day. Hunting during the daylight hours is not unknown, however.

Tigers are generally thought of as the grand gentlemen of the forest. Indeed, there is a quiet dignity to their retiring habits, and a normal tiger is a sight of beauty rather than menace. They evidently find man's proximity quite threatening, and do not generally linger long in any place near men. They avoid man as much as possible, and the fact that they still exist in large numbers after being hunted mercilessly for so long, gives testimony to their acute sensitivity. They can raise absolute havoc with domestic stock once they get a taste of this easy prey, and every effort is made to chase them out of an area once they are spotted. Hunting them on foot or on elephant back is still considered fine sport. Great beats utilizing whole villages are still organized by wealthy sportsmen, and also by the Government.

Occasionally, tigers that have been molested will attack an elephant, wild or tame, but they generally give the great beasts a wide berth. It is extremely difficult, if not impossible, for a tiger to kill a full-grown elephant, but an elephant has no trouble dispatching a tiger once contact is made. If a tiger gets onto an elephant's back, the latter can always roll and bring its greatest weapon, weight, to bear. Many elephant calves, however, are reportedly taken by tigers. Water Buffaloes (*Bubalus*) have been known to best a tiger in open combat. Generally, though, a large tiger can prevail in most disputes into which it enters willingly. Occasionally, motion picture footage crops up of a tiger, or a leopard, having it out with a large python. The contest usually is depicted as ending in a two-sided retreat. Whether or not such encounters ever really occur in nature is not easy to determine. As recorded, they have all the earmarks of something that was rigged for the camera.

Tigers live at peace when they are not hunting. They are quiet, solitary animals when well-fed, and they are assiduously avoided by most jungle creatures. When one enters an area, birds twitter in alarm and the word spreads. Wherever the great cat goes, the alarm spreads before it. Finally, the kill is made and all is quiet for days until the tiger is hungry again and starts to move. A great traveler, it may cover twenty miles or more before feeding again. This pattern, or any other, may not hold, however, when the great striped cat turns man-eater.

A man-eating tiger can disrupt dozens and sometimes hundreds of square miles of countryside. The whole normal parade of life changes to adjust unwillingly to the appetite of one cat. Religious festivals are canceled to keep pilgrims from traveling the roads and making camp in forest clearings. Markets are closed and harvests rot on the vine. Cattle are not taken to pasture, firewood is not collected, and, in the extreme, villages isolated from the main roads are abandoned. Doctors refuse to travel at night to treat the sick and injured, and people who fail to turn up before dusk are not searched for. One single great cat, wandering silently through the forest, can turn whole vast areas into ghost regions. A human being, unless armed and well qualified, is helpless against attack. Tigers, once turned man-eater, become even more wary and alert, and frequently abandon a kill after one meal. The result is more kills than normal. Victims often are taken a dozen or more miles apart, and there is no way of knowing where the next strike will be made. The most highly skilled of hunters can spend months, even years, in tracking down a man-eater. Bridges across wide and fast-flowing rivers are closed in an attempt to restrict the killer's range and permit a concentrated effort. Towers and machans, or tree-platforms, are constructed at strategic spots to permit sentries to guard paths and roadways. Inexplicably, armed men disappear from their stations, and, if they turn up at all, are little more than scattered bones and blood-soaked tatters of cloth when found.

At the height of the terror, the cat takes to raiding villages, ripping open thatched roofs, and clawing down barricaded doors. A cat that has reached the point where its disregard of man is such that it will enter a village and ignore the screams and wailings of the inhabitants, has gone too far, and is usually killed soon after. However, as long as the great cat keeps to the forest, it is nearly impossible to destroy. It avoids traps and poisoned bait with almost supernatural cunning. Once hunters think they have discovered a pattern to its behavior, the cat switches and does the totally unpredictable. If a man-eater happens to be a female with cubs, the situation can be worse yet. First, it will require more food to feed itself and its family, and the cubs *may* grow up to be man-eaters themselves. It is not clear whether or not cubs raised on human flesh become man-killers once they start to hunt on their own. Even Corbett, an authority on man-eating tigers, never was clear on this point. He expounds both points of view in his writings.

Major Charles Simpson, of Black Rock Estate in southern India, wrote me on April 15, 1962, of an encounter with normal tigers:

On my estate in 1925 I had a virago of a female who was always fighting with her husband. One evening their wordy warfare developed into fisticuffs, and the woman decided to leave her spouse, so she picked up her *cumbly* (a coarse blanket) and walked out into the night. After going a few furlongs, she found it too dark to see the path, so she laid herself down at the side of the path, under the tea bushes, and went to sleep. She was awakened later in the night by a nudge in the ribs, and on opening her eyes, found a pair of tigers sitting in the path looking at her. Petrified with fright, she stayed still, and the male tiger, after putting his paw on her again and sniffing her, walked away, with his mate following him. She stayed until light and then ran back to the quarters to tell her tale. This was so incredible that I went out at once to see if I could find the tracks, and sure enough, there were the plain imprints of two tigers, male and female, on the sandy track, and evidence that one had sat down within two feet of where the woman had lain.

Seven years later, a wounded tiger gave an altogether different account of itself:

In 1932, a party of 4 shikaris, armed with muzzle-loaders, sat up over the carcass of a cow killed and partly eaten by a tiger, in the hills at the foot of my estate. The tiger, returning at dusk to the kill, was fired at and badly wounded, but got away. In the morning, the hunters followed its tracks by the blood, and were charged by the tiger. One man was killed outright, one severely clawed, the two others escaped by jumping into a thorn tree, where the tiger could not follow.

In his book on the wildlife of India, G. P. Sanderson gives this account of a man-eater. It is condensed here from ten pages of text.

When I pitched camp at Morlay in September 1873, to commence the elephant kheddahs, the countryside was in a state of alarm from the attacks of a man-eating tigress. This tigress' fits of man-eating seemed to be intermittent, as after killing three or four persons some months before, she had not been heard of till about the time of my arrival, when she killed two boys. On November 30th, news was brought in that a man (about six miles from Morlay) had been carried off. On December 19th another man was carried off five miles from Morlay. The man had been following the cattle home in the evening. The tigress had been in the rocks, and in one bound seized him, dragged him to a small plateau, from which she jumped down into a field, and there killed him. She had then dragged her victim half a mile where we found leg-bones . . . nothing was heard of the tigress for a week. Whilst at dinner, I heard voices approaching my tent . . . the people were from a village a mile and a half away, and had come to tell me that their cattle had galloped back in confusion into the village at dusk, without their herdsman. At dawn we started on the back-trail . . . we found the man's remains; only the soles of his feet, the palms of his hands, his head and a few bones were left. We lost no time in taking up the tigress' track . . . she had recrossed the river and gone into the jungles where there was no chance of finding her. About a week after this the priest of a temple ten miles due west was jogging along on his bullock . . . tigress with her cub stepped into the path . . . seized the poojaree, and carried him off to a deep ravine. The next death was of a horrible description . . . several villagers were grazing their cattle in a swampy hollow when the tigress pounced upon one man. She missed her aim at his throat, seized the shoulder, and then, either in jerking him, or by a blow, threw him onto a thicket several feet from the ground. Here the wounded wretch was caught by thorny creepers; whilst the tigress, as generally happens when a *contretemps* takes place, relinquished the attack. Next morning the lacerated wretch was found. In his mangled state he had been unable to release himself; he was moaning and hanging almost head downwards amongst the creepers; and died soon after he was taken down. Shortly after this, work took me to Goondulpet and I returned on the 14th January 1874 . . . a woman had been carried off by the man-eater out of the village during the night. There was no jungle to cover the man-eater's advance. The attack had been most daring. At one end of the street stood a shady tree, round the base of which a raised terrace of stones and earth had been built . . . the tigress had crouched upon this terrace, from which she commanded a view of the street. The old woman had been going to her daughter's, and as she crossed the street the tigress seized and carried her off. The poor old creature was not missed till morning. The villagers concluded that they would now not be safe in their houses at night, and some of the out-lying hamlets would have been temporarily abandoned had the tigress lived much longer. But this was to be her last victim. Next day I determined upon a plan of hunting her. I arranged that Bommay Gouda and three trackers should go to one end of her usual range, whilst I remained at Morlay . . . one of them came running back to say that the party had met the tigress . . . she was then in a small hill two miles from camp. They were going across open fields and presently discovered a tiger on the far side partly hidden by a bullock which it was half dragging, half carrying towards the hill. They immediately ran shouting towards her, obliging her to drop the bullock. I need here hardly say, except for those who have had no experience of man-eating tigers, that they never refuse a bullock or other prey, if such offers, and that when opposed by man they give way at once. Their tactics in attacking man may be described in one word—surprise; and if discovered in their attempt they generally abandon it. The most confirmed man-eaters never lose the fear with which all animals regard human beings, and unless they can catch an unwary cow-herd or wood-cutter in their own fashion they are not to be dreaded. When the tables are turned they flee as readily as other tigers . . . a peahen which had been hidden amongst boulders on the hillside rose with a startling clamour and there we saw the man-eater, a handsome but small tigress. I fired at her shoulder, broadside on, with my express. On examining her we found that she was in milk . . . she was in the prime of life and condition, and had no apparent injury to account for her man-killing. I may here say that we never killed her cub. It was heard calling to its mother for several nights but we could not find it and it must have died of starvation.

The most complete and best-known accounts of man-eating tigers occur in the writings of Jim Corbett. *Man-Eaters of Kumaon* and *The Temple Tiger and More Man-Eaters of Kumaon* are certainly the most widely read books on the subject. The books are distinguished for their accuracy. There would be little point in recapitulating Corbett's accounts here since they are most revealing in their entirety, and are readily available. Corbett agreed with most serious writers, and pointed out that most man-eating cases could be blamed on old-age or injuries. Unlike lions who can turn to man-eating without understandable cause, tigers seldom do so unless forced into it. Tigers that are injured while killing porcupines, and end up crippled by quills and festering sores, have often become man-eaters due to their no longer being capable of taking swifter prey. Hunters who wound a tiger and fail to follow it up may condemn a number of unfortunate fellow humans to terrible deaths. Most of the man-eaters Corbett hunted—the Champawat, Chowgarh, Mahan Kanda, Pipal Pani, Thak, Temple, Muktesar, Panar, Chuka and Talla Des Tigers —were found to be partially incapacitated when finally destroyed. Corbett had great affection for the lordly tiger, but knew full well the chaos that ensues when an area becomes terrorized by an aberrant individual.

(During the period when the preceding paragraphs were written, a man-eating tiger was terrorizing several native villages in Sumatra. At the last count, seventeen victims had been claimed.)

Lion (*Panthera leo*).      South African Tourist Corp.

The Lion (*Panthera leo*) once ranged through all of Africa save the heavily forested and greatly elevated regions. In early historic times it inhabited Eastern Europe to Romania, and, quite probably, Italy, and ranged thence east through Turkey and the Caucasus to central India. All of the Near East was included in its range except apparently Arabia. Today, a few apparently still occur north of the Sahara, reportedly in Morocco, and a small population enjoys full protection in the Gir forest in the Gujarat region of India.

Popular literature almost invariably characterizes the lion as a creature of the jungle. Nothing could be further from the truth. It is an animal of the open orchard, bush, and savannah, the great grass plains that cover so much of Africa. You are more apt to find one in a desert than a forest.

The lion is not the largest of the cats. That honor belongs to the Siberian tiger, which exceeds it in both length and weight. Second though it may be, it is still a large animal. It can approach eleven feet in length, measuring tip-to-tip, and forty-two inches or more in height at the shoulder. Four hundred pounds is a good figure for a large specimen and some few may exceed it.

Lions are anatomically very close to tigers. With their skins off, the two animals are all but indistinguishable to anyone but an expert. The two cats can readily interbreed, giving "Ligers" and "Tiglons," the former when a lion is the father, the latter when the tiger is sire. Not only do numerous subspecies of lions (*kamptzi, nyanzae, vernayi, goojratensis,* etc.) differ in appearance, but even closely related individuals show marked variations, so that the creation of subspecific designations is thought by many specialists to be a most dubious practice. In males, manes may be extremely luxurious (although seldom so in areas where thorny brush is found) or totally absent. Colors range from golden-fawn and silver-blond, through the entire spectrum of the brown tones, to almost, but never true, black. Faces vary tremendously and individuals can be as readily distinguished by observers as can people. Game rangers and others who spend much of their time in the open, frequently come to know individuals and assign them pet names. They can pick them out of a crowd as readily as the average city dweller can identify his own bank-clerk as he passes him on the street. They differ as much in disposition as they do in appearance. It is not only in children's books that we can find "lazy" lions, "happy" lions, "timid" lions, and "brave" ones. The author is not fond of attaching human emotions to animals, but however lion emotions can be characterized, the gamut is run. One lion will stroll down a well-trafficked street on the outskirts of Nairobi, indifferent to screaming mothers and honking car horns, while another will become panicked by a sheet on a clothesline. Some individuals will go placidly through life showing real animation only when really pressed by outside influences or internal stirrings, while others will fly off into regular tantrums at the least of causes.

When lions hunt in pairs, or even groups, as they usually do, a regular pattern of cooperative effort is used. One or more approach a herd of hoofed animals in full view. The herd is panicked into an ambush of one or more females who have been stealthily circling the herd from behind as it focused its collective attention on the visible cats. It is a device that has been used by lions (and other carnivores) since time immemorial, but their hoofed prey has never learned how to avoid the obvious trap. Once the herd is within striking distance, it is over very quickly, or the cats go hungry, for, when it comes to a chase, the lion must inevitably lose out because it can't hope to match the speed of its swift and agile prey. If the lion once makes contact, on the other hand, a shattering blow is delivered with a forepaw, teeth seek the neck, and one bite usually brings the animal to ground for a few convulsive kicks. Occasionally, a lion will fail to land on the back of its prey, or won't get into position to strike a lethal blow, and will sink its claws into flanks or body and claw the prey down with its weight. Since lions hunt in the open, the whole hunting and killing procedure has been observed innumerable times. Rarely do lions hunt in any kind of cover, and dropping from a tree onto prey, characteristic behavior of the leopards, is unknown. Almost all killing is done by the female. The lion roars, the lioness kills. Dusk, dawn, and night are the usual hunting hours.

Lions, like many wild animals, have little stamina. Their speed is astounding for short distances. One lightninglike rush is all they are capable of, however, and open field running is not attempted.

Bruce S. Wright made a comprehensive survey of predator kills, which was reported in the January, 1960, issue of the *Journal of Wildlife Management*. Interestingly enough, the number of male animals killed by lions outnumbered female prey three to two. Animals killed in their prime outnumbered those past prime nearly two to one. Animals taken in good condition outnumbered those in poor condition by more than eight to one. These figures refer only to lion kills. The studies of leopard and cheetah kills were not comprehensive enough to justify conclusions. There is thus an apparent conclusion that can be made about lions. The temptation is to say that since they don't take anywhere near as many old and sick animals as they do healthy, strong specimens, they are "good sportsmen." Since they take many times as many mature animals as babies, they are "kind hearted." A better suggestion would seem to be, however, that, among hoofed prey, prime males will feed on the outskirts where the kill is most apt to be made. Females and calves keep to the relative safety of the middle of the grazing herd. Lions simply do not engage in conscious selection of prey but take that which is closest, offers the best chance for a kill, and requires the least amount of exertion.

Ivan Sanderson, in his *Living Mammals of the World*, says of lions:

They never molest men unless suddenly startled, bullied, wounded, or driven to regular man-killing by disease, excessive hunger, or a strange contagious delinquency that sometimes affects whole lion populations and notably the unmated juveniles. Senile individuals usually subsist on small rodents, scorpions, and other little things rather than plump native women and children.

Most responsible observers of wildlife are in general agreement with Sanderson. Lions do not regularly become man-eaters, but confirmed man-eaters do crop up more often than is generally realized. Young, healthy animals, perfectly capable of taking their normal fleet-footed prey, are often the culprits. This is the unexplained juvenile delinquency referred to by Sanderson. Why it approaches epidemic proportions at times is not known. Explanations are always available, but none hold up. Males and females are both guilty. Young and old, healthy and sick cats have been involved. Incidents have occurred in areas where game was scarce and where it was plentiful. There is no pattern to it. Quite simply, it is a kind of "disease" which may be contained within one animal, or spread to others. The author does not propose that "disease" indicates a bacterial infection, but rather a behavioral aberration for which there is no known prophylactic, and for which death is the only known cure.

C. A. W. Guggisberg has long studied the lion in his habitat. His superb book, *Simba*, contains priceless data and photographs. Included also is some important research on man-eaters. He gives the case history of "Chiengi Charlie" as one example:

*Place:* Chiengi, Northern Rhodesia.
*Time:* January, 1909.
*Case:* 1 woman taken from village at sunset.
1 woman taken from nearby village shortly thereafter, again at dusk.
1 man killed a week later and eaten while his wife watched helplessly from a nearby tree to which she had escaped.
2 women killed in front of their hut—one eaten.
1 man killed while working in his field.
The lion then moved off to start a reign of terror among the villages in the nearby hills.
1 boy, part of the retinue of the Chiengi medical officer, James Dunbar-Brunton, was killed and eaten on the night of February 17th.
1 kitchen boy taken in Chiengi itself.
Twice thereafter the large light-colored lion attempted to claw down the walls of native huts, but was driven off, once by a fire-brand, and once by being speared in the neck.
Then "Chiengi Charlie" joined forces with two other lions, and night after night they raided villages, while the list of victims mounted.
Finally, gun traps succeeded in ending the career of "Chiengi Charlie" and one of his cronies. Charlie turned out to be an old, very large male.

### Mr. Guggisberg comments:

The case of "Chiengi Charlie" cannot actually be considered as very exceptional, for man-eating lions turn up more often than is sometimes assumed. It also cannot be said that man-eating is restricted to a few isolated areas, for in the course of a careful study of the subject I have come across records from practically all parts of the lion's African range of distribution. . . .

Certainly the most famous man-eating lions of all were those of Tsavo. The reports of their depredations reached the floor of the British Parliament. They brought the building of a railroad to a halt for three weeks and the price in human terror and suffering cannot be calculated. The whole story was reported in full by Lieutenant Colonel J. H. Patterson, an engineer assigned to the construction of the bridge over the Tsavo River, who brought the career of the Tsavo man-eaters to an end by his skill and persistence, and not without considerable personal danger.

Tsavo River Bridge, Kenya. Bruce S. Wright.

The Tsavo is a river about 80 miles long in southeastern Kenya. It flows from Mt. Kilimanjaro into the Sabaki River, a turbid run of 120 miles eastward into the Indian Ocean. The surrounding land rolls away to the horizon in unspectacular undulations of grassy expanse and scrub thorn, except for some high hills near Voi. Some trees dot the seemingly endless plains, and rock outcroppings are relatively rare. Real lushness is reserved for the river banks and a few swampy lowlands. Game is plentiful during some seasons and relatively rare in others. Periods of flood alternate with burning arid months. It is perfect lion country. The rolling savannah and scrub thorn combination is perfect hunting country for an open-plains cat, and the few native tribes in the area do not disturb the natural order of things.

In 1898, two things happened along the reaches of the Tsavo, one quite understandable, and the other without explanation to this day. The understandable change was the appearance of a railroad destined to run from Uganda in the northwest to the Indian Ocean. The unexplained part of it concerned two male lions who went on a rampage of slaughter which wasn't ended until twenty-eight Indian coolies who had been imported to construct the line, and unknown dozens of African natives, had been killed, and most of them eaten. One European was injured. Often groups of laborers huddled together whimpering while they listened to the two cats fighting over and eating friends and relatives. The victims were not always killed outright, and their calls for help left the laborers half-mad with fright. Some nights, two victims would be taken. When Patterson finally killed the two man-eaters, he found them to be virtually maneless males of large size. Neither was incapacitated, and both were perfectly normal in all aspects save this behavior. Patterson's account of the episode is quite naturally full of shredded flesh, bodiless heads with wide staring eyes, and all of the other gore necessarily attendant upon the subject of man-eating cats.

After the two Tsavo man-eaters were killed, other cats took up the habit. Three months after the second Tsavo killer fell to Patterson's persistence, an engineer named O'Hara was killed. His wife and child were witnesses. That was March, 1899. In June, 1900, another man-eater appeared and hunted men with reckless abandon. It was eventually caught in a box trap, put on display, and later shot. None of the subsequent man-eaters who made life a living nightmare along the Uganda rail line came close to the original two in the extent of their depredations. Collectively, this episode at the turn of the century was one of the worst in history. Word of it spread around the world, it was thoroughly documented by reliable witnesses, and dozens of photographs are extant to prove quite conclusively what can happen when nature's great predators go on a rampage.

What happened at the Tsavo construction sites and subsequently in the surrounding territory has no known explanation. The cats involved were acting in an abnormal manner. For reasons completely unknown, they turned away from normal prey and took to human flesh. We know that this episode is only one of thousands of its kind. Unfortunately, there is no way of knowing when and where it will happen again. We know it has happened dozens of times since then; in Mgori, Tanganyika, in 1958, in northern Tanganyika in July, 1960. A wave of man-eating occurred in Ankole in the late 1930's; in southern Tanganyika in 1953; twenty-three known human victims were taken in Mahenge District in 1923–24. Portuguese East Africa has been plagued with killers from time to time. Accounts exist by the score. Man-eaters are, however, in a tiny minority.

Least catlike of all cats (sometimes spoken of as not being a true cat at all) is the Cheetah (*Acinonyx jubata*). With its non-retractable claws, a unique feature among the cats, long straight legs, and sway-backed profile, the Hunting Leopard, as it is sometimes called, is a very doggy feline. Common to much of Africa below the Sahara outside the closed-canopy forests, as well as to some parts of India, it once ranged through Syria, Mesopotamia, Persia, and the Caspian lowlands, but its distribution has been slowly contracting.

There can be little question that the cheetah is far and away the fastest four-legged creature on earth. It has been (scientifically) clocked up to about 60 mph, and claims have been made that it can go faster still. It is this remarkable speed that makes the cheetah the successful hunter it is,

Jane Stanton of Kibwezi and "Caesar," a male Cheetah (*Acinonyx jubata*)

and restricts it to open savannahs. Such speeds would hardly be useful in wooded country. The cheetah can run down any land animal in existence, and once it focuses on its prey, it will not stop until it has succeeded in bringing it down.

Usually seen in pairs, cheetahs are shy and inoffensive. They seldom bother domestic stock, and are nowhere as common as lions. Their prey consists of hoofed plains animals and they tend to take smaller species than the lion.

For all its flash and speed, this handsome animal is not dangerous to man except under the most unusual and accidental circumstances. Un-provoked attacks on man are, as far as can be discerned, unknown. Even provoked attacks have been extremely rare and seldom, if ever, fatal.

The one great cat of the Western Hemisphere is the Jaguar (*Panthera onca*), very often referred to in Latin America as *el Tigre*. This cat is truly one of the largest in the world, surpassed in size only by the African and Indian lions, and the big tigers of Asia. It is possibly the best tree-climber among the big cats, surpassing even the leopards, but is not limited in its range to forested areas. Generally thought of as a jungle animal, it actually ranges from the desert and semi-desert areas of the southwestern United States, where it is very rare, through the tropical rain forests of Central and South America to the open grasslands of lower Patagonia. It is an active, tenacious, aggressive, and beautiful creature of excessively stocky build. It is easily distinguished from the leopard, with which it can come in contact only in captivity, by a series of spots enclosed in rings against a variety of ground colors, just as in the tiger and leopard. Albinism is known, and melanism is apparently fairly com-mon in some areas, particularly in northern South America.

The jaguar swims exceedingly well and readily takes to water. It is essentially nocturnal in hunting habits. A big male can weigh as much as a small-sized Indian tiger, although it is much shorter. Its powerful square chest and heavy hind legs make it an amazingly powerful jumper.

Of course, the jaguar is accused of attacks on man, although waves of man-eating are not reported as they are in India and Africa. It is said to follow hunters, perhaps out of curiosity, and ambush natives. There is nothing to distinguish this cat's behavior in this regard from that of the leopard, according to most reporters, except that it tends to hold its ground with more conviction, at least at times. It does tend to melt away when approached, but appears to be quick to resent intrusion, and to be rather easy to arouse. Like any of the big cats, it can be extremely dangerous if wounded, cornered, come upon with young or when breed-ing. It has the peculiar advantage of living in extremely dense cover over much of its range. When it does ambush a man it has everything in

Jaguars (*Panthera onca*).  Smithsonian Institution.

its favor. Its camouflage is near perfect, and it is possessed of that great feline advantage—patience. Many people who have spent their lifetimes within the range of this powerful predator have never seen one outside of a zoo. The jaguar subsists on mammals, up to the tapir in size, birds, and fish.

Two characteristics of its behavior do occasionally lead to problems. First, although something of a wanderer, the jaguar establishes a range. Intruders in this area are challenged, and meetings between males frequently end in battle. Whether this open hostility is transferred to humans who inadvertently blunder into a jaguar's hunting range is not clear, but it could explain the many reports of hunters, prospectors and others whose interests have carried them into the jungles of South and Central America, who tell of being followed, or "tracked," for miles, then suddenly abandoned. In fact, the jaguar might have been "seeing them out." Tracking, in the usual sense, is not the case since the jaguar's sense of smell is probably no better than that of the other big cats. More likely, the cat follows the sounds of the intruders.

A second kind of problem can arise when jaguars take to raiding domestic stock. They can evidently become as possessive over a herd of cattle as they can over wildlife in a more natural hunting range. Laborers working near cattle herds that have been under attack have been mauled by jaguars lying up between kills. Although the literature on this cat is nowhere nearly as extensive or comprehensive as that on the other great cats, it does seem to indicate more man-killing than man-eating. More people appear to be mauled, and killed, from anger than are killed for food. This is not to say, however, that a hungry jaguar would not take advantage of a human kill, or indeed would not kill a man for food on occasion. Both apparently have occurred, though very rarely.

There is no evidence that would suggest that the jaguar is any more of a threat to man than any other great cat. Indeed, most reports of human deaths and injuries which the author has encountered involved wounded animals doubling back and attacking their attackers.[2]

Few cats have been more controversially discussed as to the danger they represent to man than the Mountain Lion or Puma; known also as the Cougar, Panther, and even the Catamount. Originally it ranged from the subarctic through all of forested Canada, the United States, and all Central and South America to the island of Tierra del Fuego, and, what is more, in both forests *and* open country. Today extinct throughout most of its eastern United States range, it still extends through more degrees of latitude than any other wild feline on earth—very close to 100! It can be found above the tree line on mountain crags, below sea level in deserts, in tropical jungles, and on forested hillsides in temperate zones. Its adaptability is truly amazing. It is beyond doubt the most adaptable cat left in the wild state. It still occurs in the Okefenokee Swamp of Georgia, in Florida, and possibly, in extremely limited numbers, in some other parts of the eastern United States. It is still found in eastern Canada. There are annual reports from New Jersey and all down the Appalachians, but these are as yet unsubstantiated. It is barely possible, however, that this extraordinary animal may in fact be making a comeback in the East.

Known variously as *Profelis concolor, Felis concolor,* or even *Puma concolor,* depending on who your expert is, the Mountain Lion in the United States today is concentrated in the Rocky Mountain states, and southward through the desert mountain ranges of Arizona, Texas, and New Mexico. The coastal ranges of California, Oregon, and Washington have a large population, it is reported. Bruce S. Wright reports that a specimen in the red-color phase, weighing an estimated 100 pounds, was taken in Somerset County, Maine, in January, 1938. Some evidence indicates the date was 1935 or 1936. A specimen was shot in Kent County, New Brunswick, in 1931. The last report from Vermont that has been substantiated was 1881. The whole matter of where the mountain lion has survived the efforts of man at extermination is a highly controversial one. The claims and counterclaims are extremely difficult to sort out and

---

[2] Not all cases however. Sasha Siemel makes several references to man-eating jaguars in the November, 1952, *National Geographic Magazine.*

Mountain Lion (*Profelis concolor*).        Wilford L. Miller.

evaluate. Quite simply, the mountain lion may possibly still survive in some areas no longer thought of as part of its range.

The amount of damage done by the mountain lion is a matter of much discussion. Those who fight for its preservation say it is a natural control on deer, and does little damage to domestic stock. Circular No. 6 of the U.S. Fish and Wildlife Service, "Mountain Lion Trapping," on the other hand, says:

> Stockmen suffer heavy losses through its depredations, for when game is scarce the mountain lion attacks young domestic stock, particularly colts, lambs, and kids, and even full-grown horses and cattle. It is practically impossible to raise young colts or sheep on open stock ranges in the rough, rocky, and broken country that forms an ideal habitat for the mountain lion.

There can be little doubt that the second point of view has prevailed. This one-hundred- to two-hundred-pound cat has been hunted as vermin since white men first arrived. Once found in great numbers on Manhattan Island, it is a tribute to the great cat's tenacity that it has survived anywhere. For over three hundred years it has been classed as an outlaw, fair game for one and all to shoot, trap, poison, and otherwise destroy by any and all means. It would be sad indeed to see this great, beautiful cat finally driven to extinction. It is unique to our hemisphere, and deserves maintenance as a species.

Early in the 1800's, a tribe of Sioux Indians living near what is now Cannon Ball, North Dakota, sent a young boy out to some buttes west of their camp to fast and go through a series of initiation tests. On the third night, some of the young men who were watching for his return heard cries. In the morning, they found his bones and blood-stained clothing, and the unmistakable pug marks of a large mountain lion. This story is still vividly alive in their oral history. To the people, and their number is legion, who insist that the puma is harmless this story is pure Indian hokum. But is it? Probably not. There are other stories, more readily verified, that support its substance. Furthermore, it is not the kind of story the Sioux would create and maintain. It contains no heroics, no vanquishing of a seemingly insurmountable foe, or any other ingredients the Indian might wish to insert and preserve to bolster up a sagging tribal image. Yet, its very preservation indicates that even to the Indians it was an unusual and memorable event, indicating that it must be an exception.

There is no doubt that the mountain lion prefers to avoid man. All cats do, even lions, tigers, and leopards. But, as we have seen with the big cats of Africa and India, this doesn't make a cat harmless. A cat will avoid trouble (and man usually means trouble for a big cat outside of protected areas), and it will hide, run, or do anything to avoid contact— *usually!* When a cat has young, when a cat is cornered or wounded, or is prone to aberrant behavior for any reason, it can be extremely dangerous. The mountain lion can be described as an animal constantly and assiduously avoiding man, but it cannot be described as harmless. Individuals have proven to be anything but that on occasion, and, although they are not by any stretch of the imagination a race of man-eaters, they are not to be underestimated.

In 1924, a thirteen-year-old boy in the state of Washington was sent on an errand to a neighboring ranch. He was waylaid, killed, and partially eaten by a mountain lion. This incident is reported by O. Earle Frye and Bill and Les Piper in a paper dated 1952 entitled "The Disappearing Panther." American big-game hunter, guide, and author Elmer Keith also refers to the incident in his *Big Game Hunting*. Keith also reports that a twenty-one-year-old man in Colorado, a schoolmarm in Washington, and a boy in Oregon were killed by these cats. He refers to them as the only four authentic cases he personally knows of. Two of the four victims were eaten.

Theodore Roosevelt had a friend who was badly mauled in 1890 when a mountain lion sprang from a ten-foot-high sandstone ledge bowling him out of the saddle. Another friend of Roosevelt's, Ed Smith, was charged by a wounded puma, but survived. General Hampton told Roosevelt that a laborer near his Mississippi plantation was waylaid by a mountain lion in a swamp and killed. These cases are reported by Roosevelt in his *The Wilderness Hunter*. Roosevelt, like most experienced hunters, considered these cases to be exceptional, but does point out:

. . . it is foolish to deny that in exceptional instances attacks may occur. Cougars vary wonderfully in size and no less in temper. Indeed I think that by nature they are as ferocious and bloodthirsty as they are cowardly.

Bruce Wright, in his *Wildlife Sketches—Near and Far,* remarks that probably more people have been killed or injured by pet deer than by wild pumas. Nevertheless, in the January–March, 1953, issue of *The Canadian Field-Naturalist,* Mr. Wright reports on three attacks in New Brunswick, where the cat, referred to locally as panther, still exists in small numbers. One took place in 1841, the second in June, 1948, and one on November 22, 1951. In the second of the three cases, a resident of Kingsclear, New Brunswick, was lying flat on his face drinking from a stream "when an animal jumped on his back." The victims in all three cases survived. Wright observes, "It appears that truculent specimens are not unknown, so that the animal should be approached with caution. The great majority, however, are timid in the extreme . . ."

W. A. Perry, in *The Big Game of North America,* reports that the six-year-old son of Mr. Farnham of Olympia, Washington, was seized in 1886. His twelve-year-old brother attacked the cat with his hands and a bottle he was carrying, and beat it off. Both children were badly scratched. In the 1880's, a Swedish sailor named Joseph Jorgenson jumped ship at Esquimalt, British Columbia, and went to work on the ranch run by Perry's father. He was attacked, savagely bitten, and clawed by a mountain lion before he finally killed the cat with a *shovel.* A Miss Mary Campbell of York, British Columbia (later Mrs. John Kelly of Sumas, Washington) was attacked in 1884, but was saved by her father's dogs, Perry reports. Mr. Charles Harmon of Mt. Vernon, Washington; Mr. Cathcart of Snohomish, Washington; Mr. John Potter of Brownsville, British Columbia; the Honorable Orange Jacobs of Washington; and Mr. John Davis of the same state, were all reportedly attacked.

The following article was released by the Associated Press in March, 1962:

## FIGHTS COUGAR
## TO SAVE BOY

Hinton, Alta. (AP)—Mrs. Elsie McEvoy, a Hinton housewife, grabbed a cougar by the ears and pulled it off a 6-year-old boy Friday.

Brian Kilbreath was in serious condition in a hospital yesterday following the attack.

Brian was playing 200 yards from his home when the cougar jumped him. Mrs. McEvoy raced to the scene, picking up a stick on the way, but could not beat the animal off.

"I did the only thing I could," Mrs. McEvoy said. "I grabbed the cougar by its ears and tore it from the frightened boy." The cougar retreated, but the boy had suffered claw marks on the face and a severe scratch to one eye.

Such a report is inconclusive, however, since it is never stated if the animal was wild, a pet, or a captive specimen, the age and condition of the animal, viz., cub *vs.* adult, and if any other factors were involved. Subsequently Bruce Wright informed the author that it was a half-grown cub in very poor condition, weighing little more than thirty pounds. It had evidently been abandoned by its mother and was starving, frightened, and quite apt to act in an atypical manner when encountered.

If it would appear in our discussion so far that we are displaying the mountain lion as an inveterate man-eater, such is not the case at all. We are trying to achieve a balance. This great cat is listed nearly everywhere as "harmless," and as an animal that can be dealt with with complete impunity. This bravado is foolish and dangerous. The mountain lion is a large predatory animal equipped, as are all cats of this size, to kill fast, strong prey often many times its own weight or size. It moves swiftly from ambush and kills with great efficiency. Such an animal is not to be toyed with. It apparently attacks man only on very rare occasions. When it does so it can be considered as acting in an abnormal manner.

It has been suggested by a number of observers that mountain lions may attack men when suffering from rabies. As far as we know, all mammals can get the disease, and if the ailment can turn a pet Pekinese into a ferocious beast, it could certainly cause the normally retiring puma to act at least as badly. In a letter from New Brunswick dated June 18, 1962, Bruce Wright reports, "Pumas do get rabies. A female puma attacked two boys near Morgan Hill, California. A young woman came to their rescue and was badly torn. Seven weeks later two of them developed rabies and died of it." Certainly, rabies could supply a logical explanation why at least this one big cat occasionally attacks the one creature from which it almost always flees.

We have now covered the true big cats that can be even *potentially* dangerous to man. Undoubtedly, lesser cats have been involved in attacks, but they are exceptional. The little-known Clouded Leopard (*Profelis nebulosa*), generally an arboreal beast, ranging from the Himalayas to Borneo and Java, grows large enough to be truly dangerous, but it is a shy animal and has rarely figured in accounts of man-killing. The other cats, the golden cats (*Profelis temmincki* and *P. aurata*), ranging, respectively, from Tibet to Burma and all across forested Africa; the various Asian leopard cats (*Felis bengalensis*, *rubiginosa*, and *viverrina*); the tabbies (*Felis lybica* and *ocreata*) of Africa; and numerous other desert, plain, and jungle cats, and all of the genus *Felis*, could be "bad news" in a cave or chicken coop, but any injury would be accidental. The servals (*Leptailurus*) and a number of other cats whose exact identification is questionable fall in this same grouping.

A number of lynxes and bobcats have bad reputations for viciousness. In the United States and Canada, the bobcat has been accused of causing considerable damage to livestock, by way of justifying the efforts being made to exterminate it. Circular No. 1 of the Bureau of Sport Fisheries and Wildlife entitled, *Hints on Bobcat Trapping,* reports that one cat has been known to kill as many as thirty-eight lambs in one night, although it couldn't have consumed more than one. Other cats have been known to go on an orgy of killing, but it is atypical of most species. Although these cats may be expensive and troublesome to man, they cannot be considered dangerous except accidentally, on rare occasions. The European Wildcat (*Felis sylvestris*) fits into this general category.

This abbreviated discussion of the cats has taken us from Siberia to South Africa, and from Canada to Argentina. We have talked of cats living on snow and ice, in desert wastes, on open savannahs, on rocky slopes, and in steaming jungles and swamps. All of these cats have much in common: they are uncommonly clever, awe-inspiringly powerful, luxuriously beautiful, and bewilderingly unpredictable. Among almost every species of big cat there seem to appear a number of abnormal individuals who seek man as food. They are exceptions to the rule, but at least among some species not so very rare as to be surprising. The facts that all of the big cats, except the African lion and the New World mountain lion have been sought for their beautiful fur, and that all big

Canada Lynx (*Lynx canadensis*).
National Museum of Canada.

cats have been adjudged fine sporting game, have kept man in rather close touch with them. Man's pursuits in animal husbandry have brought the big cats to man's doorstep. Despite all of this, man can generally live pretty much in peace with these animals, and there is rarely justification for the degree to which their kind is hounded with firearms, traps, explosives, and poisons. Unfortunately, those individuals who turn bad have, in a sense, justified in many people's minds the treatment accorded the whole. The number of these cats must steadily diminish in the coming years with the decrease in game. Unless reserves are set aside where the natural prey of these cats can flourish, and unless the ill-considered attempts at artificial predator control are re-evaluated, even the most durable species will eventually vanish. Man may not be a good enough hunter to track down and shoot every great cat in the world, but he is an efficient enough butcher to starve their kind out of existence. It will be a much poorer planet when they are gone.

# CHAPTER 2

# *Wolves*

"THE eyes have a peculiarly sinister expression. . . . They are destructive brutes, and kill large numbers of sheep, goats and children. . . . They are generally cowardly beasts, but they not infrequently take to killing human beings. . . ." So wrote Brigadier General A. A. A. Kinloch of the British Indian Army about the wolf of India in 1892.

In 1958, Lois Crisler wrote, "The wolf's clear, intelligent eyes brushed mine." And then, "The wolf is gentle-hearted. Not noble, not cowardly, just nonfighting."

Both Mrs. Crisler and General Kinloch had kept wolves as pets, and one can but wonder at the strange diversity of opinion. Indeed, as we survey large segments of the animal kingdom in this book, we will find that while some animals are misunderstood, others little understood, and yet others confusing, the wolf hides behind a smokescreen of human invective, legend, symbolism, nonsense, and half-truth. The classic villain of so much of the world's literature stands as one of the great enigmas of the animal world.

The taxonomy (or classification) of wolves is an involved subject, but has to be touched upon because of the confusion caused by the popular names for these animals. Wolves are actually *the* true dogs, and the only true wild dogs. They belong in the genus *Canis*, in which we also place all domestic dogs, as *Canis familiaris*.[1] There is no truly wild representative of the domestic dog, unless the dingo of Australia be such, and there are no other members of the genus *Canis* but wolves. (The dingo is a special case that does not concern us here.) Their nearest relatives are the Jackals (genus *Thos*), and the next of kin, though rather more widely separated, are the Foxes (*Vulpes*). The classification of the wolves themselves is also subject to the usual confusion and conflict, there being the "splitters" and the "lumpers" among canine specialists. Confusion reigns supreme when you try to break the species down into types, varieties, subspecies, or whatever, such as timber wolf, red wolf, and so on; but a surprising simplicity marks the actual number of forms. There are but three full species—the Indian Wolf (*Canis pal-*

---

[1] The so-called Cape or African Hunting Dog (*Lycaon*) is not closely related. (The Wild Dog, or Dhole, of southeast Asia, genus *Cuon*, is quite a different animal and even of another subfamily.)

*lipes*), the Coyote (*C. latrans*), and the rest (*C. lupus*), called by all manner of names, or simply the Wolf. There are those who insist that the so-called Red Wolf of the lower Mississippi valley is a distinct species and bestow upon it the name of *Canis niger*, which, of course, means "black dog." The wolf, per se, once ranged all over North America, Africa north of the Sahara, and the whole of Eurasia apart from peninsular India (which was and still is the domain of the Indian wolf) and the forested southeast of Indochina and the East Indies.

To establish a few significant points before going on to matters of behavior toward man; the wolf is a carnivore that will take what it can get, mouse to moose, quite literally. It hunts in large packs, small family units, or alone. It is evidently a very intelligent animal, with reports of great cunning satisfactorily substantiated. The wolf's brain is reportedly larger than a domestic dog's of comparable size. Captive specimens, particularly those taken while young, are extremely affectionate pets, which would seem to reflect their behavior toward each other in the natural state. Observers who have known the animal well speak of an extraordinary variety of facial expressions, and a remarkable "language," or, at least, capacity for vocal communication that ranges from a low and apparently affectionate whimper to the very familiar, but singularly variable, howl. More than one dedicated enthusiast has reported on his own ability to learn this language along with certain posturings, and thus be able to communicate directly with the animal in mutually understandable terms.

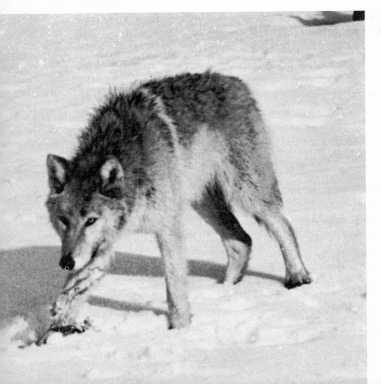

Wolf (*Canis lupus*).
Ontario Department of Lands and Forests.

The wolf becomes of special concern to man in two areas, the safety of his domestic herds and flocks, and his own personal safety. We will examine one and then the other, for they are quite distinct considerations, though they are generally run together in popular writings of the past. There can be little serious doubt that a pack of marauding wolves is a matter of grave concern to stockmen; and, historically, it was the depredations of these active hunters that brought about their eventual demise. In the United States, state and federal control programs for wolves grew out of the often well-founded lament of cattlemen and sheep ranchers, and today, although rare in most farm or even ranch areas, they still have a price on their heads. A strict program of predator control has, moreover, thinned their numbers in our national parks and wildlife reserves.

Addressing himself to the Secretary of the Interior in 1914, the acting Superintendent of Yellowstone Park wrote, "They are very destructive to game, and efforts will be made to kill them." In 1915, he reported, "Gray wolves are increasing, and have become a decided menace . . . several were killed last winter in the park." From October 6, 1915, to June 30, 1916, two special rangers were added to the regular staff on advice of the United States Biological Survey for the purpose of exterminating carnivorous animals in the Park. The two men succeeded in killing twelve wolves, bringing the total for the year in Yellowstone to thirty-six. The story is much the same in other parks, and in livestock areas. The world over the wolf is an outlaw and is hunted with hounds, guns, traps, and poison. For five cents the United States Government Printing Office will sell you a handbook on coyote and wolf trapping. The booklet speaks of their acute sense of smell, alert hearing, and keen eyesight.

Still found in very small numbers in Michigan, Wisconsin, Minnesota, and (reportedly) in Oregon, and, probably as strays from Mexico, in Arizona, New Mexico, Texas, Louisiana, Oklahoma, Arkansas, and possibly even Missouri, wolves are rare animals within the continental limits of the United States. As recently as the turn of the century they ranged over all of the nation west of the Mississippi in great numbers. When that was the case, control was an absolute necessity if ranching was to succeed. One would like to think that, now their number has been so drastically reduced, the pressure on them would be eased a little. Such, unfortunately, is not the case.

In the eastern part of the United States, man has won the one-sided war. Reuben Cary is believed to have killed the last member of the great Adirondack packs in November, 1893. Strays from Canada were killed in New York State in 1902, 1906, and 1923. The last known Pennsylvania specimen fell to hunters in 1898. They disappeared from southern New England about 1850. The last wolf in Connecticut was killed outside of Bridgeport in 1837; 1887 saw the end of the species in New Hampshire. A specimen was shot by a Mr. White in Norway, Maine, in the winter of 1907–1908. Occasional reports are heard even today, but they remain unsubstantiated. More likely, *feral* dogs (a term for a domestic animal gone wild) are the culprits, or villains. It may be that many crimes laid to the wolf were in fact committed by dogs. Even today, there isn't a year that goes by without reports of feral dogs being hunted down. In 1961, an eight-year-old boy was killed by such a pack near Cleveland, Ohio.

In reviewing what has been written about the wolf, one can't help but be shocked by the vindictive nonsense directed against this animal, even by knowledgeable people. No less a figure than William T. Hornaday, onetime Director of The New York Zoological Park, wrote in 1904:

Of all the creatures of North America, none are more despicable than Wolves. There is no depth of meanness, treachery or cruelty to which they do not descend.

Treachery to what cause, one can't help but wonder! Mr. Hornaday goes on to speak of their being "without mercy," and being "rank cowards." This startlingly emotional anthropomorphism is without value, even if written by Hornaday. It is, however, rather typical of an attitude that has prevailed for untold generations, an attitude that, when coupled with the actual facts, necessitates what is virtually an obituary of a fascinating species.

These facts are reflected, if in a somewhat exaggerated manner, in the now famous story of the Custer Wolf. This best known of American wild canines ended up with a $500 price on its head. It is said to have killed over $25,000 worth of stock in its ten years of hunting along the Wyoming–South Dakota line. Tales were told about it being guarded by a pair of attendant coyotes. Strangely, this story was apparently true, for a hunter by the name of H. P. Williams killed the two coyotes, and finally ended the remarkable career of the Custer Wolf, in 1920. There can be little doubt that the coyotes were more parasites than bodyguards, but the image of so successful a hunter attended by an entourage of smaller canines is both dramatic and in several ways rather satisfying.

The statistics of wolf damage to livestock are readily available, probably accurate for the most part, and quite convincing. Although this book purports to be an impartial study, I must confess to a strong bias in favor of the wolf. However, much as I would like to prove the animal innocent of all harm, I have to take notice of statistics.

The wolf, where it ranges in large numbers, is destructive to domestic stock, and control is justified when losses exceed permissible attrition. It is extremely doubtful, at best, however, that control is necessary, or even advisable, in natural game areas of any size. The wolf normally takes only weak and sickly individuals. To protect a herd of reindeer by killing wolves is to condemn the herd to a worse fate; weak and inferior animals live to breed and weaken the strain. Predator control of this kind is shortsighted and not at all in keeping with the best interests of any conservation project.

The charge that the wolf is a killer not only of man's domestic stock but of man himself is not by any means a sure one. Although a great deal has been written on the subject, there always has been and still is an extremely fine line between fact and fiction in this matter.

The Associated Press released the following story on May 5, 1962:

### WOLVES ATTACK VILLAGE
### IN TURKEY, KILL BOY

IZMIR, TURKEY (AP)—A score or more of wolves, believed to have rabies, attacked a hamlet in Buca district last night, killing a nine-year-old boy and biting or mauling 14 other persons.

Press dispatches said the wolves attacked the 18-dwelling village of Kaynaklar four times during the night. The villagers fought the animals for seven hours with axes and scythes.

A medical team rushed to the village, placed it under quarantine and inoculated the residents against rabies.

Similar stories, old enough now to be legend, are told of villages in Sweden, Norway, Finland, Russia, India, the United States, and many other areas. These older tales do not stipulate rabies as an ingredient of the nightmare.

General Kinloch reported:

When impelled by hunger they sometimes become bolder, and when we were encamped at Jalalabad during the winter of 1878–79, sentries were on more than one occasion attacked by Wolves, which nightly visited our camp.

The London *Sunday Express* for May 13, 1962, carried this amusing tale which reveals not so much the wolf's behavior as man's attitude:

### WOLF PAWS AT VASILY'S CAR DOOR—
### FROM INSIDE

The Soviet weekly paper Izvestia has been telling readers the astonishing story of a man's singlehanded encounter with a savage wolf, a tale as old as Russia herself, but with a modern twist.

Says the paper's Crimea correspondent: "Vasily Plashkin was driving one night along a lonely road from Sevastapol, in the Crimea, to fetch a hunting party from a remote village in the steppe.

"Suddenly, he saw in the distance dozens of flickering lights, sharp and glittering, caught in the rays of his headlamps.

" 'Wolves,' he thought to himself, pressing hard on the accelerator.

*Unarmed*

"As he approached, the wolves, instead of scattering, ran ahead of his car.

"He surged forward—right into the middle of the pack.

"The wolves dashed frantically right and left of the car. But one of the animals hit his bumper and was bowled over.

"Vasily got out of the car cautiously when he saw that the coast was clear, and looked at his 'catch.'

"It was a huge, brown-grey wolf, lying inert in the roadway.

"He pulled the huge beast into the back seat, and continued his journey.

"But he had barely gone 25 miles when he heard a strange noise from the back seat.

"He turned, and almost fainted with terror. The 'dead' wolf was standing upright on the back seat, breathing balefully, its enormous jaws extended and snapping.

"Hardly knowing what he was doing, Vasily braked to a halt and jumped out of the car.

"He slammed the car door hard behind him, and as he leaned against it he realized he carried no weapon of any kind with him.

"Inside the car, the enraged animal was battering against the car's windows.

"At any moment, thought Vasily, the glass would break.

"The night was cold and chilly, and Vasily began blowing on his frozen hands wondering what he should do.

"Then he noticed the exhaust fumes coming out of the exhaust pipe—he had forgotten to switch off the engine.

*Idea*

"Suddenly an idea struck him.

"He rushed round to the back of the car, pulled out the box of tools and a length of rubber hose.

"He hacked a hole in the body of the car and connected the hose to the exhaust pipe, then pushed it through the hole he had made.

"In a few minutes the interior of the car was filled with suffocating fumes.

"The wolf tossed about and finally quietened down, overcome by the poisonous exhaust fumes.

"Then Vasily continued his journey, with a dead wolf in the back of his car—and the best hunting story of his career."

Writing to the author in May, 1962, American hunter-author Elmer Keith reported:

I know of one case on an island in S.E. Alaska where they found a man's skeleton and a rusted .357 S & W,[2] and three wolf skeletons together, no doubt on that one . . . talked with several men who had been in Russia in the old days when they hunted wolves with sleds and 4 to 6 horses and used buckshot

[2] The specification of a .357 S & W by Keith, an arms expert, marks this as a recent report, possibly one of the most recent on record. The .357 Magnum caliber was developed in the middle 1930's. The first revolver designed to use this cartridge was presented to J. Edgar Hoover in 1935.

. . . sometimes whole outfits were not only run down, but eaten up, horses and men both, and the harness, where the wolves travel in big packs of 100 or more. No fiction about this.

In reviewing references to wolf attacks on man, two interesting points become readily apparent. Most such references are old, and relatively few come from North America. One is forced to two conclusions, *if* the accounts are taken at face value: first, wolves vary in habit, at least in their attitude toward man, from place to place; and, second, attacks on man were more common in earlier days. The first conclusion is quite probable, the second is somewhat more difficult to accept since the reduction in the numbers of reports of attacks on man did not necessarily coincide with the decimation of wolf populations. Even in the last century, when thousands and perhaps tens of thousands of wolves ranged through the American West, reports of attacks on man were relatively rare. It is entirely within the realm of possibility that an ingredient of the "wolf as dangerous to man" problem is man's own need to fictionalize the subject.

Dingo (*Canis familiaris dingo*).
Courtesy of the American Museum of Natural History.

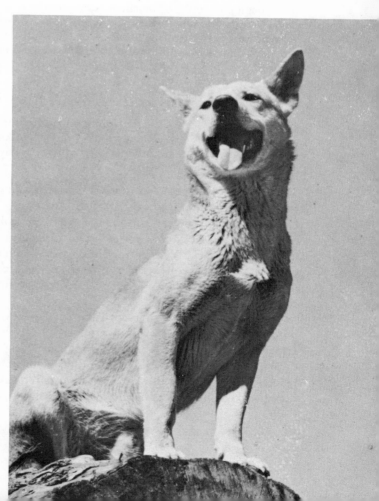

In their classic study of the wolf (*The Wolves of North America*), Young and Goldman cite many old references:

In the Scotland of James VI (16th Century), wolf attacks became so numerous that houses, called "spittals," were provided for travellers at night, specifically as places of retreat from the marauding packs. (Harting, 1880)

Camden wrote, in 1586,

Wolves, which, to the great damage of the country, not only furiously set upon cattle, but even upon their owners themselves, to the manifest danger of their lives. . . .

In 1890, St. George Mivart wrote,

In 1875 one hundred and sixty-one persons fell victims to wolves in Russia.

T. Thornton, 1806 . . .

. . . by attacking children, whom they carry off and devour.

Ross Cox is quoted as saying, in 1831,

Although the wolves of North America are the most daring of all the beasts of prey on that continent, they are by no means so courageous or ferocious as those of Europe, particularly in Spain or the South of France, in which countries they commit dreadful ravages both on man and beast; whereas an American wolf, except forced by desperation, will seldom or never attack a human being . . .

Young and Goldman themselves observe,

European comments of earlier times regarding unprovoked attacks on humans are numerous while those relating to North America are much fewer. Whether these stories are products of the fertile imagination, or are truth, is difficult to determine.

They go on to suggest that there is more than enough smoke to indicate that there exists or at least existed a fire of sorts.

In a twenty-five year period of a wolf-control program, the United States Fish and Wildlife Service failed to substantiate a single reported unprovoked attack. A newspaper in Ontario, in an area known for blood-curdling tales of wolf attacks, offered a $100 reward for proof of an unprovoked attack. It went uncollected for the fourteen years we know about.

There is no shortage of records from North America although, as we noted earlier, they are fewer in number by far than those from Europe. Experts rally to both banners, some declaiming that no proven cases of unprovoked attack exist, and others countering with names, dates, places, and even witnesses. Where human remains have been found on blood-soaked snow laced unmistakably with wolf tracks, it is impossible to tell whether or not the person died from any of a number of causes and was later eaten as carrion, or whether he was attacked and killed. There is a distinct difference, certainly. Where human and wolf remains have been found together, *unprovoked* attack is impossible to establish. In short, it is extremely difficult to come to any conclusion about this matter of wolf versus man. It looks very much like a small amount of fact liberally spiced with fiction.

There may be certain factors that affect the wolf's attitude toward man which could account for the contradictions apparent in the subject. Wolves probably reproduce according to food supply. Lions, for example, breed more often and produce larger litters in captivity where food is always available, than they do in the wild state. Quite probably, wolves are similarly responsive to their environment. If a series of four or five very mild winters followed in succession, the hoofed prey on which the wolf essentially depends might increase markedly in numbers. Although this is not substantiated, the number of wolves in a given area might increase correspondingly, not just as wolves from other areas drifted in for the easy pickings, but because the local animals might have increased their reproductive rate. Also, their migratory, or at least far-ranging, hunting habits might be cut back from lack of necessity.

If a particularly severe winter followed this period of increase and plenty, the needs of the wolves would be likely to exceed the food supply available to them. Desperation might bring on a whole series of bold attacks not attempted under other conditions. If a migration of hoofed animals was diverted, or failed to materialize for any reason, wolves that, historically, congregated along a migration route might similarly be driven to excesses of behavior. Whether hunger alone drives wolves to such attacks, or if other mechanisms of physiology and behavior are involved, is not known. Overpopulation, as is known to be the case with other mammals, could trigger mechanisms of which we know little or nothing.

The possibility of rabies being at the root of many attacks by individual animals cannot be overlooked. Coyotes, close relatives of the wolves and frequently their range mates, are known to be a great reservoir of the disease, and wolves are certainly subject to it as well.

Several reports exist of smallpox epidemics ravaging Indian tribes and bringing scavenger wolves in droves. Wolves thus emboldened (they reportedly did not always wait for Indians to die before moving in to feast) might continue to seek human flesh when the available supply of corpses was used up. This is believed to be the case with leopards in India, as we have noted. Wars in Europe have, historically, been followed by an intensification of the wolf problem, as have epidemics of large proportions.

Joy Adamson, famed author of the *Born Free* saga, with tame wolf belonging to George Wilson of St. Louis.

The wolves of North America, when they were plentiful, had one of the richest harvests on earth available to them. Nowhere, save on the African plains, have there ever been such enormous herds of wild game as were once here. Neither Russia nor Siberia ever boasted anything to equal the millions of bison and pronghorn that roamed the prairies of North America, while the woodlands were rich in various deer and the Moose (*Alces*), and the uplands swarmed with the mountain goat and wild sheep. It is quite possible that these were prime factors in keeping down attacks on man. Unlike other parts of the world, even vast wolf populations simply did not need man.

A review of the literature on the subject leaves the distinct impression that many more attacks occurred in winter than in any other season. Here, too, a food shortage would seem to account for the difference. Also, a wolf attack in the bleak and harsh winter night makes for better fiction and people are more apt to sit around a fire and tell such stories in winter than in the summer. Almost certainly, there are many factors that can account for great differences of behavior in animals of one species. One man's experience in a given place may be totally different from another's at the same place at a different time. The carnivores of the world are at the extreme end of a food chain. All the factors that affect the food source of other animals eventually affect them. Carnivores must work for a living in a way unknown to grazers and browsers and a certain seasonal desperation is not only discernible but understandable. Just what the mechanisms are that trigger marked alterations in behavior are not known, but it can be assumed that the severity of the seasons and the available supply of hoofed prey lie at the root of it all. All that has been said and written cannot be discounted. Almost certainly, wolves have attacked men; probably provoked for the most part by the rigors of their environment.

The best we can hope to do in this particular matter is strike a medium. As we deal with other reputedly dangerous animals we will find that there exist medical reports, government statistics, names of doctors, and photographs of victims. Such is not the case with the wolf. Wolves are predators—large predators—and thereby at least potentially dangerous, at least part of the time, or under certain conditions. Wolves are not the despicable, treacherous, and cruel villains of Mr. Hornaday's emotional prose, either. Wolves are animals, devoid of human emotions, capable of very sociable behavior among their kind, and worthy of further study.

# CHAPTER 3

# *Bears*

A REVIEW of the popular literature on the bears, and much of the alleg-edly scientific writing as well, makes poor reading due to the amount of rhetoric employed to prove these animals harmless on the one hand and dangerous on the other. Bears tend to be cranky after they reach maturity, and are immensely powerful creatures. Any bear is harmless at a distance, and any bear is potentially extremely dangerous at close quarters. Occasionally, moreover, an individual specimen will take the initiative in closing that all-important safety zone, and it is then that the animal must be considered dangerous to man. In dealing with these ani-mals we must keep foremost in our minds the realization that bears are individualists to an extraordinary degree. Experience with one is no guide in dealing with another. To be safe, one must take the position that all are dangerous and should therefore be treated with great respect.

The bears, or Ursines, are a relatively recent development in the ani-mal kingdom, and are very closely related to the dogs, or Canines. Ivan Sanderson describes them as "nothing but gigantic, tail-less Canines." Until modern times, bears were spread all over North America, from the Arctic to central Mexico; throughout the Andes in South America; and all across Eurasia, including Japan, Formosa, Borneo, Sumatra, and Java, and along the southern Mediterranean coast. Being far too tempting a target for anyone with a gun, they have been driven out of much of their range and, apart from the North American Black Bear, are generally found today only in more remote areas. Yet, throughout most of the mountainous terrain encompassing their original range, they can still be found, and some lowland wilderness regions still have limited populations. The far (American) northern populations are still comparatively intact, although the advent of light, private aircraft, extremely high-powered rifles like the .375 Magnum, and a class of moneyed big-game hunters who have all but exhausted the supply of other trophy-caliber game, probably mark the eventual doom of the more impressive species. The great Grizzly Bear (*Ursus horribilis*)—actually one of the American Brown Bears—once ranged throughout much of North America in large numbers, while today fewer than a thousand are believed to be left in the United States exclusive of Alaska.

The classification of the group is a matter of constant controversy and at times appears to be rather arbitrary. Certainly, the space allotted to us here will not permit a presentation of the interesting taxonomic arguments, and we will say in passing that, except for the Sloth Bear of India (*Melursus*), the Spectacled Bear (*Tremarctos*), and the small-headed Polar Bear of the Arctic (*Thalarctos*), most of the world's bears are remarkably similar in most respects.

For our purposes here, the following generic breakdown will suffice:

| | |
|---|---|
| *Ursus* | Brown Bear—including grizzly, kodiak, etc.—North America and Eurasia. |
| *Tremarctos* | Spectacled Bear—South America. |
| *Helarctos* | Sun-Bear—Southeast Asia. |
| *Selenarctos* | Moon Bear—Middle to Far East, centered around the Himalayas. |
| *Euarctos* | American Black Bear—North America. |
| *Melursus* | Sloth-Bear—India. |
| *Thalarctos* | Polar Bear. |

There are wide variations in appearance, size and behavior among geographic races or mere populations of individual species, but proportionately not so much among the species, or even genera, themselves. Animals as adaptable as bears do not need to differentiate into endless species to survive; individuals within a species or genus make the necessary adjustments. For instance, the American Black Bear (*Euarctos*) ranges through every type of terrain and environment found in the United States, from mountains to coastal swamps, and from deserts and plains to deep forests.

The Brown Bear makes a good starting point in our discussions of bear behavior, for not only is it the most impressive of the *Ursidae*, but one form constitutes the largest terrestrial carnivore left on earth. This, the

Grizzly Bears (*Ursus horribilis*).          Wilford L. Miller.

Kodiak Bear (*Ursus middendorffi*), limited in range to a few islands off southeast Alaska, can weigh close to a ton and have a maximum length of nearly a dozen feet. The so-called "grizzlies" belong in the genus *Ursus*. About 75 "species" have been described but, while these animals vary greatly in color from area to area, all may be varieties of but a single species.

Early American history and prehistoric Indian lore are full of harrowing grizzly bear tales. In point of fact, the American Indian probably avoided the animal before the advent of white man and his firearms, though it once roamed the prairies in great numbers. Reliable accounts of large specimens taking several heavy slugs from big-bore rifles and still pressing home a determined, albeit usually defensive attack demonstrate how ineffectual even a tightly drawn bow must have been. Certainly, they were killed by Indians, but the toll that could be taken by an angry, adult grizzly probably limited its tormentors to the bravest of the braves.

Plantigrade, or flat-footed, and equipped with nonretractable claws (characteristic of all bears), the grizzly bear is truly omnivorous. It hunts, fishes, gathers, and browses, eating anything from grass, roots, berries, and fruits to insects, honey, reptiles, fish, and other meat. Essentially restricted to the Northwest today, most sleep away part of the winter, and all females normally produce two cubs in late January or early February. Indeed, two cubs constitute the standard litter among all of the world's bears. Single births occur, and triplets and even quadruplets may be born on occasion.

Hornaday said of the grizzly bear:

Down to the advent of the breech-loader, the Grizzly was a bold, aggressive and highly dangerous animal. When attacked, he would charge his enemies with great ferocity, striking terrible blows with paws that were like sledge-hammers armed with huge hooks of steel. The combined swiftness and strength with which any large bear can strike must be seen or felt to be fully appreciated.

I . . . am convinced that naturally the disposition . . . is rather peaceful and good-natured . . . no animal is more prompt to resent affront or injury. . . . The Grizzly temper is defensive, not aggressive. . . .

Lewis and Clark wrote a great deal about this animal, and at one point spoke of it as "a creature of extraordinary ferocity." Theodore Roosevelt wrote, "No Grizzly will assail a man now unprovoked . . . though if he is wounded or thinks himself cornered he will attack his foes with a headlong, reckless fury that renders him one of the most dangerous of wild beasts." John M. Holzworth described the animals as "fighting machines of the first order." The same author says that unprovoked attacks are all but unknown, and poses the very interesting question, "Who is to say when a bear is provoked?"

The people who have been hugged to death by bears in fiction are uncountable; the number who have met their fate this way in real life is almost certainly zero. Bears bite. They may take a swipe at an enemy in passing, or if the encounter occurs in thick brush, but a normal bear attack (if there is such a thing) generally involves a man running and a bear running after him. In such cases, teeth are the weapons used. Pulp magazine artists invariably have these impressive creatures wading into a fight in a standing posture like steel-clawed prize fighters. Since this makes for better composition on a page, it is in a sense understandable. However, a bear is an animal that moves on all fours, and it is in that position when it closes for combat. The bear goes up on its hind legs to reach for things, and to see over obstacles like dense brush, but generally not to attack.

Ernest Thompson Seton wrote:

Notwithstanding the sinister reputation that has won for him the names "*horribilis*," "*grisly*," "*ferox*," etc., the Grizzly, according to all the best authorities, never attacks man, except when provoked. That is, he is a harmless, peaceful giant, perfectly satisfied to let you alone if you let him alone.

Seton quotes a number of sources discussing the reputation this animal has acquired down through the years. They are in general agreement with the observations already cited above. However, the World Wildlife Fund described the grizzly as "about the only really dangerous mammal in early America."

There can be little doubt that grizzly bears in the United States, and in Canada, have made apparently unprovoked attacks on men, with fatal results to one or both parties. The problem, as obliquely presented by Holzworth, is that it is really impossible to determine if a bear has been provoked or not. A man on foot who approaches a thicket and is suddenly charged by a female bear may think himself unfairly set upon, never knowing that he had approached two concealed cubs. A man on horseback who is attacked and sees his favorite mount killed by an enraged grizzly may similarly feel himself victimized, not knowing (or caring!) that the last one, two, or three mounted men encountered by the animal had taken shots at it, possibly inflicting painful wounds. With man's record of trophy-hunting in mind, the term "unprovoked" has little or no meaning.

Provoked attacks have occurred in great numbers and have often been disastrous. Many men have survived attacks, mainly because the bear bit and ran, perhaps charging half by accident in the direction of the noise. Other men have been terribly mutilated. Bears, as we said, are immensely powerful and have extremely long claws which, while not razor-sharp, are capable of inflicting great damage when employed. All indications are, however, that most injuries have been caused by the bear's impressive teeth.

American Black Bear (*Euarctus americanus*).

National Museum of Canada.

The North American Black Bear (*Euarctos*) has a perfectly vast range, from northern Alaska to southern Florida; across all of Canada, south along the West Coast, the Rockies all the way into Mexico, around the Great Lakes, through New England, New York, and, in fact, throughout just about every wilderness region left on the continent. They frequently range into suburban areas in many parts of North America.

The black is not big as bears go, but large males can approach 500 pounds and reach a length of over six feet. Nonetheless, it is the smallest bear on the continent, and the most common. Color phases include cinnamon and nearly white (in areas of British Columbia), with the black phase always having a brown muzzle and generally some white on the breast.

Like the other North American species, the black bear is omnivorous, shy, and short-tempered. It is a powerful animal and not to be toyed with. Protected today in many areas (although still a bounty animal in others), it tends to become more bold where not hunted. A close encounter could be disastrous and, indeed, a young girl was killed *and eaten* a couple of years ago in Michigan. A specimen newly out of hibernation or with cubs can be downright ferocious.

*The National Observer* for September 2, 1963, carried a report from Anchorage, Alaska, where four attacks were made by black bears. One man was killed and two severely mauled. The report suggests that the summer of 1963 produced a poor blueberry crop driving the bears to seek other food. Charles W. Major of Fairbanks was dragged from his sleeping bag while on a hunting trip. A companion shot the bear, but not before Mr. Major was badly injured. A few days later, an electronics engineer from Fairbanks, George P. Roberts, was driven from his tent and badly bitten and clawed before a companion killed the animal. William Strandberg was killed and his brother found his maimed body with a bear standing over it. Larry J. Bidlake was chased up a tree and bitten on the legs. The Fish and Wildlife Service warned people in the woods to be alert until the cranberries ripened. It was taken for granted that the

Warning poster for national park in Canada.

Minister of Northern Affairs and National Resources, Canada.

# WARNING !

BEARS are WILD animals. Many have lost the fear of man because they are protected in the National Parks. All are **dangerous** if approached closely.

Food is essential to all wild animals and bears seek food when they approach a person or a car. **They may attack you** without warning and for no apparent reason.

For your protection Park Regulations prohibit feeding bears.

## PLAY SAFE · DON'T TAKE CHANCES

attacks, all of which took place within a space of a few weeks, were prompted by efforts at man-eating.

Hand-feeding from automobiles, or approaching on foot in an effort to "get a good picture," is a singularly foolish practice. This is particularly true in park areas where protection reduces the animal's apparently natural fear of man. In remote wilderness areas, a normal black bear will move off at the approach of man. In parks, specimens climb onto parked cars and often attempt to reach in through the windows to get handouts from the inhabitants. Clearly, the last set of circumstances is the most dangerous, and I would suggest that the more nearly tame a bear is, the more likely it is to cause injury. This does not weigh in a discussion of animals actually provoked by an approach toward their cubs, or wounding, of course. In fact, leave this animal alone, and get out of its way with as little noise or fuss as possible.

The Polar Bear (*Thalarctos*) probably has been implicated in more unprovoked attacks than any other species. It is possible that some of these attacks have been prompted by hunger since, except in the brief Arctic summer, the animal cannot fall back on honey, berries, and other vegetable food when the hunting is poor. Bruce S. Wright says of them:

> The polar bear is truly one of the most dangerous land animals alive as they are the only bears that live entirely on meat. There is no other large land carnivore that has had less contact with man, and consequently has less fear of him. This is why they are so dangerous.

Kaare Rodahl wrote, in 1953:

> . . . at times will stalk and attack a man, at other times he will flee like a ghost at the slightest scent of human beings.

He goes on to tell the amusing story of a sailor who was charged on the ice and who threw off his jacket to be able to run faster. The bear paused to examine the garment and then took up the chase again. The sailor kept discarding diversionary articles of his apparel as he ran toward his ship. He arrived at his destination, quite naked, at the same time as the bear who caught up with him and began licking his hand. True or not, the story will probably be around for a long time!

Stories of these bears retreating, and of others attacking balance each other out, it would seem, leaving no conclusion possible. Polar bears are often accused of attacking open boats, and almost certainly some of these tales are true. There are factors that enter into the picture that lend plausibility to even diametrically opposed opinions. First and foremost is the consideration of individual differences. There can be little doubt that some polar bears are more shy than others of the same group and

Polar Bear (*Thalarctos maritimus*).
Courtesy of the American Museum of Natural History.

even sex. Previous experience with man certainly would be a contributing factor, as would degree of hunger. Females will fight to protect their young, particularly since there is good evidence that they must protect them from males who will eat their own offspring if hungry and given the opportunity. A very important factor is probably latitude. As Seton put it:

The White Bear, like the Grizzly, has learned that guns are very much more dangerous than arrows or spears. Along his Southland, where he commonly meets whalers or explorers he is shy, fearful as a fox. Farther north, where he never meets a gunman, he is much more aggressive.

Most reporters point out that attacks on men more often occur in winter than in summer, which strengthens the theory that the polar bear can be regarded as a potential man-eater, at least in parts of its range.

Second in size only to the Kodiak and other giant races of brown bears, the polar bear is a formidable creature on the ice, or in the water. It is a true hunting animal, swift, silent, well-camouflaged, and quite cunning. Under no circumstances should one be trusted. The unknowns that combine to create the bear's "personality" are too variable and the animal far too powerful to permit any license in dealing with them at close quarters.

Writing of the Indian sloth bear in 1896, G. P. Sanderson said: "Bears are dangerous to an unarmed man. Woodcutters and others, whose avocations take them into the jungles, are frequently roughly handled by them." Dividing the bears of India into three species, *Snow*,[1] *Himalayan Black*, and *Indian* or *Sloth*, Brigadier General Kinloch wrote of each in turn . . .

1. I think I am justified in saying that it is very seldom indeed that one of this species (*Snow*) will deliberately attack a man.

2. Occasionally, certainly, the Black Bear proves a formidable antagonist, and I have known more than one British Officer killed by them, while one constantly meets with natives who have been terribly mutilated in encounters with one of the species; but these accidents have usually occurred, when the animal has been attacked or suddenly met with, in thick cover where the bear had every advantage.

3. The Indian Bear has the character of being very savage, and in some parts of the country it is dreaded by the natives as much as, or more than, the Tiger.

General Kinloch then goes on to describe mutilated, faceless natives and similar living testimonials to the animal's reputed ferocity.

The Sun-Bear (*Helarctos*), referred to earlier, ranges from the eastern Himalayas to Sze-chwan in China, and south to Burma, sections of Indo-

---

[1] Known as *Ursus pruinosus* or *Ursus arctos pruinosus;* a gray or silvery form of Brown Bear. There is, however, much confusion here as *Ursus isabellinus*, an almost white form, has also been described from the Himalayan-Tibetan area, and called the "Snow Bear."

china, Malaya, and Borneo. It is a pleasant-looking creature between four and five feet long with a rudimentary tail. Basically black, it has a light muzzle and a characteristic yellowish ring on its chest. Essentially arboreal, it has long claws, particularly on the forefeet. Often kept as a pet, reports vary as to its actual tractability and there is every indication that it is probably as unpredictable as the other bears. It would certainly be unwise to trust an adult specimen too far! Reputedly, at least, it has attacked men in the wild, without apparent provocation. It is probably one more case where proximity can lead to an unfortunate chain of events culminating in a dead bear or a badly mauled man.

In reviewing scores of references, and in corresponding with dozens of people with wide experience with one bear or another, the author has been unable to find any serious disagreement with the following capsule summary of any bear's position relative to man:

1. Bears are extremely adaptable, variable, and therefore individualistic. Generalizations or predictions about the behavior of any individual animal are hazardous in the extreme where they involve close proximity.

2. Bears vary greatly in behavior from season to season in some parts of their range, and are equally variable from one range to another.

3. Bears do sometimes attack without any apparent provocation. In most cases, "hidden" provocation is probably involved.

4. Although bears can use their extremely formidable claws in devastatingly powerful swipes, biting is a more characteristic form of attack. Similarly, bears can and do rear up on their hind legs, but the quadrupedal position is more likely to be employed in an assault.

5. Bears are quite nearsighted, and do not have particularly good hearing. Their sense of smell is very keen, however, and the downwind position is the safest for man.

6. It is never safe to approach any bear, and this includes feeding them through the bars at zoos, or from car windows in national parks. More than one person has lost a hand or arm by disregarding posted warnings.

One point of clarification is needed while we are on the subject of bears. The two favorite "bears" of picture books, the Koala "Bear" of Australia and the Giant Panda "Bear" of China, are not bears at all. The former is a marsupial much more closely related to kangaroos than to any bear on earth, and the latter comes closest to the raccoons.

# CHAPTER 4

# *The Leopard Seal and Walrus*

Victor B. Scheffer estimates, in his *Seals, Sea Lions and Walruses*, that the total world population of the pinnipeds is between fifteen and twenty-five million individuals. There are currently recognized but three families, twenty genera, and forty-seven species and subspecies. Considering the vast pole-to-pole range of these active marine mammals, they constitute a small and highly specialized group.

Categorically, all of the pinnipeds are flesh-eaters. They dine variously on fish, squid and octopus, shellfish, sea birds, macroplankton, other seals, perhaps an occasional small cetacean, and, reportedly, some carrion. The reports of seaweed found in the stomachs of slaughtered specimens almost certainly represent accidental ingestion. With forty-seven seals, sea lions, and walruses to choose from, popular writers have generally chosen only a few to accuse of being dangerous to man, the leopard seal, and the walrus leading the list.

In fact, the Walruses (there are two subspecies, *Odobenus rosmarus rosmarus*, Atlantic, and *O. r. divergens*, Pacific) can be extremely troublesome if cut off from the water. Like most intelligent animals, and walruses are quite intelligent, they fear man and generally seek to escape when approached on rocky shore or ice floe. Restricted both in distribution and numbers, they seldom range very far south of the Arctic Circle in summer, or south of Hudson Bay and Bering Sea latitudes—58 degrees north—in winter (one record indicates 42 degrees north). The total number of specimens alive today is estimated to be under 100,000. Walruses could have no interest in man as a potential meal for they eat shellfish, principally, and possibly some carrion such as small dead whales. With the exception of the characteristic tusks, actually enormously elongated canines and found in both sexes, their teeth are flattened or rounded, and adapted for crushing molluscs.

Walruses grow to great size, the male approaching a ton and a half, the female nearly a ton. During breeding season, or with young in tow, they can be quarrelsome and attacks on small boats are reported from time to time. Certainly a wounded and enraged animal would be a handful with which to contend. A staple item in the economy of the Eskimo tribes, walruses are hunted assiduously, but are seldom encountered by anyone not actually hunting them. To the Eskimo in a skinboat who misjudges his

Walrus (*Odobenus rosmarus*).
Courtesy of the American Museum of Natural History.

harpoon throw, or to the adventurer who stumbles into a harem during the breeding season, walruses can be a lot to handle. While they are extremely affectionate in captivity (the author has had the good fortune to "cuddle" a couple of specimens brought to the New York Aquarium by Dr. Carleton Ray) they are less desirous of human attention in the natural state. On the unlikely chance that you encounter one, and it doesn't flee, don't press the issue. In close quarters, the walrus would certainly prevail with all that weight, and those tusks, to throw around.

The Leopard Seal (or Sea-Leopard of earlier writers), *Hydrurga leptonyx*, belongs to the subfamily *Lobodontinae* of the family *Phocidae*. It is believed to be represented in the world today by about a quarter of a million individuals, and all of these are resident in generally inaccessible Antarctic and sub-Antarctic areas. It is found, but never in great numbers, all around the edge of the Antarctic continent, off South Africa, the southern tip of South America, New Zealand, and Australia. Isolated islands in the southern Atlantic. Pacific, and Indian Oceans have limited populations. The leopard seal is thus quite rare, retiring, asocial, and doesn't characteristically seek the company of man or his works, but like most seals is inquisitive.

There can be no doubt that the leopard seal is a fierce animal which could be very dangerous to any man foolish enough to tangle with one at close quarters. Large males grow to ten feet in length and weigh over six hundred pounds. Females grow to over twelve feet and may weigh half a ton. They have long, pointed, incurved teeth, and powerful jaws. Like most of the pinnipeds, they don't chew but rip and shake their prey apart when it is too large to swallow whole. Their teeth and jaws are made for grasping, but that would not keep them from giving a serious bite should the occasion call for one.

Swift and agile in the water, leopard seals are somewhat cumbersome on land or ice. They can, however, lunge with great determination and even put on rather surprising bursts of speed when pressed. The body is streamlined and the neck is flexible and muscular. At best, out of the water, peak performance of short duration would still not be as fast as a man can run. In the water it would be another story; their agility would be something with which to reckon.

Leopard seals dine on ice-front marine birds, especially penguins, and on other species of seals. When times are bad they undoubtedly take what they can get in the way of fish. In years past, some popular writers went so far as to suggest that they attack man as a potential meal. The suggestion was never taken very seriously, apparently, since such stories have had limited currency. The picture of a seal dining on an explorer is somehow more comic than ominous. An argument given in support of this theory was the very questionable claim that many Antarctic seals regularly hunted by the leopard seal are two and three times the weight of a large, full-grown man. It is much more likely that it is the young of these preyed-upon seals that are generally taken. In fact, there isn't a shred of evidence even to suggest that any leopard seal ever attempted to make a meal of a man.

It is interesting to note a few recorded encounters. On May 29, 1911, Captain Robert Scott, with his companions Wilson and Bowers, came upon a young leopard seal on the ice off Inaccessible Island. To set the stage for this drama, Inaccessible Island is an ice-locked bit of frozen ground about three quarters of a mile long. It lies about a mile-and-a-half south of Ross Island, and not far off the Antarctic continent, just about due south of New Zealand. When Scott and his men spotted the young leopard seal, they decided to collect it for their scientific series. Antarctic explorers have never had reason to walk around armed, so they attacked the animal with clubs. In Scott's words, "This poor beast turned swiftly from side to side as we strove to stun it with a blow on the nose. As it

Leopard Seal (*Hydrurga leptonyx*).
Courtesy of British Antarctic Survey. (Photo by F. G. Bird.)

turned it gaped its jaws wide, but oddly enough not a sound came forth, not even a hiss." On his earlier expedition, Scott had noted (March 1, 1904), "We have also passed two or three Sea Leopards asleep on the floes: one we surprised greatly by ramming the floe on which he was taking his siesta, whereat he opened his formidable jaws and threatened us in the most ferocious manner." In describing the animal in his report on Antarctic fauna, Edward A. Wilson, Scott's zoologist, commented: "This seal is a carnivore of the most aggressive type, and probably in the Antarctic has but one enemy to fear, and that is the still more aggressive carnivorous dolphin, the Orca or Killer Whale."

In his report of his Antarctic Expedition of 1907–1909, Sir Ernest Shackleton included a dramatic account of the leopard seal's tenacity:

When he (Joyce) got close he found that the animal was a sea-leopard. He was armed only with a club, and came running for a pistol, for the sea-leopards are savage and aggressive, and can move very rapidly on the ice . . . the animal was still in the same position, and he shot it twice through the heart, and then twice through the skull. It had remarkable tenacity of life, for it still struggled, and even after a fifth ball had been put through its brain some minutes elapsed before it turned over and lay still.

Shackleton went on to say that when they dissected the animal it appeared to have two hearts! Unfortunately, some sled dogs got to the specimen and the extremely doubtful matter was not verified. Elsewhere, Shackleton reported that one of his men was attacked when a leopard seal left the water for an ice floe and found he was not alone. Leopard seals have not had enough experience with men to get used to them. As aggressive carnivores they undoubtedly have a rather bullish attitude.

In the foregoing accounts and, indeed, in almost all reliable accounts that can be found, the topic heading would best be "Man Dangerous to Leopard Seals" since they inevitably report on man attacking the animal, and the animal attempting to remain alive. Aside from a flood of emotional adjectives like "ferocious," the worst that seems to be reported about this animal's behavior is that it does attempt to defend itself against being slaughtered and it apparently is capable of giving a rather good account of itself.

Is the leopard seal dangerous to man?

In a letter written to the author on August 8, 1962, Philip Law, Director of Australia's Antarctic Division, says:

. . . we consider the Leopard Seal much maligned. . . . It is a shy creature on land and is generally only dangerous if you stand on the beach between it and its escape route to the water. It is curious in the sea and will follow a boat but we have no record of it ever having attacked one.

Victor B. Scheffer wrote to the author on May 11, 1962, from Seattle, Washington:

"It does not seem likely that any pinniped would attack a man without provocation. . . ." Scheffer later added, "The approach of a man during the frenzy of the mating season may represent to the dominant male no more and no less than the approach of a 'rival.' "

What is provocation? Many seals, including the leopard seal, are apparently possessed of a short temper. They are carnivores themselves and are in turn preyed upon by killer whales and sharks. In some species the males are highly competitive during the breeding season and a "harem" system prevails in the social structure of most of them. Females are for a period very attentive to their pups. All of these factors—being keyed to the hunt, being alert to attack, being quarrelsome about sex, and being concerned for the safety of their young—make many of the pinnipeds dangerous animals to tamper with; worse, no doubt, during certain seasons. Most pinnipeds, and certainly the leopard seal, can inflict painful and even serious injuries. Many biologists have been badly "nipped" by species far less aggressive than the leopard seal when their intensity of interest in matters scientific overran their common sense in dealing with wild animals. Provocation is quite simply a matter of giving an animal good reason to fear, resent, or otherwise object to your proximity. As a result, the leopard seal is dangerous to man only if molested or led to believe it is going to be interfered with.

# CHAPTER 5

# *The Killer Whale*

EARLY in the morning of Thursday, January 5, 1911, six or seven large Killer Whales (*Orcinus orca*) surfaced aft of the *Terra Nova*, the Antarctic research vessel of Captain Robert Falcon Scott. She was anchored to the floating ice shelf of McMurdo Sound, approximately 2,200 miles due south of New Zealand. In the few minutes that followed, expedition photographer Herbert G. Ponting very nearly lost his life. Using a cooperative pack tactic peculiar to these animals, the hungry cetaceans smashed the ice on which he was standing in an effort to catapult some tethered Eskimo dogs and, presumably, Ponting himself into the near-freezing waters. Captain Scott witnessed and recorded the incident in his journal, which was published and republished a number of times. Nearly every author who has discussed the killer whale at any length since has made some reference to the affair. I told the story in detail in my *Antarctica: Land of Frozen Time*. This celebrated adventure has stood for over half a century as proof positive that the killer whale is a man-eater. Other adventures, recounted on considerably less authority than Captain Scott's journal, could be disproved in almost any intelligent discussion, but Ponting's close scrape was always available to anyone who wanted to show the killer whale to be man's deadly enemy. Seeking the truth about the killer whale has proved to be the most intriguing investigation in all the research for this book.

John D. Craig tells a tale in his *Danger Is My Business* of a killer whale trapping a diver in a submarine grotto and biting and battering at the rocks of the entrance to get at him. Before passing on to other deep sea monsters, Craig retreats to the safety of the ice-battering business without actually naming Ponting. He goes on to say "they will attack and smash small boats, and eat whatever falls into the water from them." Since man is the one animal currently building and using boats, we can assume that he means they eat men.

Frank T. Bullen, in his *Denizens of the Deep*, has the killer whale and Swordfish (*Xiphias*) joining forces to slaughter large whales and their young. This delightful fiction, I believe, arose from the fact that the name *swordfish* was reportedly once used for the killer because of its extremely long dorsal fin. Other writers have the orca swimming beneath large whales and slashing their bellies open with this same fin.

Killer Whale (*Orsinus orca*), breaching.

Official U.S. Navy Photo.

That would be a neat trick since the six- to seven-foot fin is so limp it often flops over like a spaniel's ear.

Dr. Tedford L. Greathouse of Oxnard, California, writing in *Skin Diver* magazine for January, 1960, says, "It has been known to bite holes in small boats in an attempt to get at its occupants." Writing in *Skin Diver* for July, 1961, Aden F. Romine says, "The killer whale is the bitter enemy of man . . . because there is not a fact on record to disprove it." Of all the statements one encounters about the killer whale, that is probably the least logical! However, Mr. Romine's article is a classic collection of inaccuracies, and some of his other observations are equally suspect. He claims that there is one known incident of men being eaten by the killer whale and this involved one which smashed up a fishing boat off Cape Town, South Africa, and ate its four occupants. He mentions that another stove in the hull of a fishing craft off northern California but failed to get the two anglers.

Let us first identify and locate the animal in question, and then examine some of these stories in detail.

*Orcinus orca* is the largest of the dolphins.[1] The name Killer *Whale*, however, is not inaccurate since the dolphins and porpoises are all small whales, members of the mammalian order of *Cetacea*. The male grows to thirty feet while the female seldom exceeds half that length. They are communal animals traveling in small herds, packs or pods, or in great convoys reportedly numbering in the dozens and even hundreds. Hundreds of killers together almost certainly represent a migration in search of food rather than a normal hunting pattern. They are, of course, warm-blooded, air-breathing mammals with, it is believed, a very high order

[1] Porpoises (*Phocaenidae*) are not dolphins (*Delphinidae*) though some of the latter, such as the bottlenose dolphin (*Tursiops*) commonly seen in our great aquaria, are erroneously though popularly called "porpoises" in the United States.

of animal intelligence, perhaps the intellectual equal of the apes. This last point, it must be pointed out, is still well within the realm of speculation.

There can be no doubt that the killer whale prefers a diet of warm-blooded animals and its depredations on seal herds, penguins, porpoises, and dolphins have been too often recorded to warrant repeating here. They are stated to attack the largest animals that ever lived on this planet, the great baleen whales or *Mysticeti!* It is reported that they prefer the tongue, and will attack a 100-foot blue whale to get this choice two or three ton morsel.

It is also reported, on good authority, that an aggressive bull baleen whale can put a pack of killers to flight if he gets his dander up. The percentage of successes realized by the killers in their attacks on these huge giants of the sea cannot be estimated. They may succeed most of the time, or only rarely. There is no way of knowing. It may be a matter of individual disposition on the part of the big whale, and possibly a question of leadership among the killers. The social structure of a killer pack would be an interesting thing to study but the odds against such a study ever being done are enormous.

Certainly, the smaller mammals have no defense when attacked. Even their speed can be matched by these large and aggressive predators. Seals have the one advantage of being able to get out of the water. In the open sea, they don't stand too much of a chance, although their quick turning ability may save some. It is also reported that other whales will ground themselves and smother rather than face an onslaught by these powerful carnivores. Such reports are apparently speculative, however, and are usually offered as a probable explanation for the periodic beaching of whales reported from all over the world. Since killer whales themselves are sometimes found high and dry for no apparent reason, the explanation may not be of universal application. From the British Columbia area alone have come several reports of killer whale strandings: twenty at Estevan Point, Vancouver Island in 1945, and eleven at Masset on Queen Charlotte Island in 1941. There have been many, many others, of course. Actually, the reason why whales, including killer whales, beach themselves is not known.[2] When they do, they are condemned to death from suffocation. Even their great muscles cannot keep pushing their enormous weight up enough to allow their lungs to fill.

The killer whale ranges from the Arctic to the very edge of the Antarctic continent. It has been reported from just about every sea in the world. It is reported in the open sea, in harbors and bays, and even along beaches in sheltered sounds.

[2] It has recently been reported that an outbreak of contagious disease is involved, of a pulmonary nature.

Unfortunately, the literature on the killer is almost inevitably colored with misleading adjectives. Even the *U.S. Navy Diving Manual,* which gives the killer a 4 plus or top danger rating, describes it as "ruthless" and "ferocious." That is hardly more clinical than Romine's description of it as the "meanest thing in the sea." A run-down of the literature on this animal will reveal that it is "cruel, heartless, vicious, treacherous, nasty, devilish, monstrous, and pitiless," to name a few things, and not to mention the fact that it is possessed of a violent "bloodlust" and "kills for the joy of it." I would suggest that before we start to investigate some of the crimes against mankind of which it has been accused, we discard all of these descriptive words and take the cool, zoological view that the animal is merely hungry. It has a huge body, it is very active and requires a lot of food. Because, even if the killer whale has eaten a man a day since the dawn of the age of mammals (*and it hasn't!*) it is not cruel, heartless or any of the rest. Those are human emotions and however bright the killer may be, it does not possess them! The simple fact is that we have no yardstick for measuring the emotions of these animals; they are as foreign to us as are the mouselike squeaks with which they communicate among themselves in the darkness and the mystery of their realm. The danger in using human emotions to describe the ways of animals is not merely a semantic one. Their use has done a grave injustice, not so much to the animal (who certainly doesn't care what man thinks of him), but to our own powers of reason and understanding. So overpowering has been this flow of fictional invective that today it is universally taken that the orca is an incorrigible man-eater. As we shall demonstrate, no facts exist to support this belief.

Let us take a long hard look at the most celebrated case of a supposed killer whale attack on man in recent years. Only Ponting's adventure as recorded by Scott has received more attention. For a decade, this story has been told and retold as final proof that the killer whale does attack man.

On the front page of the 7th Sport Night Final of the Friday, March 28, 1952, edition of the San Francisco *Call-Bulletin* (now the *News-Call Bulletin*) there appeared the following headline and story:

### WHALE BITES CAL. BOAT; 2 MEN RESCUED[3]

#### FISHERMEN WIN BATTLE OFF COAST

Two men in a small fishing boat were attacked by a killer whale off the Sonoma County coast today but escaped with their lives when one of them fought off the creature with an oar.

[3] Mr. Robert W. Lee, Managing Editor of the paper, has kindly consented to our quoting the story.

The deep-sea monster—a modern day "Moby Dick"—circled the pair's 14-foot craft several times as they rowed frantically to escape him.

Then he made one preliminary pass underneath the boat, turned, and charged, sinking his teeth into its hull.

### *"Poked Him in Eye"*

He thrashed and twisted, his teeth grinding on the wood, until one of the men grabbed an oar and "poked him right in the eye."

With that he unclamped his teeth and drew away, permitting the pair— H. W. Van Buren, 50, and A. L. Anderson, 72, both Petaluma poultrymen—to reach safety on a nearby island.

Their boat, a six inch hole bitten in its hull, swamped just as they touched the shore.

They were picked up by a Coast Guard helicopter and carried to safety after waiting on the island about an hour and a half for aid.

### *Half Mile off Shore*

The episode—almost unheard of in these waters—took place shortly before 8 A.M. about half a mile off the shore of Bodega Head, a peninsula jutting obliquely off the coast about 30 miles north of San Francisco.

Van Buren and Anderson were approaching the small island in their outboard motor boat with the engine stopped as they coasted toward an intended landing to gather abalone.

In another smaller craft nearby was their companion, George Stewart, also of Petaluma.

Van Buren—who confessed his knees were shaking a little bit after the rescue—told the story:

"We were just about 75 feet from the shore of the rock, about a half-acre island, when we saw him circling us.

"There were a lot of seals in the water, but he wasn't going for them. He seemed to be eyeing us.

"We started rowing as fast as we could to get away. But we didn't get more than 50 feet. Once he came close and went underneath, bumping the boat.

"Then he turned and charged right at us, and hit us as hard as he could.

"He sank his teeth in the boat, one set on the rail and the other underneath on the keel.

"He was hanging on and chewing and twisting, trying to break the boat.

"I was sitting down, trying to hold on. Anderson was doing the same.

"Then I grabbed the oar and I just jabbed him right in his eye. I don't know whether I ruined the eyeball or not, but I poked pretty hard. I sure did.

### *Dark Brown Whale*

"His head was right there in front of me. He was kind of a dark brown.

"When I hit him, he just let go—opened his mouth and went away. I don't know where he went to. We didn't see him again."

Water began gushing in through the gaping hole in the hull and the two men just managed to make the final 25 feet to the shore of the rock.

The boat swamped as they reached it.

Stewart, in the other boat, joined them, but his craft was too small to take all three to the mainland.

In the meantime, a man who witnessed the deep-sea drama from shore notified Coast Guard boatswain's mate first class Norman Paulsen, in charge of the light at Bodega Bay.

### Land on Island

He notified San Francisco headquarters and a helicopter piloted by Lieutenant Tommy Hynes with Lieutenant Milton L. McGregor as his aide, took off from the South San Francisco field.

Hynes landed the ship on the island itself, took Van Buren and Anderson aboard and landed them on a sandspit off Bodega Bay, where they had left their cars when they started their fishing trip.

Stewart returned in his own small boat.

Were the men scared?

"I sure was!" said Van Buren.

The Coast Guard said killer whales—one-ton creatures, from 15 to 20 feet long—are not uncommon in these waters. They ordinarily attack other whales, seals and other large sea creatures, but rarely man.

*Outdoor Life* magazine[4] recapitulated the story in a series of nine drawings under the heading, "This Happened to Me! Killer Foiled." The drawings show a killer whale biting a huge hunk out of the side of the boat. Presumably, it was this incident Dr. Greathouse referred to in his 1960 article when he said, ". . . has been known to bite holes in small boats." Romine probably referred to this episode when he said an orca stove in a fishing craft off northern California. Many other writers have referred to it and so the matter has stood, duly recorded in print, worthy of a banner headline in a large and reputable metropolitan daily. Hence, the killer whale must be a threat to men in small boats. But is it?

Clearly, if the mystery was to be solved, this was the case to study. It happened recently, it is clearly recorded, and the area involved is nearby. This was no rumor of sea monsters, drifting in tardily from some distant and mysterious clime! This happened less than thirty-five miles from San Francisco in 1952.

Step number one was to locate and question the most reputable single source of the story. What was the most authoritative voice repeating it? The answer came in the Biology Laboratory of the United States Antarctic Research Program at McMurdo Sound on frozen Ross Island, just a few miles off the Antarctic mainland. There, just a few miles from the spot where Ponting had his big adventure in 1911, the author found a copy of what is almost certainly the most up-to-date and respected study of the pinnipeds, the afore-mentioned *Seals, Sea Lions and Walruses*. The

[4] *Outdoor Life,* Vol. 119, No. 4 (April, 1957), p. 36

author of that book, Victor B. Scheffer, is a world-recognized authority on marine mammals and a scientist whose integrity is beyond question. Facing page 151 in the book was a photograph of the boat and a caption outlining the adventures of Anderson and Van Buren.

On May 5, 1962, the author wrote to Mr. Scheffer and on May 11 an answer was received which contained the following paragraph:

An important point: I am now convinced that the identification by the fishermen of the attacking beast as a killer whale was wrong. It was quite certainly a great white shark . . . the dentition of the shark, clean and sharp, corresponds to the injury sustained by the dory. A killer whale would have left a coarser, more crushing kind of mark.

Mr. Scheffer's new view of the episode provided the key! Dr. Raymond M. Gilmore, another world-recognized authority on marine mammals, wrote from a whaling station at Richmond, California, on July 13th:

The photo of a boat in Vic Scheffer's book, said to represent attack of killer whale, showed tooth marks of shark . . . I have spoken with two biologists who examined the boat and they agreed it was a shark.

With the permission of the *News-Call Bulletin,* a closeup of the boat is reproduced.

In examining the photograph, keep in mind that the killer has large conical teeth, as much as two inches in diameter at the base. Such teeth,

Boat showing alleged Killer Whale bite.
*San Francisco News-Call Bulletin.*

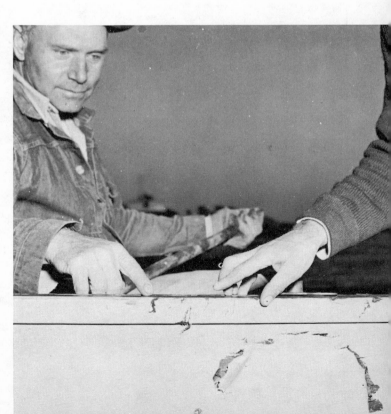

crushing down on wood, could not tear and puncture, but would crush. A shark has exceedingly sharp teeth, the kind that would penetrate, rip, and tear. Clearly, the boat was attacked by a shark.

That is only the conclusion. What of the facts of this story? How was such an error made?

Both killer whales and very large sharks are found off California at the same latitude as San Francisco. A 15-foot Great White Shark (*Carcharodon carcharias*) was taken in a net off San Miguel Island in March of 1958. The distance from Bodega Bay was about 260 miles. However, seeing either animal close up, at least close enough to poke with an oar, is an unusual experience. Although Mr. Anderson was seventy-two and Mr. Van Buren fifty at the time of the incident, it is likely that neither man ever got very close to a killer whale at sea before. A shark, particularly a very large shark (and some sharks grow every bit as large as killer whales) partially submerged, with a hide discolored from age, and probably covered with scars and various marine growths, would look like a whale, particularly if you were under attack, scared half out of your wits, and fighting for your life. There is no question here of misrepre-

Skull of Killer Whale (*Orcinus orca*) with Dr. H. E. Anthony, formerly scientific director of the American Museum of Natural History.

Courtesy of the American
Museum of Natural History.

sentation. Killer whales are known to appear in that area, they are believed to be a threat to man, and an attack by one would not be much of a surprise to anyone who hadn't stopped to question the matter before. The report in the *News-Call Bulletin* was not sensational and was probably very, very close to the actual interview granted by the two terrified men. The account in *Outdoor Life,* five years and one month after the episode, was within the bounds of reasonable reporting although not quite as cautious as the original newspaper account. Apparently, Messrs. Anderson and Van Buren made a very human error and everybody followed suit, for a time, at least.

Aden Romine referred to the eating of four men by a killer whale off Cape Town, South Africa, and it seemed only right to at least look into the matter. The search was a short one. A year and a half earlier, the same magazine, *Skin Diver,* carried an article by the world-renowned scientist, Professor J. L. B. Smith, Ichthyologist at Rhodes University, Grahamstown, South Africa. Fortunately, Professor Smith's article is more characteristic of this interesting and informative magazine than Mr. Romine's. In his article, Professor Smith tells that on July 30, 1956, a large whale attacked a fishing boat in False Bay, at the Cape, and wrecked it; four of the six-man crew drowned. He further reports that it had been suggested that the attack was made by a killer whale. He discounts the idea on a number of points, mainly size. The attacking animal was a *large whale* and the killer is a small one, not even a third the length of a big Blue Whale (*B. musculus*).

Professor Smith had been most helpful to this author in the preparation of other portions of this book and another letter was dispatched to Grahamstown in an effort to find out if the killer who ate four men off Cape Town was, in fact, the non-killer whale who drowned four men in the same area. It is not possible, of course, to nail such a point down. Professor Smith did say, however:

We certainly have no information here about the alleged attack and devouring of four men off Cape Town. While this may have occurred, I think it most unlikely that it would not have been greatly publicized and we should certainly have heard about it.

The author might add that Professor Smith knows his home waters well. It is very difficult to accept the idea that he would not have heard about such a significant thing as a whale, any whale, eating four men in his own back yard! Other reliable sources in South Africa report knowing of no such incident.

In the same letter from which we quoted above, Professor Smith says:

There have been attacks on boats by sharks in that area and in one case a large shark badly battered a fishing boat and so great a hole in it . . . , etc.

On this same point, Dr. V. M. Coppleson, an authority on sharks, wrote in a letter to the author from Sydney, Australia, in June, 1962:

. . . an attack which occurred in Safety Bay, Tasmania, about two years ago in which some claims were made that the attack was made by a killer whale, but those who investigated the attack came to the conclusion that the attacker was a shark and not a killer whale.

Certainly, all of this reflects on the California incident of 1952! We will have more to say about this when we review the alleged shark menace and attempt to evaluate it.

Quite simply, there have been no authenticated reports of attacks by killer whales on men, *outside of the Antarctic*. If there have been, this author has been unable to locate them after exhaustive research. However, the Scott-Ponting affair did happen. During Operation Deepfreeze, a young naval lieutenant, Morton Beebe, had a very similar adventure, also in the Ross Sea area. The color photograph he took of the attacking killer whale (no mistake about sharks in this case!) is the frontispiece of the author's book on the Antarctic. Here, then, at least, are two cases where men on ice were seriously endangered by these animals. Why is it that man, who has been in contact with these animals for thousands of years, has recorded *authenticated* attacks only in the Antarctic?

The killer whale of the polar regions, north and south, is the same animal, as far as we know, as the killer whale of Long Island Sound, San Francisco Bay, and the English Channel. The difference lies not in the animal but in the behavior of man.

There is a standing axiom concerning any dealings with large carnivores—if you act like their natural prey, you stand a good chance of getting into trouble. Animals function, no matter how bright they are (if I may borrow a human value), on basic, natural instincts. They respond to stimuli in rather rigid patterns, and when conditioned or instinctive reflexes are triggered in a hungry beast, trouble can ensue. We offer here the not altogether new theory that, in the Antarctic, man inadvertently acts like the normal prey of the killer whale, and that is how Ponting and Beebe, and a number of others, nearly got into serious trouble.

In the Antarctic, seals and penguins regularly retreat to the often questionable safety of the ice whenever they suspect killer whales are near. Many times, killers have been witnessed and photographed rising out of the water six or eight feet and looking across the surface of the ice for escaping prey. If they spy a likely meal, they attempt to smash the floe or tip it up to get the victim into the water where it can be dealt with. Ice has strange effects on vision and even at short distances it can be extremely difficult to get a clear outline of an object. We don't know how good the killer whale's eyesight is but we can assume it has the same problem. Its eyes are best adapted for use underwater and probably are less effective in the air. Man probably looks like a seal to the killer when it sees him on the ice. Many Antarctic seals are at least as big as man (they may outweigh man by 800 pounds), and even the Emperor penguin gets to be nearly four feet tall. It is a mistake a killer whale easily could make. Even if a man doesn't exactly look like a penguin, the killer whale probably doesn't have the mental facility to understand the difference at once, even if its eyes could detect it.

Of course, if a man ever gets caught off guard and does fall to a killer whale, it will be a purely academic question, to the unfortunate victim, that it was just a case of mistaken identity! It is important, however, to us in our effort to determine whether or not the animal is by nature a man-eater. Before going on to draw our conclusions, let's see what some of the experts have to say. The following quotes are from previously unpublished letters received by the author on direct inquiry and are printed here by permission:

Donald P. de Sylva, research assistant professor, The Marine Laboratory, Institute of Marine Science, University of Miami, June 22, 1962:

. . . I know of no authenticated attacks . . . except to say that these animals are certainly potentially dangerous by their size alone.

Gilbert L. Voss, chairman, Biological Sciences Division, The Marine Laboratory, Miami, July 25, 1962:

Concerning the killer whale, I have been also unable to find any information concerning attack on man. Dr. Paul Hansen, at Charlottenlund Slot, Denmark, who is in charge of the Danish fisheries at Greenland, told me in conversation, that in his many years in killer whale infested waters there has never been a case of a killer whale attacking an Eskimo in a Kayak, regardless of distance from shore; although the Eskimos are fearful of them.

W. D. L. Ride, director, Western Australian Museum, Perth, July 25, 1962:

. . . no authentic reports at all here.

George Mack, director, Queensland Museum, Brisbane, July 11, 1962:

I have no record of . . . the killer whale causing any harm to a human being. . . . In my opinion, the fanciful tales . . . are the creations of novelists and newspapermen. . . .

Stewart Springer, U.S. Fish & Wildlife Service, Bureau of Commercial Fisheries, July 21, 1962:

I have not noticed an authenticated report of death to man caused by . . . the Killer whale. I am quite sure that the Killer whale is dangerous if only because of its size and power.

Bruce S. Wright, director, Northeastern Wildlife Station, Fredericton, New Brunswick, June 18, 1962:

I would still rate the killer whale to be as dangerous to a man in the water as any shark, although records of its attacks on men are almost non-existent.

John E. Randall, professor, Biology Department, University of Puerto Rico, Mayaguez, May 14, 1962:

I know of no injuries or deaths resulting from man's contact with killer whales. . . . I suspect that the killer whale is a very intelligent beast like the porpoise. It certainly has had ample opportunity to attack man. It is most distinctive in color pattern and morphology, as you know. If more than just a very rare attack on some poor Eskimo on an ice floe has occurred, I think we would have accounts of it. But I must confess that I would be more than just a little uneasy if I were to share the same part of the ocean with a hungry killer whale.

Raymond M. Gilmore, biologist, and writer-lecturer, and consultant on whaling, Richmond, California, July 13, 1962:

The confusion between man and the emperor penguins to a killer whale may result in the interest shown by killer whales to men on ice, but close inspection by the killer whale has revealed strangeness of man and reluctance to attack. This explains the absence of records of attacks on man.

Victor B. Scheffer, U.S. Fish and Wildlife Service, Seattle, May 11, 1962:

. . . I have been aware of the need for documented accounts of attacks by killer whales . . . but do not recall having seen any. . . . I would feel very uneasy if I were in a small boat or were swimming in the vicinity of killers, particularly if the animals had just made a kill and were excited.

Paul Hansen, Ministeriet for Grønland, Grønlands Fiskeriundersøgelser, Charlottenlund, Denmark, October 30, 1962:

. . . have never heard that Killer Whales have attacked human beings. The Greenlanders are, however, very much afraid of that whale, and we have heard that Greenland seal-hunters in many cases have taken refuge on small islands with their kayak, when Killer Whales have appeared.

It is an old experience of the Greenlandic seal-hunters that Killer Whales do much harm to their hunting by chasing away the seals. Therefore Killer Whales are outlawed and all crews on board motorboats and schooners are asked to fire at them whenever they meet them.

A. S. Hourston, assistant director, Fisheries Research Board of Canada, Nanaimo, British Columbia, August 16, 1962:

Mr. Pike, who is in charge of our Marine Mammals Investigation, does not know of any confirmed incidences of attacks by any of these creatures in British Columbia waters. While we do not maintain a close check on these matters, it is unlikely that any such attacks would not come to Mr. Pike's attention. Since killer whales are relatively abundant in our waters, it appears unlikely that they are a great menace to man.

P. G. Law, director, Australian Antarctic Division, Boulder, Colorado, August 21, 1962:

I too believe the stories of Killer whales to be grossly exaggerated. They seem to stem mainly from the account in Scott's expedition. . . . I have never heard of a case where a Killer whale attacked a man.

The Long Island Dolphins, Inc., a skin-diving club, issues a news letter called "The Snorkel Snooper." Page four of the December, 1962, issue carried the following account:

Fifteen killer whales showed up at the individual competitive spearfishing meet of the Greater Los Angeles Council of Divers. They just nosed around the divers and in the process turned one over with the swirl from his tail. Another diver pushed a bull away with his speargun. Now get this . . . only six divers of the 43 contestants left the water because of the killers.

[The author has not checked this story. It is repeated here as reported.]

A noteworthy addition to the above extracts is a brief report on a conversation the author had with Captain Jacques-Yves Cousteau, famous underseas explorer. From his own experiences with marine animals, from his observations, research, and general knowledge of matters marine, Captain Cousteau feels that the danger from this creature is minimal. He has known of cases where skin-divers were in the water with killers and were not bothered. He feels the tales of their so-called ferocity are exaggerated.

Antony Alpers, in his well-researched and very interesting book, *Dolphins: The Myth and the Mammal*, reports at some length on the fabled cooperation between a pack of killer whales and whalers of Two-fold Bay, Australia. Men still alive swear that the stories of the orcas assisting the whalemen to get their prey in return for the tongue and lips are true. For over fifty years, the whalers of Eden on the Bay were supposed to have been on the best of terms with three distinct packs of killers. In view of other incredible stories that have proven true about other small cetaceans playing with children, etc., it could be true.

What, then, can be our conclusion—if any?

The killer whale, particularly an adult bull, is a large and formidable creature. Although small as whales go, it is a big animal, the biggest of the dolphins. It is very fast in the water, and is armed with a really terrible array of teeth. The crushing power of its jaws is apparently immense. It can snap a seal or a porpoise in half with a single bite; or so it is reported. A man in the water would be absolutely helpless should one attack. Any small boat, unless especially designed with a sheathed hull or planking inches thick, could easily be broken up by an enraged orca. In brief, *if* a killer attacks, it is as dangerous to man as any creature on earth.

Does the killer whale attack? The temptation here is to reverse Mr. Romine's odd logic that the killer whale is dangerous because nothing proves that it isn't, and say that it isn't because nothing proves that it is. We will avoid that trap, however, and say that it is surprising, even startling, that there aren't reports of death and injury to man. It would seem that there would be enough rogue bulls on the prowl to cause at least some trouble! Eskimos in their skin boats are surely at the mercy of the killer every time they put to sea. Where are the reports of attacks? There is an extremely effective grapevine that operates on an international level carrying information of interest to biologists into libraries and laboratories from Sydney to Tokyo, from Bombay to London, Paris, and New York. Where are the reports of the killer whales? There are thousands of attacks by the big cats on record; a man killed by an elephant in the African forests is recorded sooner or later. Why, in thousands of years, has there not been one single authenticated attack by an animal whose appearance in the vicinity of small craft could be reported daily from some place on the oceans of this planet?

This author does not believe the killer whale is disposed to attack man unless it mistakes him for something else, something it normally eats. If there have been attacks on man, intentional or in error, they have been very, very few and far between. The killer's appearance is such that one would think that he must be dangerous; and, quite simply, this author believes, that is how the stories started.

To those who may challenge this point by asking me if I would go over the side and cavort with a killer, my answer is "No. I would not." There *is* the danger of aberrant individuals, "rogues," extremely hungry migrants, near-sighted old-timers, sexually excited bulls, and mothers with calves.

# CHAPTER 6

## *The Elephants*

THE following account was received from Major C. H. Simpson in April, 1962. It was sent from Blackrock Estate, Nagercoil, Kanjakumar District, South India. Major Simpson is a well-known hunter and planter with many years of experience in the forests of India.

In the same year [1932], six men went up into the Mahendragiri Hills to collect cardamoms. They had a muzzle-loading gun, although this was prohibited. They found a large male elephant feeding in a patch of cardamoms and the gunner of the party crept up close and let fly his weapon, charged with bits of iron and slugs, and propelled by country-made black powder. The pain of the wounds, the noise of the shot and the smoke, combined to cause the tusker to go crashing off down the hillside, trumpeting with rage. The cardamom pickers moved away some distance to camp for the night. Three of them slept under an overhanging rock, the other three put up a shelter of wild plantain leaves and slept just alongside. The elephant returned at dark, took up the scent of the men, and came to their camp. He rushed the camp and killed all three men under the shelter, those under the rock, he could not reach.

Two years later this same elephant was walking through Woodlands Estate in broad daylight when he was seen by an overseer named Singarajan. The tusker was below on a steep slope, so thinking he was safe, Singarajan flung a large stone at him. The stone hit his tusk, and he immediately gave chase up the slope. Singarajan ran for his life, shouting warnings to other men who were working further up the hill. All scattered except an old man, who squatted under a bush beside the path. The tusker rushed after Singarajan, ignoring the others. As he passed the old man in the bush, his fore foot hit the man who rolled over into the path, and the tusker's hind foot came squarely on his head, squashing it. Singarajan, though young and active had no chance, he was caught in the tusker's trunk, thrown to the ground, and torn in two. Not satisfied with this, the tusker trampled him until not one bone was left unbroken, and then left trumpeting his pean of victory.

Less than a year later, a party of men were going down from Mahendragiri Estate to their homes in the village in the evening. One man was running to catch up with the others, when he ran into the rogue tusker. He was immediately seized and killed. The other men heard his shrieks and the trumpeting of the elephant, and ran for their lives. The corpse was found next day.

I had been continually writing to the Government about this elephant giving them a detailed description of it, and asking for it to be declared a rogue, which would entitle it to be shot. Elephants being preserved in Travancore State, shooting one not proscribed would lead to prosecution. I was managing several estates, and was kept busy driving away the rogue when he was near.

On the morning of 16th April, 1936, the man who brought the morning muster from Seafield Estate, turned up late, and pitched me a harrowing tale of how he had been waylaid, and had escaped only because of his superhuman agility. I gave him a restorative in the shape of a tot of rum, and taking my 450/400 H.V. rifle told him to lead me to the spot. Getting on the slope overlooking the ravine in which the rogue was said to be, I sat scanning every clump of bush for a sign of it, and listening for the crack of breaking branches as he fed. Seeing and hearing nothing, I told the man to get back to Seafield, and that I would stay and cover him over the ravine. He had gone little more than half way when the rogue burst out of a clump of brush hardly big enough to conceal a cow, and made for the man with a scream. I roared to the man to run, at the same time firing two shots into the air to deter the elephant, but with no effect. I fired at the root of the elephant's neck, just as he stretched out his trunk to grab the man. He reeled and staggered a few paces and collapsed below the path. The man dropped a few yards further on, and I had to administer another tonic to bring him round.

In addition to these instances, there have been several cases of elephants causing deaths, the last being barely a year ago on the Mahendragiri Road, there was an instance of an elephant attacking a lorry and piercing the radiator with its tusks, when the hot water squirted out and put him off further mischief. A cart was broken up and the bullocks killed on the Baaiamore Estate Road, the cart driver escaped by running for his life.

Let us examine the subject of this account, the largest land animals left on our planet, the elephants.

Of the more than three hundred and fifty kinds of elephants (Order *Proboscidea*) that once lived on earth, two genera and three species are left. The African Bush Elephant (*Loxodonta africana*) has a range extending over the greater part of Africa south of the Sahara, but with large pockets excepted. The African Forest Elephant (*L. cyclotis*) has a range approximately one third that size. The Asiatic or Indian Elephant (*Elephas maximus*) ranges through much of India, Ceylon, East Pakistan, Burma, Laos, Cambodia, Vietnam, Thailand, Malaya, Sumatra, and parts of Borneo, and has an indefinite number of subspecies. There is no way of accurately estimating the world's wild elephant[1] population, but it is considerable. Vast herds still range wild, and majestically independent.

For many reasons, the elephant has long attracted the attention of man. To protein-starved populations, a slaughtered elephant is a cause for great rejoicing. Reports of natives descending on a still-warm carcass, and literally hacking and eating their way into the mountain of raw flesh exist by the score. Few observers have been able to resist a description of the event. In most cases, their own protein-rich diet has given

[1] Some zoologists prefer to call the African elephants "Loxodonts," but "elephants" covers all pachyderms with trunks, except in works of a highly technical nature.

Indian Elephants (*Elephas indicus*).

Information Service of India.

their reports a rather short-sighted, supercilious air. Elephants have supplied a highly treasured commodity to the world's artisans since long before the dawn of history. One example of ivory carving, a mask from Nigeria, recently brought $20,000 at auction. In large areas, the elephant is essential to the logging industry, and performs other heavy industrial chores as well. Elephants pull man's vehicles, carry men at work and play, lift his loads, and assist in the capture of more elephants to help with the labors. Should the elephant suddenly disappear, whole economies would suffer. When man hasn't been using the elephant to work or supply raw materials, he has used it as a symbol, as a sign of wealth, and as a mystic image. From the hardwood forests of Burma where it supports a major logging industry, to the national parks of Africa where it supports a major tourist industry, to the circuses of Europe and America the elephant is an animal close to the hearts of men.

All of the attention directed to these magnificent beasts has resulted in a veritable mountain of legends, beliefs, and misinformation. In India, wealthy princes still dress their stables of ceremonial elephants in lavish tapestries. Everywhere in the world, primitive and sophisticated people alike dress elephants in robes of fine-spun fiction. Why it is more enticing to record and repeat nonsense than sense when dealing with such honestly amazing animals will forever remain a mystery.

Although someone will almost surely mount an expedition within the next twelve months to find the great, secret elephant graveyard, it doesn't exist. The lure of untold tons of free ivory has caused this particular legend to persist right up to the present day, despite all evidence to the contrary. Elephants do wander away from the herd to die, but the idea that they trek to some secret valley is without foundation.

Elephants do not live to be hundreds of years old, not even one hundred. To the best of the author's knowledge, there isn't a record known to prove that they pass seventy years on any but rare occasions. Some almost certainly do, of course, but a seventy-five or eighty-year-old elephant would be very old indeed. (Our knowledge of the longevity of African elephants is very limited.)

The idea that elephants never forget *is*, surprisingly, close to *a* truth. Of course, *never* is a strong word, and elephants differ as individuals. They are not improvisers but function well within certain confines, and can learn an astounding variety of tasks. They learn slowly and apparently retain what they have learned almost indefinitely, and they keep learning all their lives. These animals are slow to be born (twenty-one months is normal gestation), slow to grow up (they are kept on milk for years), slow to learn, and slow to forget. Just what the memory span and the saturation level are has not really been determined, but certainly there are limits to both.

Reports of charging elephants leaping ravines and galloping or trotting in pursuit of man mark themselves as fiction. An elephant cannot leap or jump under any conditions. If the maximum stride of an individual is six feet, it will burn to death before it will cross a moat six feet six inches wide to escape a fire. Quite simply, it can't; its body does not have the bone-muscle-tendon combination necessary for any form of saltation. As for running, trotting, or what-have-you, never! An elephant has one form of locomotion on land, it can walk! It can walk fast, to be sure, faster than a man can run by a very good margin, but nothing more. At the height of a charge, an elephant is walking despite a thousand adventure stories to the contrary.

The question of maximum size is often discussed, and some really

African Bush Elephant (*Loxodonta africana*).

South African Tourist Corp.

fantastic claims have been made. The bigger of the two African elephants, the so-called Bush Elephant, actually does grow to be slightly over eleven feet at the shoulder, and weighs around seven tons. (However, a thirteen-foot-two-inch specimen is in the Smithsonian Institution.) The smaller African Forest Elephant grows to be eight feet tall, and weighs proportionately less. The Asiatic animal is intermediate in stature and bulk. There are any number of differences between the two genera, and between the two African forms, but these are of significance only to the specialist. It is enough, generally, to be able to distinguish between the Asiatic and African elephants and this can be done at a glance. The

African elephants have huge ears, the Asiatics' are very much smaller. The Africans give the impression of having little or no neck, due largely to their great ears, the Asiatics appear to have their heads set out well in front. African elephants have sloping foreheads, while the Asiatics have two very pronounced bumps at the top and front of the head. The other differences are less apparent at a distance but are nonetheless quite distinctive. Side by side, the two types of living elephants are obviously very different animals, even to the most casual observer.

Are elephants dangerous to man? Under certain conditions, decidedly so. They have enormous strength, are capable of a speed estimated at twenty miles per hour maximum, and frequently tend to be quite short-tempered. Left alone, they generally won't bother man, but man very often does not leave them alone. When he hasn't been hunting them for their flesh, hide, and tusks, he has been capturing them for use as work animals. When he hasn't been tracking them down for any sensible use, he has hunted them mercilessly to prove his own manhood. The mystic rite of slaying a magnificent beast that nature has taken forty or fifty years to grow, to prove that you are brave, is not generally practiced by primitive people. Only supposedly civilized people seem to feel that manhood can be obtained by a blood bath at the expense of our most impressive land animal. This endless, and aggressive pursuit of elephants has resulted in a lot of dead and mutilated hunters, but we won't consider the animal dangerous in this context. If an individual wishes to pit his skill and his $2,600 double rifle against the biggest and potentially most dangerous game in the world, in the estimate of many, there is always the chance that he'll be rather the worse for the experience. We'll consider the danger posed by these animals in a different light, here.

An adult elephant will consume up to six hundred pounds of food a day, it has been estimated. Much of this is wasted since a great deal of undigested matter is passed out. The enormous stomach of the creature indulges in endless churnings and rumblings known as borborygmus. The digestive process is quite staggering in its proportions. All of this attention, however, is lavished on vegetable matter. Elephants, of course, do not eat meat, and reports of their turning carnivorous are without substantiation. Although the elephant is therefore never a man-eater, its appetite can make it dangerous to man in another way. Elephants like many of the same foods enjoyed by man, and this puts them in direct competition with hunting-gathering tribes, and makes them particularly troublesome to agricultural people. The invasion of cultivated lands by wild elephants is a common occurrence, and human deaths have resulted from the practice. A herd of wild elephants trampling through a farm can lay waste many acres in a single night. Farmers often find it necessary to hunt them down, or bring in professionals to do it for them. Elephant control is still a major problem in many places. An inexperienced hunter attempting the job himself can get into serious trouble. Elephants move like ghosts through the thickest of cover, and can hide most expertly in almost any cover at all. Knowing how far you can push a foraging herd before triggering a charge, or even a stampede, and how far a bull will retreat before turning and waiting in ambush, are calculations for the expert to make. Should the herd have young, and since the young are not weaned until years after their birth most herds always have young around, the cows can be very touchy. A herd of wild elephants, in or out of your garden, is a thing to be respected. These animals are short-sighted, and short-tempered. They have incredible hearing, and a most delicate sense of smell. They are quite fearless, and if provoked will attack anything in sight, trucks and cars included.

Oscar "Ed" Pearson of the South African Tourist Corporation told the author of a successful attempt to enclose an area near a national park with an elephant-proof fence. Railroad track was driven deep into the ground with a pile-driver, and laced with elevator cable. It apparently worked, although it was never put to the test of a charge or stampede. Even if it did resist the determined efforts of a herd (and that is very doubtful), it would hardly be a practical way to enclose a farm of many thousands of acres! The systematic control of elephants by trained naturalists and really expert hunters is essential to all agricultural areas within their range. Surely, there are few jobs requiring a higher level of skill in the ways of the wild than this. Some friends of the author do it in off seasons in Africa when the safari trade is slow. They confess that even the most skilled of professional hunters approach a herd of wild elephants with their hearts in their throats. Only novices, and slightly deranged old-timers, *like* killing elephants. That last squeeze of the trigger is accompanied by a thunderous roar, and a feeling of real guilt in all but the most unfathomable of minds.

The fearlessness and temperament of the wild elephants are in part demonstrated by an adventure enjoyed by friends of the author. Christian and Barbara Hansen, a remarkable team of nature photographers, returned from their fourth African safari with some priceless motion picture footage. Late in 1961, having negotiated the Sahara Desert by car, they were motoring south through East Africa. They camped in a clearing in a heavily forested area, and spent an uneventful night although there were signs of elephant all around. The following morning, while Chris was checking some camera equipment, Barbara set up breakfast on a folding camp table outside their tent. Chris looked up, and shouted for Barbara to run. An enormous bull was striding out of the forest directly for her. She ducked into the tent, the nearest available cover, and prepared to escape through the back should matters get any more dangerous. Chris took up his rifle, but, as always, reluctant to kill, he held fire until he could determine the bull's intent. The animal made no signs of charging, nor did it hesitate in the slightest from its apparently predetermined path. While the Hansens, now more amused than terrorized, watched, the bull polished off their oranges, took a full box of cereal into its mouth and spat it out empty, rummaged around for a minute or two and then moved off, doing no real damage.

The story of the Hansens' breakfast makes the elephant sound like an amusing, if somewhat oafish fellow. Nevertheless, it would have been a serious mistake for the Hansens to have relied on that quality at such close quarters. A precipitous act by either of them could have enraged the bull, and set it off into an orgy of destruction. An elephant is not an easy creature to kill, and even if Chris had used his rifle, there would have been no guarantee that Barbara would not have disappeared underfoot before a telling shot could have been placed. On the other hand, a snap of the fingers might have frightened the beast and set it crashing off into the forest in headlong flight. The trouble is, with elephants you can never be sure.

Theodore Roosevelt, in his *African Game Trails*, describes the graves of two hunters at Nimule, in British East Africa. Both men were killed by elephants, one was dismembered by an infuriated bull. Carl Akeley, father of modern taxidermy, was seized by a bull and terribly mutilated. A series of miracles, not the least of which was the great hunter's astounding stamina, enabled him to survive. One can believe that the incident contributed to Akeley's belief that the elephant is the most dangerous game in the world.

In his *Large Game Shooting in Thibet, the Himalayas, Northern and Central India*, Brigadier General Alexander A. A. Kinloch says:

Elephants usually go in herds, varying in number from four or five to sixty or seventy. When in herds they are generally quite harmless, and a child might put a hundred to flight; but a solitary bull is often a savage and dangerous brute, attacking and killing everyone he can. Occasionally one of these "rogues" will haunt a certain road and completely stop the traffic as long as he remains. There was one which used to haunt the Dera Dun, and which was said to have killed many people, and even destroyed houses. I fancy, however, that the depredations of several Elephants were laid to the charge of one.

A. Blayney Percival, of the Kenya Colony Game Department, in his *A Game Ranger's Note Book*, wrote:

. . . it was impossible to know what the herd might do; elephants have been known to charge a camp at night when they blunder on it thus in the dark. . . .

G. P. Sanderson wrote, in his *Thirteen Years Among the Wild Beasts of India*,

Single male elephants spend their nights, and sometimes days, in predatory excursions into rice and other fields in the immediate vicinity of villages. They become disabused of many of the terrors which render ordinary elephants timid and needlessly cautious. These elephants are by no means always evilly disposed. A solitary elephant I knew intimately at Morlay was a most inoffensive animal, and, although bold in his wanderings, never injured anyone. Some male elephants, however, as much wandering herd tuskers as really solitary animals, are dangerous when suddenly come upon, but rarely wantonly malicious.

Of cases recorded of really vicious animals perhaps the most notable is that of the Mandla (near Jubbulpore, Central Provinces) elephant, an elephant supposed to have been mad, and which killed an immense number of persons about five years ago. It is said to have eaten portions of some of its victims, but it probably only held their limbs in its mouth whilst it tore them to pieces. The Mandla elephant was shot, after a short but bloody career, by two officers.

One is unlikely to read a book by a hunter, game conservator, missionary, or just plain traveler who has known the habitat of the elephant, without finding some reference to the depredations of so-called "rogues." Since this special kind of elephant is the one generally accused of being the man-killer, it is on it that we should concentrate in our discussion of danger to man. Webster defines a rogue elephant as "a vicious elephant that separates from the herd and roams alone." Semantically, this may be correct, but it is not clear if it is an accurate zoological description. The only thing that is certain is that some elephants spend part of their time away from the herd, and tend to be more dangerous than a normal herd animal. Perhaps the solitude they endure, not characteristic of a highly social animal, makes them uneasy and defensive. Perhaps some infirmity keeps them from staying with a herd on the move; and most herds, generally, are transient. This same infirmity could make them unusually cranky. Since all solitary animals are not old and not bulls, the idea that rogue elephants are old bulls past their sexual prime is open to question. A herd bull past his prime, and who was displaced by a younger and more vigorous male, might quite readily develop a personality disorder. This may account for some so-called rogues but not all.

Male elephants fight among themselves, the sexual drive probably being at the base of most disturbances, and very extensive wounds often result. Untreated, these huge puncture wounds and massive lacerations undoubtedly fester and cause great pain. Many rogues have been identified as pain-maddened, once shot and examined.

Jokes are often heard around the elephant pen at the zoo to the effect, "How would you like to have a toothache in that?" To an elephant whose tusk has been injured and is decaying, this is hardly a joke. The nerve in the base of the tusk is immense, as big around as a man's arm, and an ache there must be monumental. Certainly, an elephant with a tusk-ache might very well be disposed to attack.

The elephant has a surprisingly small brain for an animal so large. It is set low, and far to the rear. Most of the massive frontal portion of the skull is given over to air pockets to help reduce the load of the broad foundation required to support the tusks. For this reason, the brain shot so often attempted by the hunter is frequently unsuccessful. When successful, the brain shot is the best way to stop a charge, but it is a difficult assignment. Many bulls go through life with heavy particles of metal imbedded in their skulls. The loads used in elephant rifles, .450 to .600 calibre, fire projectiles weighing from 480 to 900 grains. Since most big tuskers who wander outside of game reserves get shot at sooner or later, one can wonder just how many majestic headaches an old bull will endure before taking a decided dislike to all mankind. A number of rogues have been shot and found to have one or more bullet wounds. Such an animal can almost be excused for its disposition, except by the innocent victim who is plucked off a path while en route to market. It cannot be demonstrated at this point that the elephant is capable of so complex a motive as revenge. It would seem that way, however.

This author has never faced a charging elephant, and cannot offer a firsthand account of the experience. Conversations with people who have survived these spectacular displays have provided some impression of what it must be like. A bull African would rather avoid a showdown and prefers to rely on bluff. It tastes the air with that wonderful trunk, casting it up, from side to side, and then straight out. Its ears are spread wide, many feet across at the extreme, to force every small sound into its ear canals. Its wholly inadequate eyes glisten, and its feet practice a nervous little prancing shuffle as it takes one step forward, and then two back. Suddenly, rocking slightly from side to side, the first charge is made. A cloud of dust and debris billows up around its chest and forelegs, and a shrill blast issues forth with stunning impact. The first charge, a last bluff, carries it twenty feet or so before it hauls up and half turns. It snorts, shuffles, and tastes the air once more. Any structure or vegetation at hand is apt to get smashed down as the rage mounts. Perhaps it holds its advanced position and shrieks again, or perhaps it turns in a small circle, or backs off a few steps. At any rate, it is soon again facing the cause of its irritation. Its ears snap forward again, its trunk seeks the direction its eyes can't locate, and then it comes, with all the force of an express train as the giant presses home the charge. The first few strides are misleadingly slow, in a moment the pace is far in excess of any speed a man can approximate. In a moment, the elephant is either dead with a bullet in the heart or brain, or the object of its attentions is in grave peril.

Reports of just what elephants do to their victims vary. Some animals evidently catch their victims in their trunks and variously dismember them, smash them against the ground or an upright object, or simply toss them into the air or back over their shoulders. Some elephants impale the object of their charge on their tusks, while others simply run over people; others are reported to take great pains to totally mutilate their enemies. Some angry beasts are satisfied with one crushing charge, while others return again and again to their victim after he is quite dead.

Thousands upon thousands of elephants are slaughtered every year, so the animal is not beyond the destructive powers of our midget race. Charging elephants have been stopped dead in their tracks by a lethal shot on untold occasions. Nonetheless, a charging elephant is as dangerous to man as any animal can be.

In this chapter, so far, we have concentrated on the danger these animals *can* represent. It remains to put this into perspective.

The elephants are one of the most magnificent natural heritages we have left on earth. Basically, they are orderly herd animals, very intent on minding their own business. An adult has no natural enemy save man and disease. Other animals, even the great predators, leave it alone for the most part, although an unguarded calf may be taken. The average elephant in normal circumstances is not dangerous to man. It confines its attentions to herd behavior, migrations, foraging, and seeking water. Although quick to go on the defensive, it is normally a peaceful animal. Most elephants will flee the sound or smell of man. They will frequently vacate an area if man moves in. From their earliest days, baby elephants come to associate the strange and unpleasant smell of man with great agitation and nervous rumblings within the herd. Nature thus teaches her young how to survive; what the mother doesn't like, the baby learns to dislike from the disturbance in routine that it causes. (An orphan, however, will readily "adopt" human parents if it is taken young enough.)

On occasion, a herd will ignore man and raise havoc. Crops are ruined and structures destroyed. For reasons not clearly understood, lone animals will become killers with behavior as far from the norm as the murderous cunning of a homicidal psychopath among humans. These aberrant individuals must be dealt with, naturally. Elephant control is essential to agricultural areas, and few people can argue with the logic of a game ranger tracking down a known insane specimen. Sometimes a herd becomes diseased, and it is essential that it be destroyed before it can migrate to new areas, carrying diseases like anthrax. For the most part, however, there is little excuse for considering the elephant an animal to be destroyed on sight. We have perfectly good plastics from which we can make our piano keys and billiard balls, and these magnificent creatures are worth any and all efforts to preserve. Fortunately, they respond well to sensible control and are for the moment not in danger of extinction. Surely, if there is an animal on earth worth preserving as a monument to the primeval state of nature as it once was, the elephant is the prime candidate.

# CHAPTER 7

# *Venomous Mammals*

EVERYONE knows there are venomous snakes; a great many people realize there are venomous fish; but very few people, apparently, are aware of the fact that some mammals come equipped with venom and envenomizing apparatus.

There are venomous mammals; just how many is not yet known. To the author's knowledge, the ability is limited to two groups, the extremely isolated, egg-laying Monotremes of Australia, Tasmania, and New Guinea, and an unspecified number of specialized Soricids, or shrews. All of these animals are shy, retiring, and, if not actually rare, extremely difficult to find. By no stretch of the imagination can any of them be considered aggressively dangerous to man and they are discussed here only to establish this fact, and because a review of the world's venomous animals must logically make some note of them.

*Blarina brevicauda*, the Short-tailed Shrew of North America, has red-tipped teeth. It is a minute creature with infinitesimally small eyes and a perfectly foul disposition. It makes its home under trash and vegetation and builds a cozy little nest where it hibernates and where the young are born. It eats an absolutely amazing quantity of insects, worms, arachnids, slugs, and other animal prey, and will turn to cannibalism if denied other food for a few hours. It is apparently almost constantly in a "rage" which is magnified by its atom-splitting metabolism. Its shrill shriek is partially beyond the range of human ears, and it is evidently seldom still. Al-

Greater Short-tailed Shrew (*Blarina brevicauda*). Ernest P. Walker.

though superficially mouselike, it is really related to the moles and is an insectivore. If it was as big as a collie, and kept the same rate of metabolism, it would be far and away the most dangerous animal alive, venom glands or no. What a really large shrew could do to the natural balance of any region is terrifying to contemplate.

Near the base of the Short-tailed Shrew's lower incisor teeth is an opening to a pair of ducts. These ducts lead to a pair of modified salivary glands where the venom is produced. The two pairs of lower incisors project forward markedly, forming a sort of groove along which the venom flows. No great amount of venom is stored, but it has been demonstrated that mice can be killed by a small fraction of the dose the shrew has available. Partial paralysis, protruding eyes, and convulsions occur in small mammals injected with an extract prepared from the glands. Death follows these symptoms in a few minutes. There have been no human deaths recorded as resulting from the bite of the one known venomous shrew; only a few, mild, localized reactions have been noted in humans.

The folklore of Central Europe contains many references to venomous shrews, and it is quite likely that others will eventually be identified. There is no particularly valid reason why *Blarina brevicauda* should be the only venomous one. Once again, there is no danger to man unless you want to count the various witches' brews that crop up in Gypsy legends. They have apparently been stirring shrews into their magic broths for generations. Aside from that, a shrew could hardly bite a man who wasn't handling it, and even if a venomous shrew did manage to bite, the venom is too mild to have any systemic effect.

The *Monotremata* are generally represented in most people's minds by the famed Duckbilled Platypus (*Ornithorhynchus anatinus*) of Australia. This single member of the family *Ornithorhynchidae* has close relatives in the family *Tachyglossidae*, the so-called Echidnas, or Spiny Anteaters, of Australia, New Guinea, Tasmania, and some adjacent islands. Although quite different in appearance, the echidnas and the platypus share certain remarkable characteristics; they lay eggs, and have only one body opening for all eliminatory and reproductive purposes. They have hearty appetites; and are extremely shy and retiring. They are among the most fascinating animals in the world, representing a number of reptilian as well as mammalian features.

On the inside of the male platypus' rear ankles are matching, one-half-inch spurs that lead to ducts running down from the animal's thighs. The females are not so equipped. These spurs can be driven deep into the flesh of anyone handling the creature by a convulsive little kick. It is obviously a defensive device only, and of little threat to man. As a matter

Platypus (*Ornithorhyncus anatinus*).

Australian News and Information Bureau.

of fact, as shy as this animal is, it is hard to see how anyone could become involved with the device without picking the platypus up. An actual venom is introduced by these spurs.

David Fleay of Queensland, Australia, the outstanding authority on the living platypus, kindly responded to a letter from the author by publishing a request for platypus envenomation case-histories in the *Brisbane Courier-Mail,* on May 30, 1962. He himself told of a Mr. Warrian of Injune who accidentally hooked a platypus in 1950 while fishing in the Dawson River. While attempting to free the creature, he received both spurs in his hand up to the hilt. He was in great pain and dangerously ill for weeks. Ten years later, his arm was still "useless." In reply to Mr. Fleay's column, two letters were received, attesting, as Mr. Fleay pointed out, to the rarity of incidents. A Mr. Richards wrote from Liston in New South Wales and told of a nine-year-old girl named Gillespie who was struck on the arm by a platypus caught in a fish trap. The incident occurred in the tiny village of Vacy near the junction of the Allyn and Paterson rivers, in 1895. Mr. G. H. Sargent wrote from Currumben

Poison spines on hind feet of male platypus.
David Fleay, Queensland, Australia.

to tell of his own adventures fifty years ago. As a boy of twelve, he caught a young male platypus in the North Pine River and tucked it in his shirt. From 9 A.M. until 1:30 P.M., it cuddled up against the boy's body without any sign of aggression. He then transferred the animal to a wooden crate. He removed it several times to show it off, and never encountered any difficulty. Toward evening, he took the creature out to show to some people from a traveling circus. Among them were "three very brightly dressed, rather loudspoken ladies." Their effect on the young platypus was evidently electric, and young Mr. Sargent received one spur in the front of the wrist and the other in the back of the hand. Mr. Sargent describes his injury in this way: "The pain was very severe, like a nerve pain, and left me feeling shocked and sick for some minutes. The hand immediately began to swell and was soon so 'puffy' that no knuckles were visible. The whole arm became very hot and a lump developed in the arm pit." A doctor at Sandgate who had previous

Echidna (*Tachyglossus aculeata*).
U.S. National Zoological Park (via Smithsonian Institution).

experience with platypus envenomation prescribed hot baths for the arm. Mr. Sargent concludes, "My arm was O.K. again in a few days and except for stiffness, for a day or so longer, in the hand and fingers, no lasting ill effects occurred." The platypus was lucky in that young Mr. Sargent was a real animal lover. Despite his sorry injury, the boy returned the animal to its river home unharmed. One can speculate that the youngster was lucky to have picked on an immature specimen.

Strangely enough, most Australians don't realize that their platypus is venomous. People who speak of being stabbed by one often get very strange looks.

There is reason to believe that the echidnas may also be similarly equipped. Mammologist Ernest P. Walker suggests that the spines of the echidnas *may be* to a degree venomous. He developed a localized reaction after being jabbed and writes that a Japanese researcher reported a case of envenomation from the spines. Stanley P. Young of the U.S. Fish and Wildlife Service reports that all monotremes have venom glands. The question is as academic as the case with the platypus. It is interesting information, should be noted in a book dealing with venomous creatures, but must be off-set with the statement: *Within the context of this book, not dangerous to man.*

# CHAPTER 8

# *Other Mammals*

THE Cynocephaloids, or Dog-faced Monkeys, are a widely varied group of true monkeys represented by more than two hundred different kinds. They are found from Gibraltar in the West to Japan in the East and far to the north (Amuria) in the eastern part of their range. They are, for the most part, restricted to the south of the great desert belt in Africa and Asia. Their range is quite enormous and their habits as varied as their appearance. Though by nature retiring for the most part, some forms grow large enough individually to be dangerous to lone people, while a high degree of social organization among some species has led

Baboon (*Papio* sp.).
South African Tourist Corp.

to apparently deliberate attacks on even parties of people. Of the dog-faced group, the baboons (*Papio*) have the most advanced social organization and are possessed of an equally remarkable level of intelligence. They mass attack in self-defense, and can put a marauding leopard to flight. They are powerful creatures with truly enormous canine teeth set in formidable jaws. They kill livestock, notably sheep, and are omnivorous. Their raids on gardens, and even homes, have made them a real pest animal. Human children have been stolen by them on at least a few extremely rare occasions, although the motive was more likely adoption of a new baby than intended harm. Eugene Marais recounts an incident in *My Friends the Baboons*. In those cases where an over-stimulated troop attacked a man, the punishment they inflicted was quite appalling. Wise enough to be afraid of man, they are nevertheless damaging to man's enterprises in many areas, and are altogether too much animal to be taken on bare-handed.

A Salvation Army medical missionary with two score years of service in India told the author that monkey bites are more common in many

Rhesus Monkey (*Rhesus mulatta*).

Lynwood M. Chace.

Siamang (*Symphalangus syndactylus*).
Zoological Society of London.

parts of that country than snake bite. The true significance of that observation will be appreciated more fully when we examine the case of the venomous snakes. Rhesus Monkeys (*Macaca*) in India, because they are emboldened by the freedom afforded them by the Hindu religion, do attack and bite children. Buttocks and leg muscles are badly torn in these ill-tempered assaults, and rarely a death will occur. Monkeys enjoy various degrees of protection in a number of social orders erected by man within their range, and they are generally nuisances in all such situations. On occasion, as we have pointed out, attacks on human beings take place, particularly by the Langur Monkeys (*Presbytis*), temple animals in India. For the most part, monkeys are shy and quite harmless when unmolested. And, the larger species definitely discourage molestation by any but the most skilled animal handlers.

The Anthropoids, or Apes, are among the most dramatic (and overdramatized) creatures on earth. Their range today is strictly limited to parts of forested Africa south of the desert, and the Oriental region. The lesser apes are generally regarded as six species, five Gibbons (*Hylobatidae*) and the Siamangs (*Symphalangus*). The gibbons range from the Himalayas to Hainan, throughout Indochina, Borneo, Sumatra, and south to Java. They are superficially "monkey-like" but tailless, are equipped with very long arms, a comical bipedal gait, and a normally gentle disposition. They are shy but very intelligent and are frequently kept as pets by natives. However, when so kept, they can be among the most unpredictable of the mammals, attacking suddenly for no apparent reason. They are then terribly dangerous.

The great apes are much better known. The Gorillas (*Gorilla*), Chimpanzees (*Pan*), and Orang-Utan (*Pongo*) constitute this group. The orang-utan, found in Borneo and Sumatra, although immensely strong is retiring and peaceful. There is every indication that it is extremely intelligent. Unless actually attacked or threatened it never bothers man. Even when molested it is much more apt to retreat than to take the offensive. It is within the realm of reasonable speculation to suppose endangering the young of a troop might bring on an attack, but it is an unlikely set of circumstances that would elicit such behavior on the part of these large, startlingly human creatures. In dealing with captive specimens, however,

Chimpanzee
(*Pan satyrus*).

Courtesy of the American Museum of Natural History.

their normally docile behavior should not cause their great strength to be overlooked. In one case, a newly caught specimen was crated for shipment to a zoo. It was packed in a crate made of teak held together by ten-penny spikes. The creature managed to wrap a finger around an inch or so of one spike that had been left protruding. The startled keeper, assigned to its care, watched the orang draw the spike out of the wood, with one digit!

Chimpanzees, still widespread in the equatorial forests of Africa, are brash creatures as individually variable in behavior and appearance, it would seem, as are men. Normally retiring, they watch the movements of human beings within their realm from a safe distance, and with great interest. It is reported that they can be annoyed into attacking, but surely these are exceptional cases. Among the brightest, best known, and most engaging animals on earth, they should be respected for their great strength, strong teeth, and occasional outbursts of bad temper. They are not, however, normally any threat to man. Young specimens displayed in circus acts and on television are quite misleading as to size. Old males grow to be very large, very, very strong, and very cranky, particularly during parts of their sexual cycle. The bite they can administer is seriously damaging, although a zoo keeper is far more likely to be the victim than even an unarmed traveler in their natural habitat.

The mighty gorillas are probably the most maligned of all animals. Almost certainly of two distinct types, Mountain and Lowland,[1] they are restricted today to widely separated areas in equatorial Africa. Some specialists suggest that they are the same animal. The matter is very confused, however, and no definitive statement seems possible. Three quite different classifications exist today.

The gorilla is apparently at least as intelligent as the other apes, but the somewhat sullen attitude of adults in captivity has frustrated efforts of investigators to determine what the real level of that intelligence is. They are very large animals (an adult male will have an arm-spread of nine feet), and outweigh man by several hundred pounds, although they are generally shorter in stature. Their strength is prodigious, their teeth formidable, and their behavior when encountered in the forest conducive to wild flights of fantasy which indeed has marked much of the literature on them.

The nature libraries of the world were enriched in 1963 by the publication of George B. Schaller's *The Mountain Gorilla.* This remarkable study examines these fascinating animals from all angles, and in depth. Not ignored is the matter of danger to man, and Dr. Schaller's findings are in keeping with most of the serious writings of recent years. Apparently, man is coming to his senses as regards, at least, some of our wild

[1] Most of the "Lowland" forms, however, live in mountainous areas!

Gorilla (*Gorilla gorilla*).

New York Zoological Society.

creatures, and tales of gorillas raping women and carrying off living victims to sacrifice in some mystic jungle rite have become increasingly scarce.

Gorillas are generally harmless animals. Attacks on man have been made when the troop was pressed too far, but these were exceptional cases. Gorillas, like so many large and formidable-looking creatures, are big bluffs. Their actual powers of destruction are so marvelous that they seldom have to employ them. They do quite well by simply threatening to do so. They *do* pound their chests, they *do* roar and bellow, and they *do* make terrifyingly realistic charges. This great show usually puts all but the most persistent or best armed observer to flight. Those who have witnessed these anthropoid histrionics, who have shot the animal, or turned tail and run, have come away with harrowing tales (and even motion picture footage) of matchless ferocity. Those observers who were interested enough in the animals to steady their nerves and call the bluff, came away with a true evaluation of these remarkable melodramas. Until recently, this latter type of observer was lost in a rash of fiction about these mighty apes and their supposed homicidal tendencies.

Like the bears, the gorilla has been worked into an erect posture by pulp magazine illustrators and is usually depicted as a hairy gladiator wading into battle. Gorillas generally travel on all fours, using their knuckles in front. They certainly travel that way when in a hurry; and when they charge, in bluff or in earnest, they are in a hurry. In the words of Dr. Schaller, "Prolonged bipedal locomotion is rare." On those rare occasions when the gorilla actually presses home and attacks, the subject may receive a perfectly devastating sideways slap that can just about break a man apart, or a vicious, rending bite with enormous teeth and extremely powerful jaws. The gorilla usually makes one punishing pass and is satisfied to move off into the thick forest in which it is always found. These attacks are rare, however.

Certainly, only a fool would knowingly involve himself with a gorilla at close quarters because one of these animals has the strength of a number of the biggest men. The chances of being injured by an unmolested specimen are very slight, though apparently unprovoked attacks do occur. Although man did not "descend" from these apes, as so much popular literature would have it, the common ancestors we shared with them were sufficiently recent to make looking into the eyes of these endlessly fascinating animals a haunting experience.

One of the most remarkable adaptations made in the world of mammals is the modification of the fore-limbs as organs of flight. This power is restricted to members of the order *Chiroptera*—the Bats. Some rodents (the so-called flying squirrels) and a few other mammals soar rather

Blood-lapping, or true Vampire Bat (*Desmodus rufus*).

Charles E. Mohr, from National Audubon Society.

effectively, but the true power of flight is limited to these almost mythical creatures. Only rodents, among mammals, outnumber the bats in actual numbers and kinds. Bats are harmless to man with one odd exception, and this only secondarily—as a disease-carrier. These are the blood-lapping Vampire Bats (*Desmodus* and *Diphylla*), animals that feed only on blood and will take that of any animal from man to toads. The wounds they make are small and not very damaging; and the amount of blood consumed, although a disquieting contemplation, does not usually approach a dangerous level. One can suppose that an unprotected infant could be set upon by a number of vampires and bled to death, but this is stretching a point too far, though a ten-year-old boy once sustained a dozen bites in one night. Indeed, it must be something more than annoying to wake up in the middle of the night to find a bat enjoying the seepage from a freshly gouged big toe, but the bat itself will do no real harm. Secondary infections are certainly possible as a result of these nocturnal ministrations, but here again the real damage is a result of microorganisms, and not bats. The very real harm that *can* result from these encounters is discussed in Appendix B, *Rabies*.

Many bats are capable of giving a good bite if handled, but the group as a whole is harmless. Most of the stories that exist about them are pure fiction and, except perhaps in appearance, they are entirely inoffensive. In plain fact, the world would be a sad place without bats, for the quantities of insects consumed each night of the year by the insectivorous varieties must be measured in tons. Bats have a very important place in the natural scheme of things. (Incidentally, they will not descend upon, or stick in, women's hair.)

Cape Hunting Dogs (*Lycaon pictus*).

C. A. W. Guggisberg.

In several chapters preceding, we have discussed the most impressive of the meat-eaters: cats, wolves, and bears. Many of these forms are on occasion dangerous, and some of the lesser creatures remaining in the order can be troublesome as well. Aside from those already discussed, the Carnivores include: the remaining *Felidae*, the lesser cats and near-cats; the *Viverridae*, or civets, mongooses, and their allies; the hyaenas or *Hyaenidae;* the racoons and related forms such as coatis and kinkajous, called the *Procyonidae;* the other *Canidae*—the true wild dogs and jack-als, foxes, and fennecs; and finally the *Mustelidae* or weasels, minks, martens, badgers, wolverines, skunks, and otters.

A number of the jackals and the so-called Hunting-Dogs of Africa (*Lycaon*)[2] are reputed to occasionally mass an attack on lone humans, but certainly these are rare instances. All of these animals, as hunters, live by their wits, and most, if not all, are intelligent enough to fear man. It is a rare carnivore that doesn't give man a wide berth.

The case of the hyaena is a particularly interesting one. Once wide-spread throughout Europe, Asia to eastern China, and all of Africa, they are today restricted to that latter continent, India, and the Near East. They are strictly meat-eaters and tend to do more scavenging than actual hunting. Together with the African Aard-Wolf, a harmless, aberrant hyaena, they constitute the group known as *Hyaenines,* which appar-ently falls somewhere between the Canines and Viverrines.

[2] This curious piebald beast, although resembling a calico wolf, has only four toes on each foot, and is a descendant of some long-vanished Canid stock, not closely related to others still living.

Spotted Hyaena (*Crocuta crocuta*).

South African Tourist Corp.

Hyaenas are generally characterized by the tellers of animal stories as "cowards." They supposedly just slink about, cackling in a demented fashion, and eat only carrion. While the "laugh" of the hyaenas does have a deranged quality, and while the hyaenas do clean up carrion, they are animals equipped with some of the most powerful jaws in the class Mammalia. They can crack bones that would resist efforts by much larger and apparently more formidable forms. They also appear at times to be aggressive. Witness these reports.

### 9 CHILDREN CARRIED
### AWAY BY HYENAS

BHAGALPUR—Nine children have been lifted away during nights by beasts of prey, believed to be Hyenas in six weeks in Bhagalpur town and its outskirts.

The last, a six-month-old child, was carried away from Waraligunj Mahaila on Sunday night.

The police have been trying to locate and liquidate these beasts but without any success so far.

That report, from the Madras *Mail* of May 5, 1962, does say *believed to be Hyenas*, but no surprise is expressed at the idea. Recently, four-year-old Terry Anderson, son of Baptist minister Douglas Anderson of Kroonstad, South Africa, was dragged from his father's tent in Kruger National Park by an adult hyaena and carried thirty yards into the brush before his screams brought rescue. Other such reports are on record and it does seem fairly certain that a helpless human being, small child, or invalid, might occasionally be taken. It is believed that many old lions, who have spent their lives feeding these essential scavengers, eventually fall prey to them. An animal given to cleaning up derelict carcasses may not necessarily wait for a body to be dead before starting to feast. It is often reported that this is the case with hyaenas, known to take the young of normal prey animals, doing the killing themselves.

Theodore Roosevelt said of them; "The hyena is a beast of unusual strength, and of enormous power in his jaws and teeth . . . on occasion the hyena takes to man-eating after its own fashion . . . it will enter native huts and carry away children or even sleeping adults." In 1908 and 1909, Uganda was scourged by sleeping-sickness and hyaenas emboldened by the supply of corpses took to raiding native villages, graduating from corpses to the sick and helpless, and eventually to healthy people as well. A native hunter working for Sir Alfred Pease was seized by a hyaena and had part of his face torn away. Major R. T. Coryndon, administrator of Northwestern Rhodesia, was attacked in his sleep, and, in 1910, a hyaena entered the outskirts of Nairobi and carried off a man. Many other such reports are on record.

Many of the other carnivores such as Viverrines (mink, weasels, badgers, wolverines, and ratels are good examples) can give very bad bites, and, indeed, do so when mishandled. Few, if any, however can be accused of attacking man, unless rabid. The civet tribe of the Viverrines are particularly vicious but, strangely, often make safe and reliable pets.

Carnivores are among the "cleverest" animals on earth, second, perhaps, only to the primates and whales. They make the best pets, and the best stories. Few, however, ever really are dangerous to man unless cornered, or otherwise molested.

The *Rodentia* is the largest of mammalian orders. A third of all the known genera and half the total species belong to it. Five thousand is the current estimate for species, and three hundred for genera. They are among the world's most adaptable animals and certainly range further than any other mammalian order. There are very few natural habitats without some, and their reproductive rate is so great and so easily accelerated that often, when a new area is involved, unless predators or starvation conditions are present to exercise control, the population explodes and the area is overrun. Rodents are the most destructive mammals on earth, except for man, and the annual toll amounts to billions of dollars.

Crop spoilage by rats[3] alone reaches a staggering figure. The United States Government estimates that there are over fifty million rats on farms today, thirty million in towns, and twenty million in large cities. It further estimates that each rat costs over $10 per year, or more than one billion dollars in damages. One state alone conducted a survey of cereal grain storage facilities and found 43 per cent had infestations by rats, and 59 per cent by mice. In one section of the United States, only 3 per cent of the corn shipped to terminal markets was free from rat and mouse filth. A state chemist found rat hairs in thirteen out of forty-three different canned food products. A single recorded incident involved the spoilage of 1,800,000 pounds of sugar by rat urine!

The Government of the United States issues warnings that hundreds, and perhaps thousands, of baby chicks, ducks, and geese are killed by rats every night of the year. Small pigs, lambs, and calves are injured and killed. Among the diseases carried and spread by rats, or the fleas they in turn carry, are plague, typhus, amoebiasis, infectious jaundice, salmonella food poisoning, tapeworm infections, and rat-bite fever. Discounting the people killed by these diseases, and the people who die in fires caused by rats eating the insulation off electrical wiring, rats are dangerous "in the first person." Hundreds, and perhaps thousands, of people, particularly children, are attacked each year and bitten. Some are injured badly enough to die.

In 1961, a man and wife on Manhattan's upper East Side were awakened by the screams of their eighteen-month-old son. They approached his crib and found him bleeding from several bites on his ear, cheek, and neck. Glowering defiantly from a position on the child's pillow was a rat measuring "nearly two feet long." The father took a broom and attacked the rat which in turn attacked the man and bit him deeply on the leg. The wife was similarly attacked by the maddened animal, and all three members of the family required medical attention. The family's cat, kept as protection against rats, had been killed by one the week before! Exterminators, ordered into the building at the cost of the landlord by an outraged judge, killed 43 rats in the one tenement with no guarantee that the infestation had been eliminated. Such cases are not in the least unusual, unfortunately.

No mammal on earth causes man more pain, discomfort, food, and money loss than does the rat. It is far and away the most troublesome, and at least indirectly, the most dangerous mammal. Rats travel far and wide aboard ships and evidently have for a very long time. An area visited by an infested ship soon has its own population. Unless checked by predators, the rats soon destroy the natural balance of the area by putting

[3] That is, the Black Rat (*Rattus rattus*) and the Brown Rat (*Rattus norvegicus*); both probably originated in Asia.

to an end the career of many native species. Many of the world's ground-nesting and flightless birds were wiped out largely by rats.

Rat control is an essential and costly process for which man must pay each year. With the breeding cycle as short as it is, a single year without control would seriously endanger many of man's enterprises, and life. Few city dwellers realize that their welfare is in such critical balance with so small an animal, but such is the case.

Compared to rats, the other rodents are harmless, save for rabid specimens. All can give nasty bites, but few if any attack man.

Collectively, all of the hoofed animals of the world are called ungulates. Those with an odd number of toes (including the horses, asses, zebras, tapirs, and rhinoceroses) belong to the order, *Perissodactyla,* and those with an even number of toes (pigs, peccaries, hippopotamus, camels, llamas, chevrotains, deer, moose, reindeer, okapis, giraffes, cattle, buffalos, bison, antelopes, gazelles, sheep, goats and dozens of related forms) to the order, *Artiodactyla.*

Whereas the rodents are the most significant mammals from a negative (to man) point of view, the ungulates are so on the positive side. It is safe to say that man could not have reached his present state of social development and welfare without the domestication of these animals. Leather, wool, and meat, and uncounted scores of other products come from this group. Fortunately, a great many ungulates are easily domesticated and readily bred into new and more productive forms. Early overland transportation was entirely dependent on members of this order and, in many parts of the world, they are still essential to the economy. The ungulates are truly the animals that carried the primates to a place of dominance on earth today.

Most wild ungulates are shy. They are the primary food source of not only hunting man but of most of the world's carnivores. As a group, the bears alone, of the great carnivores, are not largely dependent upon ungulates for survival. As browsing-grazing animals, the ungulates have developed the skill of escape rather than that of attack. Some few have learned how to fight back, and some of these are dangerous to man under certain conditions, and not always in mere defense.

Our planet once swarmed with rhinocerotine animals of great variety, and, frequently, great size. Today, only four genera and seven species are left as far as we know. Two genera are in Asia and two in Africa. Having either one or two "horns," depending on the species, the rhinoceros is a formidable animal. [The so-called horn of the rhinoceros is not of a horny substance at all, but a matted, hairy conglomeration akin to human fingernails.] These creatures are near-sighted, and short-tempered. Most of them will charge quite readily when disturbed and they can be

Indian One-Horned Rhinoceros (*Rhinoceros unicornis*).

Information Service of India.

exceedingly dangerous to molest. They are powerful, thick-skinned animals and have been known to overturn cars and trucks when in a particularly truculent mood. This behavior, however, is defensive and predictable, although their habit of going for the first thing they detect, when they charge, makes it quite hazardous to get near to them, unless you really know what you are doing. Except on rare occasions when they are encountered by unwary men on foot, there is little excuse for getting into trouble with them. Most of their charging is sheer bluff, pulled up short of contact, or veered aside, and if you are downwind you won't be detected even a few yards off unless excessively noisy. They are, by and large, inoffensive brutes of no great intelligence, but they are best avoided by anyone not familiar with their rather odd behavior and habits, particularly the African Black Rhino.

The swine have many wild members and many of these are decidedly dangerous to encounter at close quarters. Various Wild Hogs (*Sus*), and particularly the related Peccaries (*Tayassuidae*) of the New World are very well equipped to take care of themselves. Large cats have more than enough to do in making a kill, and a man on foot who threatens a pack can find himself the object of slashing tusks and fierce determination. Although not strictly vegetarians by any means, the wild pigs and peccaries do not kill large animals for food, but have developed a formidable counterattack—a characteristic that advises caution in any dealings with them.

Men have had their horses killed out from under them by White-Lipped Peccaries (*Tayassu pecari*) if reports from Central America are

African Wide-Lipped Rhinoceros (*Cerathotherium simum*).

South African Tourist Corp.

Eurasian Wild Boar (*Sus scrofa*).
Courtesy of the American Museum of Natural History.

to be believed. Writing of the Collared Peccary, or Javelina, of the south-western United States, Hornaday commented: "An enraged Peccary, athirst for blood is to any one not armed with a rifle or a firstrate spear a formidable antagonist." A report published in 1940 tells of a camper who was run up a tree by a pack of two hundred javelina and held at bay for twenty-four hours. The pack refused to move off although the man killed two dozen before he ran out of ammunition. The same report warns against attacks on riders where tendons were ripped on horses' legs.

In 1880, hunter A. G. Requa was run up a tree by a pack of collared peccaries in Sonora, Mexico, and observed the following:

Collared Peccary (*Tayassu tajacu*).
Courtesy of the American Museum of Natural History.

They were chewing the tree, and climbing over each other trying to get at me. Each shot laid one out, and each shot seemed to make them more and more furious, as they would rush at the tree, and gnaw the bark and wood, while the white flakes of froth fell from their mouths.

He finally had to tie himself in the tree to keep from falling out. He never hunted javelina again. Similar reports are told of Wild Boars (*Sus scrota*) in Europe, Red Forest Hogs (*Potamochoerus*) of Africa, and feral "razorbacks" of southeastern United States. The wild swine of the world, while not man-eaters, or even man-hunters, are extremely dangerous to approach.

The great and ponderous Hippopotamus (*Hippopotamus*) of Africa (except for a pigmy form (*Choeropsis*) on the same continent), is unique. Of great bulk, and puzzling ancestry,[4] they are startlingly fast swimmers and quite dangerous in the water. When man does get into trouble with them, however, it is usually through his own ignorance. A herd of hippos is a matriarchy. The females rule from a central sandbank or sandbar in the middle of the established herd territory called the *crèche*. Only the babies and very young males of the herd are allowed in the crèche area with the grown females and an intruder on foot can bring on a charge. Surrounding the crèche are several refuges inhabited by the older males of high social standing. Further out, and less accessible to the crèche and therefore breeding possibilities, are the less well-defined refuges of the younger males. The hundreds of photographs that have been pub-

---

[4] They are now thought to be possible survivors of a line of ungulates called *Anthracotheres*, elsewhere extinct.

Hippopotamuses (*Hippopotamus amphibius*), on land.

South African Tourist Corp.

Hippopotamuses in water.

South African Tourist Corp.

lished and circulated showing hippos "yawning" are actually pictures of hippos warning others of their kind who have intruded on a refuge. If this warning is not heeded, a violent fight can ensue. A man in a boat who unwittingly paddles from the refuge area of the younger bulls into the refuge of a cranky or insecure old bull, can find his boat suddenly broken in two. Also, lonely "rogues," usually old males, seem to occur in certain areas.

Hippos are generally peaceable creatures, despite their seemingly rigid social structure and territorial divisions. Most often a herd will scatter, or at least submerge, at the approach of man, but attacks are not uncommon, and because of their sudden and violent nature, are well to avoid.

The deer of the world are of great variety, and great numbers. They are usually the last big animals to die out once civilization starts to impinge on a wilderness area and their high reproductive rate keeps populations fairly intact even close to urban centers. Usually retiring and shy from overhunting (as they once were from predation), these large sharp-hooved, often well-horned animals can be most formidable under certain conditions. They make dangerous pets once they reach maturity and a sexually excited stag, triggered to fight off challengers to its harem, will readily charge an intruder. The occurrence of these sometimes damaging and rarely fatal charges seems to vary from place to place. In areas where there has been a great deal of hunting, fear is the dominant factor and a charge is unlikely. In very remote wilderness areas, such an occurrence is more possible. Moose (*Alces*), called elk in Europe, are particularly quick to take offense, and a fatal encounter is reported from time to time. Generally, the victim is a hunter who has placed his shot badly, and the incident cannot be looked upon as unprovoked.

Discounting wounded specimens, for the moment, charges are evidently made when a man on foot infringes on an established territory. A couple of years ago, two automobiles were attacked and wrecked by moose in Canada, and in one instance the driver was killed. Approaching 1,000 pounds, with antlers as much as seven or eight feet across, the moose is a formidable animal. Some years ago, six lumberjacks on Clear Water River, Idaho, attacked a swimming moose from an open boat with axes. They wanted the animal for meat. Turning on the boat, although over its head in the fast-running current, the moose easily destroyed the heavy wooden craft and killed two of the men. Hunter-writer Newton Hibbs shot badly, on one occasion, and broke a bull moose's shoulder. Although floundering, half-crippled, in snow seven feet deep, the enraged animal charged again and again, until finally dispatched with a bullet between the eyes.

Moose (*Alces alces*).                    Wilford L. Miller.

The ubiquitous White-Tailed Deer (*Odocoileus virginianus*), found over most of the United States and Canada (and replaced by the Mule Deer—*Odocoileus hemionus*—in those few areas where it is not found; their ranges overlap in many places) is truly a creature of the shadows. Alert, shy, with extremely keen senses, it is the most heavily hunted game in North America. Twice-a-year hunters who never even see another species of big game seem, eventually, all to get their buck. This extraordinary onslaught (even bows and arrows are used on them by sportsmen today) has made the animal excessively shy in most areas. Still, the animal can be formidable and reports of attacks are not uncommon. One evening in 1961, a housemaid left her place of employment in Westchester County, just north of New York City, and was waiting for a bus on a dark street corner. A white-tailed buck charged out of some bushes and pinned the hysterical woman to a tree. Only the timely arrival of the bus kept the woman from being killed. The white-tailed deer is equipped for flight. It can clear amazingly high obstacles with graceful, arching leaps, can run with remarkable speed even in dense cover, and has excellent camouflage. However, caught in unusual circum-

Virginia White Tail Deer (*Odocoileus virginianus*).

Wilford L. Miller.

Wapiti (*Cervus canadensis*).

Wilford L. Miller.

stances, the white-tail will turn and fight with sharp hooves and slashing antlers. Territorial infringement during the breeding season undoubtedly accounts for some attacks.

Ernest Thompson Seton wrote (in *The Whitetailed Deer and Its Kin*): ". . . the bucks not only fight among themselves, but occasionally attack man; and more than one unfortunate person has been gored to death by them."

Merriam reported:

I was once sitting quietly on a log in a Deer park when a buck approached and, making a sudden spring, dealt me such a powerful blow on the head, with the hoofs of his forefeet, as to render me unconscious. No sooner was I thrown upon the ground than the vicious beast sprang upon me, and would doubtless have killed me outright had it not been for the intervention of a man, who rushed at him with a club and finally drove him off.

Cape Buffalo (*Syncerus caffer*).

South African Tourist Corp.

*Field and Stream* magazine on December 26, 1898, carried an account by J. Park Whitney of a similar incident that occurred in Maine. Seton adds, "If, however, the Deer is the conqueror, he never ceases to batter, spear, and trample his victim as long as it shows signs of life." Reports like these, made by competent observers, are quite common. The deer, as a large animal, should be treated with due regard for its capabilities in the art of close combat.

Similar incidents are reported of the magnificent American Elk or Wapiti (*Cervus*), a race of the Eurasian Red Deer. A Mr. McLaughlin, a rancher in Stinking River Valley, Wyoming, barely escaped with his life when charged by a stag. His pack horse was thrown off a cliff to its death by the impact of the assault. John Fossom of Gardner, Montana, had a similar narrow escape when attempting to photograph a wapiti.

It seems fairly apparent that any large hoofed animal can be dangerous to man on foot or horseback, and should be approached with extreme caution; this applies most particularly to males in the autumn when their conditioning for mating predisposes them to fighting. Many descriptions indicate that the males become wild with rage at the first sign of intrusion.

The various true buffalos (not to be confused with the bisons of North America and Europe) are without question the most dangerous of the ungulates. The great "Buff" of Africa (*Syncerus caffer*) is considered by many to be the most dangerous animal on the continent, exceeding in this respect even the elephant, rhinoceros, leopard, and lion. Their great bulk is not a deterrent to speed, and their charge is more apt to be carried through than that of any other animal. When a buffalo charges a man on foot, one or the other usually dies. It takes great skill to get a bullet into a fatal spot when the head is down with its spread of heavy, deflecting horns meeting across the skull. Stories are told of men driven into low trees and held at bay there by an infuriated buffalo until death came in a most unorthodox fashion. Parts of the body exposed to the buffalo were rasped clear of flesh by the animal's file-like tongue. Such stories are quite common in literature, but I must confess that no effort was made in the preparation of this book to check them. Suffice it to say, the buffalo is a particularly cunning ungulate, with great slashing horns, a penchant for lying in ambush, and a very short temper.

Bush-Cow (*Syncerus nanus*).
Jardin Zoologique d'Anvers.

Gaur (*Bos gaurus*)—mounted specimens.

Courtesy of the American Museum of Natural History.

The smaller Red Forest Buffalo, or "Bush-Cow" (*S. nanus*), of Africa is reportedly even more deadly. It has an almost uncanny way of stalking passers-by and hunters alike and attacking with deliberate intent, even hours after first encounter.

Speaking of buffalo in general, Theodore Roosevelt described them as "tough animals, tenacious of life and among the most dangerous of African game." He also said, "The list of white hunters that have been killed by buffalo is very long, and includes a number of men of note, while accidents to natives are of constant occurrence." In some areas, destruction to crops and attacks on people have reached such proportions that buffalo have been ranked as vermin. Writing in *Harper's New Monthly Magazine* in 1898, Arthur C. Humbert commented, "My guide who has lived in this country for the past ten years, relates many stories of men who have been mauled by lions, and who have escaped death, but he knows of no instance where the African buffalo has left a human being until the life was trampled out of him." References, observations, and reports like these exist by the thousand, the only conflict being whether the buffalo is the most dangerous animal in all of Africa, or only the second or third most dangerous.

Asiatic Water Buffalo (*Bubalus bubalis*) in the Philadelphia Zoo.

Courtesy of the
Philadelphia Zoo.

The mighty Gaur (*Bos gaurus*), the Wild Ox of India, Burma, Thailand, and Malaya, is another animal given to charging molesters; and being hit by one is almost certain to prove fatal. The Gaur or *Gaor* is the largest member of the bovine family, and in India, in height at least, second only to the elephant. Kinloch wounded one on a hunt in the Satpura Hills, and, in his words, "Back he came, at a fast gallop, evidently looking out for some one on whom to wreak his vengeance. I was ahead of my men and stood my ground, while they, being unarmed, very wisely scrambled up trees. I allowed the bull to come on to within forty yards, when I fired my right barrel at the point of his shoulder. . . ." The domestic Water Buffalo (*Bubalus*) of the Oriental region still exists in some areas as a wild animal. It is powerful, and short-tempered. Accidents with them and apparently unprovoked attacks by them have been reported, strengthening the thought that no wild bovine can be trusted. All of these great bovines are hunted as trophy animals and many are the hunters who have paid with their lives for their dangerous sport.

There are a number of reports on record of various antelope charging their tormentors with extensive damage done by their often spectacular horns. Certainly, some of these stories are true but it is, once again, stretching a point to call them specifically dangerous to man. Many species, indeed, could be extremely hazardous at close quarters, most because they would thrash around in blind panic. Spectacular accidents have occurred when hunters have approached animals they thought dead, though only wounded. Supposedly dead antelope can come to life with amazing speed and energy!

Whales do not generally seek issue with man, but man has been hunting the whale for many hundreds of years, perhaps, in fact, thousands. Whaling from open boats was a hazardous occupation at best because of the size of the prey-animal. Stories of stove-in boats and lost harpooners are legion. The great historic period of American whaling was well reported. Many, many such stories were true, and are occasionally reported today as witness the following UPI release of January, 1963:

### WHALE SMASHES FISHING BOAT

SYDNEY, AUSTRALIA—A 70-foot whale smashed a fishing launch off Coogee Beach near here yesterday, killing one man.

Police said William Morris, 64, was killed. Companion Jack Banning, 39, was pulled out of the water.

The mighty Sperm Whale (*Physeter catodon*) is one of the most formidable creatures on earth. Males reportedly reach a length of more than sixty feet, although fifty is the average size of a large bull. In his definitive work on Cetacea, *Whales*, E. J. Slijper, says:

Sperm Whales, like elephants, have the occasional rogue male, i.e., a solitary individual which obviously cannot fit into any school, and which is therefore particularly aggressive. Such rogues were Moby Dick, New Zealand Jack, and many other famous whales from the great days of Sperm Whale hunting, all of which tore up men and boats alike. . . .

In August, 1851, the *Ann Alexander* out of New Bedford lowered two boats on order of Captain John S. Deblois. Both were sunk by an angry sperm. A few minutes later the ship itself shuddered as she was struck below the waterline by the infuriated animal. She sank in a few minutes.

Sperm Whale (*Physeter catodon*).

From *Follow the Whale*.

Captain George Pollard took the *Essex* out of Nantucket in 1820, never again to return. A sperm twice smashed her bow, sinking her. Most of the crew perished. There are dozens of such stories on record, with no reason to doubt them. One added hazard has humorous overtones. Sperm whales are extremely sound sleepers and are often encountered floating on the surface in deep slumber. In 1956 alone, three ships are believed to have collided with sleeping sperms; the Russian whaler *Aleut*, the American liner *Constitution*, and the Dutch ship *Willem Ruys*. The S.S. *Amerskerk* collided with a sleeping 32-footer while doing seventeen knots in March, 1955.

Approaching whales in light watercraft is not a wise practice. If the animal is a cow with a calf near-by, a charge is not unlikely in many species, especially in relatively shallow water. Old bulls can be quite short-tempered, the great size of these creatures alone suggesting that they are dangerous to molest. Most whales will sound and disappear at the approach of man, but if one doesn't, it is usually an indication that something is wrong, or may be very shortly thereafter.

Most marsupials are quite harmless to man. While a kangaroo at close quarters can deliver a stunning clout with its powerful hind legs, most of these animals are extremely shy. But two forms reputedly have been involved in attacks on human beings; both are today apparently on the brink of extinction. The Tasmanian Devil (*Sarcophilus harrisii*), now restricted to Tasmania, once ranged over much of Australia. The last specimen there is believed to have been killed about sixty miles from Melbourne, at Tooborac, in 1912. Although small, the creature attacked larger animals including domestic stock. Occasionally caught in the act of raiding farms, it reportedly turned on its would-be tormentors with a reckless fury. Quite possibly this is so, and some settlers may have received painful bites, but no deaths are known to the author.

Tasmanian Devil (*Sarcophilus harrisii*).
Australian News and Information Bureau.

Thylacine, or Tasmanian Wolf (*Thylacinus cynocephalus*).

Australian News and Information Bureau.

The Tasmanian Wolf, or Thylacine (*Thylacinus cynocephalus*), is roughly the marsupial equivalent of the wolf, although far removed from any true canine. Today, it is found in only the most remote regions of Tasmania, although it once, like the Tasmanian devil, inhabited mainland Australia. When cornered, the thylacine is said to have counter-attacked and human injuries are on record. However, although an active predator, the hunting of man was not reported. A supposed attack occurred in Tasmania a few years ago in which a young boy was badly bitten.

For many years reports have been drifting out of the Queensland bush of a savage marsupial "tiger" that does attack man. There have been too many of these accounts to dismiss the matter out of hand, but to date the animal has not been identified, much less its danger to man established. An animal that has escaped all efforts (and there have been many!) to capture it and identify it, is certainly far too rare and remote to consider as much of a menace. It is interesting to think, though, that on this planet, there probably still remains to be discovered a large (leopard-sized) predaceous mammal.

With this brief survey, we have reviewed the great order of mammals. Many others have behavioral characteristics unpleasant to man, but, all-in-all, mammals cause fewer deaths and injuries today than most other groups of vertebrates containing reputedly dangerous forms. The great size and often colorful behavior of many mammals will continue to attract the attention and imagination of man for many years to come. As long as this is so, whatever danger they do represent inevitably will be exaggerated.

# PART II

## *The Birds*

# CHAPTER 9

## *Are Any Dangerous?*

AT THE TOP of the so-called "tree of life" there are two main branches, the mammals and (it may come as somewhat of a surprise) the birds.

Birds are actually nothing much more than warm-blooded reptiles with some odd features such as feathers instead of scales, and a four-chambered heart like our own. Perhaps it is the latter development that has given them, like the mammals, a great advantage over their cold-blooded ancestors the reptiles. But, by whatever means they achieved their prominence, they are today one of the most numerous groups both in forms (over 8,600 species) and numbers of individuals. Are any of these forms dangerous to man?

The answer is a qualified "Yes." This statement, however, requires some explanation.

Peacock (*Pavo cristatus*).
Courtesy of the American Museum of Natural History.

Sclater's Cassowary (*Casuarius philipi*).
From *Wild Animals In and Out of the Zoo*, Smithsonian Institution Series.

Unlike mammals, birds are, as the old adage goes, "bird-brained"—and this despite the fact that some birds have brain capacities larger in proportion to their bodies than we do. Nevertheless, whether actual gray-matter capacity does or does not indicate intellectual capacity, there is no doubt but that birds do have very *different* "brains" than mammals. Anybody who has handled animals professionally will tell you that, if you get into a fight with a bird, you cannot expect any respite, since a bird, unlike a mammal, never gives up. Mr. Larry Taylor, past president of the Pheasant Breeders Association of America, gives a most graphic description of an unprovoked attack on his person by a peacock (*Pavo*) in an enclosure that resulted in multiple injuries necessitating stitches. The incident could have ended in hospitalization had aid not arrived unexpectedly.

You may say, however, that such encounters are provoked, in that the birds are confined. This is not necessarily the case. Man's dealings with wild mammals are almost wholly provocative, even if only by infringement of territories, as I have pointed out; with birds this is not so, for we keep many large birds around us that are not truly domesticated. In various parts of the world, these include ostriches, swans, eagles, peacocks, and so forth. And it is these that are the most dangerous and the most likely to attack. As some writer once said—I have a note of this, but no record of who said it—All birds are nuts but sometimes they go completely balmy. But, first, to deal with the birds that we do not normally encounter or keep around.

Astonishingly enough, while all but a handful never molest man, there are a few that will do so deliberately. They are the Cassowaries (*Casuariidae*) of New Guinea and Australia. There are reports of other birds, large and small, performing in the same way, and I have one word-of-mouth account of a barn owl (*Tyto*) so attacking the recounter's grandmother in a wood in England. It proved to have a nest in a hole in a tree alongside the path.

The cassowaries[1] are quite another matter. Few people are likely to

[1] *Casuarius:* six species known, all from northern Australia, New Guinea, and adjacent islands. The height: five feet plus, and flightless, with strong legs.

Ostrich (*Struthio came-lus*).
Zoological Society of London.

come in contact with these strange distant relatives of the ostrich and emu, except natives of the countries where they live. However, during World War II, Allied troops encountered them in dense scrub in New Guinea, and several times confirmed native reports that they may attack by leaping into the air and slashing down with their enormously long and powerful first claws. Oliver L. Austin reports that "many" natives have been killed by these pugnacious creatures. Whether such attacks are truly unprovoked, or just random panic on the part of these remarkably stupid and hysterical creatures, is difficult to say, but, judging by accounts given by zoo keepers, they must be formidable to say the least.

It is manifest that, to be truly dangerous, attacks must be by large birds. An interesting case is the largest—the Ostrich (*Struthio*). Not only are these birds now farmed, they roam about in considerable numbers in game reserves visited by tourists, and they have ostrich races in California. Thus, man is in contact with them. Like all birds, and perhaps more so, they are a bit "balmy," and if they get particularly excited they kick out hysterically. They can give a terrible kick with their huge piston-like legs that end in a shaft of almost solid bone and two toes with strong claws. It is a curious fact that, if for some extraordinary reason, you find yourself confined with a lot of hysterical ostriches, you should fall flat on your face. Even in extreme panic these strange creatures will not tread on you! The cock ostrich in the mating season is, in the opinion of Peter Ryhiner the big game collector, probably one of the most dangerous animals on earth, and not, according to him, only in a zoo enclosure.

For centuries the Mute Swan (*Cygnus*) has been semi-domesticated, but there are greater numbers of truly wild ones. There is little doubt that they will attack if their nests are too closely approached either deliberately or by mistake, and they can and have broken peoples' arms,

Trumpeter Swan (*Olor buccinator*).

Wilford L. Miller.

Jungle Fowl (*Gallus gallus*)—mounted specimen.

and the legs of some children.[2] They half-jump, half-fly directly at you and then pound you with their half-folded wings. Their "elbow" joints are hard knobs of bone, and their wing muscles are very powerful so that they can deliver a terrific wallop. Like all birds, they keep at it once they have launched an attack. Swans, moreover, seem to be of rather high "intelligence" for birds, and appear to employ real strategy when they fight.

The so-called game birds include the fowl, peacocks, partridges, and so on, and are lumped together as gallinaceous birds. Many are armed with long, sharp spurs on the backs of their legs—hence cock-fighting—and, as in the case of Mr. Taylor, mentioned above, they can do extraordinary damage with them. A lone man so attacked by a peacock (*Pavo*) is at a disadvantage because he has to protect his eyes at all costs, and at the same time ward off a sort of living hover-craft that usually goes for the back of his neck. I have a report from private sources of an unprovoked attack by a bantam rooster! This occurred to Mr. James Rorty, the well known poet, in northern New Jersey in 1951, in the presence of three witnesses. The party was visiting the house of a friend and Mr. Rorty was ahead on a narrow paved path between tall, old, clipped hedges when, without warning, the tiny cockerel flew over the hedge

[2] In fact, a child was killed in Ranelar Park, England. It was reported some years ago in *The Field*. A child was forced underwater and drowned by one in Methuen, Massachusetts, in 1938.

Bald Eagle (*Haliaeetus levcocephalus*).

Wilford L. Miller.

and inflicted a deep gash on the back of his neck. It then repeatedly flew up from the ground, its legs flailing, and caused two further wounds before Mr. Rorty's companions literally beat it off.

It is naturally more than just improbable that any such attacks by this group of birds ever occurred in the wild, but, in view of their behavior in confinement and also loose around a house, it is conceivable that anyone stumbling on a nest in the bush might be so attacked by the cock bird.

The birds which have from time immemorial been most feared by people, though notably by those who know little about them, are, needless to say, the eagles (*Aquila, Haliaeetus*). The stories about eagles carrying off human babies, and even small children, are absolutely endless. In my opinion it is pure myth;[3] yet the stories persist. Applying

[3] Doug Storer, author of *Strange But True*, seems to have authenticated one true case in Norway several decades ago. Apparently, a very large eagle attacked a very small seven-year-old girl and hit a powerful updraft at just the right moment. Mr. Storer has assembled an impressive collection of documents and his evidence would be difficult to refute. It is all very startling, but it would appear as if this one case must be accepted for the moment, at least. (Personal communication.)

Vulture (*Gyps fulvus*).
Courtesy of the American
Museum of Natural History.

Adjutant Stork (*Leptop-
tilus javanicus*).
Cy La Tour and the Detroit
Zoological Park.

logic, at least insofar as I can determine it, these stories are all false except Mr. Storer's case. An eagle attacks small mammals, reptiles, fish, and, perhaps, some other birds. It is not equipped by nature to lift great loads and the endless tales of these birds acting like a giant helicopter airlifting Army supplies, are not at all in keeping with the actual physical structure of the creatures. I recall seeing a scene of an eagle carrying off a child in an old movie. This badly stuffed and rather moth-eaten prop, suspended from the studio roof by an all-too-visible wire, was about as convincing as the stories one encounters!

Eagles, as a matter of fact, are, of all birds, probably the calmest and most serene. They are also really rather timid. I have photographed specimens in the Florida Everglades and on Cape Breton Island, Canada, and can testify that it is extremely difficult to get near enough to make even a 135 mm. lens pay off. They can be tamed and become lifelong companions of men, and are even patient in face of molestation. People examining or robbing eagles' nests may very well have received some pretty determined attention from the mother and sometimes also the father, but I do not know of any case where the "attack" was carried through to the point of actual physical harm to the intruder.

The lesser cousins of the eagles—the falcons and hawks—can sometimes give a very good account of themselves if molested; and they probably don't hesitate to do so. I do not know of an unprovoked attack that resulted in a significant injury. Occasionally, a handler engaged in the ancient sport of falconry, will get clawed by one of his charges.

If you deliberately walk up to a group of vultures when they are feeding, you may, according to some people with long experience in the countries where they are found, be confronted by a lot of hissing avian monsters that will even run at you. For the most part they are very wary and just flop up into the nearest tree and wait for you to go away; but

Skua (*Catharacta skua*).
K. J. Salmon.

sometimes, it is alleged, they do not. You have to be very wary of certain individual vultures in captivity as they don't wait to be provoked, and it may be possible that some in the wild would adopt the same attitude toward interference.[4]

There remains then a somewhat different aspect of danger from birds. This is in handling them. Many birds can give really terrible bites. Many of the long billed birds, like the Maribou and Jabiru storks (*Ciconiidae*), can make a nasty puncture in you and there is always the ever present danger, in handling birds, of damage to the eyes. Never hold any bird with a long neck and sharp pointed bill at less than arm's length.

The Skua (*Catharacta skua*), an aberrant gull-like bird, turned hawk, ranges from the Arctic to the Antarctic, and is the southernmost vertebrate animal on earth. Specimens have mysteriously appeared within a few miles of the Geographical South Pole, over eight hundred miles from the nearest possible food source. It is a powerful predatory bird of the

[4] *South African Scope* (Vol. 6, No. 7, Summer 1963), an official government organ of the Republic of South Africa, reports that on March 3, 1963, Miss Bessie Smit on a farm named Aminnis was attacked by a large southwest African vulture. The deliberate assault carried Miss Smit to earth but a rock within her reach enabled her to escape.

Macaw (*Ara macao*).
Courtesy of the American Museum of Natural History.

coastal regions, and some, at least, prey on young penguins. It has earned an unfortunate reputation for itself by attacking men who approached its nest. I do not know of any specific injuries received, but attacks do occur. One can suppose that eyes could be lost, and other painful injuries inflicted if an unwary explorer failed to duck in time.

The *Psittaciformes*, parrots and their allies, have particularly powerful beaks. Anyone who has ever handled them to any extent can testify to the kind of bite they can give. This is a defensive measure, though, and hardly a danger in our context.

The birds of the world are a source of never-ending joy. They are color, life, and movement personified, and their very being graces the natural world in a way typified by no other class of animal life. It is sorely tempting to go on discussing them here at great length, but hardly justified in light of this book's avowed purpose. Mountain climbers may have been toppled off cliffs by "dive-bombing" eagles defending their aeries; zoo keepers have been hospitalized by ill-tempered ostriches, men have been variously pecked, scratched, even bullied by geese, swans and other forms, but, all-in-all, birds are not dangerous to man. In rare cases this may not be an accurate generalization, but the threat, when it does exist, is so slight statistically (and generally involved with human molestation, or at least provocation) that I will stand by it as a conclusion.

# PART III

*The Reptiles*

# CHAPTER 10

# *Venomous Lizards*

In all the world today, there are approximately three thousand known species of lizards, suborder *Sauria* of the order *Squamata*. There are a few hundred more species of lizards than snakes, but while more than two hundred species and innumerable subspecies of snakes are more-or-less dangerous to man, only two species of lizards are known to be so.

Antarctica is the only continent on our planet that hasn't been accused of housing a venomous lizard, but so far as anyone has been able to demonstrate, North America alone has that distinction. One could argue that there are lizards yet to be scientifically described, in jungles, deserts, and forests, and caves (yet to be explored), but there is still no really good reason to run contrary to current scientific thought. This states, quite categorically, that the ancient family *Helodermatidae*, found exclusively in the United States of America and Mexico, has the world's only venomous lizards.

The family is respectably old, with fossils dating back from thirty to forty million years on record from Colorado. Today, there is only one genus, *Heloderma*, with two species and five subspecies. For the records, here are all of the world's venomous lizards:

### THE VENOMOUS LIZARDS OF THE WORLD

#### Family: Helodermatidae

#### Genus: *Heloderma*

| Species | Common Name | Range * |
|---|---|---|
| H. horridum horridum | Mexican Beaded Lizard | Pacific drainage of Mexico—sea level to at least 5,000 feet—coastal regions to at least 170 miles inland. |
| H. H. exasperatum | Rio Fuerte Beaded Lizard | Very limited—drainage of the Rio Fuerte and Sonora Rivers in Mexico. |
| H. H. alvarezi | Black, or Chiapan Beaded Lizard | Very limited—Rio de Chiapa drainage in Mexico. |
| H. suspectum suspectum | Reticulated Gila Monster | Arizona, New Mexico, and Mexican state of Sonora. |
| H. S. cinctum | Banded Gila Monster | Arizona, Nevada, Utah. |

* Rough, overall outline only.

The origin of the venom apparatus is the same as that of the snakes' —i.e., modified salivary glands. There, however, the similarity stops. While the venom glands of snakes are above the upper jaw, those of *Heloderma* are in the *lower*. While the snakes' venom is channeled from the producing glands to the injecting teeth, the venom glands of *Heloderma* have no connection with the animals' teeth. *Heloderma* have grooved, not hollow, teeth in both upper and lower jaws. Between eight and ten upper teeth, and six and eleven lower ones are grooved, always on the front but sometimes also on the rear edges. Instead of one duct, as in

Simplified drawing of single heloderma tooth, showing venom lumen at gum-line.

Chris Bottomley

the snakes, the venom glands each have a number of ducts which open into a mucous fold situated between the lip and the lower jaw. The venom flows along this groove until it reaches the teeth where it is then literally chewed into the victim, not injected in any sense of the word. The whole system is quite diffuse when compared with the crisp and efficient hypodermic system used by snakes.

To replace the neat injection apparatus they never had, *Heloderma* use tenacity. Almost everyone who has had anything to do with them has used the comparison, "like a bulldog," to describe this trait. When a Gila (hee-lah) monster or beaded lizard grabs, it hangs on. At times, it is reported, pliers have been required to make them let go!

It is not characteristic for bites by animals with neurotoxic venom to be particularly painful at the site of the injury. The bite of the Gila monster, although a nerve toxin is involved, has been described as very painful. The pain is caused by the chewing and tearing as the tenacious little animal works its venom into the flesh.

The Gila monster is not a large animal, about twenty inches being the record length. The beaded lizard reaches thirty-two. They are generally slow-moving, rather sluggish animals with blunt heads, beady eyes, and powerful digging claws and digits on short legs. They have a very thick tail which is, in fact, a storage vault from which they draw nourishment during hibernation. One of the more inane legends that has grown up around these animals is the story that the poor creatures are unable to dispose of body waste, and that it is all stored in the tail. The putrefaction of this fecal matter is said to supply the animal with its venom. For the record, the Gila monster and kin dispose of their waste quite naturally.

We have said that these animals are sluggish. This they are, unless pressed. If escape is not practical, or if the creature is injured or unduly teased, it is capable of remarkably swift, and surprisingly determined lunges and twists. When it does grab hold, its mild and non-combative disposition undergoes a sudden reversal.

*Heloderma* feed on eggs, nestling birds, and baby animals. They do not attempt to catch fast-moving prey. They have highly developed chemical senses—smell and taste—and use these to track down their prospective meals. They are great blood-hounds.

If disturbed, *Heloderma* generally seek cover under rocks, or in scrub. They will, on occasion, hold their ground with loud hissing, and short but exceedingly determined lunges.

To round out our capsule description of these interesting animals, they are egg-layers, take readily to water although they are essentially a desert animal, and hibernate during the colder seasons. Their scales do not overlap, but have a decided beaded look. The differences in marking are quite distinct, and readily apparent when different subspecies are placed side-

Gila Monster (*Heloderma suspectum*).

Roger A. Caras.

by-side. Actually, they look like no other lizard and are especially easy to recognize. It is almost inconceivable that a case of mistaken identity could account for an accident, except where it involved a small child.

In their exhaustive study of these animals, *The Gila Monster and Its Allies*, Charles M. Bogert and Rafael Martin Del Campo supply some of the vernacular names by which these animals have been known. The list is a long one, full of intriguing Indian sounds, but, most important is the fact that the animal has for long been known by variations of the Spanish name *Escorpion*. One can't help but wonder if some of the black deeds of which *Heloderma* have been accused aren't, in fact, the results of confusion in popular literature with the scorpions which inhabit the same region, and which are much more dangerous to man on an encounter-incidence basis.

We have already written off the comic notion that these animals are without elimination processes, but it might serve some good purpose to examine a few other long-standing legends about them. The breath of *Heloderma*, while reportedly quite evil smelling, is harmless except to the non-herpetologist's sensitivities. The animal can cause damage only by latching on, and chewing. They do not spit venom, although they may spray a little saliva around when pushed into their defensive-hissing attitude. Although these animals can pivot rapidly on their hind legs, and lash out to either side with startling agility, they do not leap on their prey. They just aren't built for saltation. The teeth of these animals are made for grasping, and not for cutting; they are incapable of cutting out a piece of flesh as they have been accused of doing. Their tongue is harmless although if you are close enough to be touched by their tongue you may be in for a bit of trouble. They are essentially immune to their own venom. Heloderms are not a cross between a lizard and an alligator, but have a respectable lineage as a pure, unadulterated, albeit rather singular, lizard. As far as is known, the Gila monster possesses no magical powers and is quite killable, although it *is* very tenacious of life. All-in-all, these animals are just about what a sensible person might expect them to be; they are all lizard, not terribly bright, not at all affectionate, very poor pets, very intent on minding their own business, but different in that they are (1) large, as North American lizards go, and (2) venomous. They have many distinct features, of course, but these are of interest mainly to the specialist.

Are the Gila monster and its allies dangerous to man? A qualified "yes." Bogert and Martin Del Campo discuss thirty-four known cases of injury to man, eight of which were reportedly fatal. It is pointed out that most of the fatal cases involved men in poor health, or decidedly *drunk* at the time of the incident. Most of the injured victims were handling the animals either in laboratories, zoological collections, or dis-

Mexican Beaded Lizard (*Heloderma horridum*).

Lee Ball, Staten Island Zoo.

plays of some sort. Two cases involved the victim carrying the creature in a shirt pocket, or inside a shirt next to the body. A number of cases occurred when drunks or near-drunks were teasing or otherwise mal-treating captive specimens. Very rarely are cases recorded involving a chance encounter in the wild. One victim was bitten when he pushed or struck at a Gila monster that crawled over him as he slept in a cave.

Even with all of the above before us, we should not be deluded into thinking of *Heloderma* as completely harmless. They possess a powerful neurotoxin, and can cause respiratory paralysis if they get sufficient venom worked into the tissue of a human being. Records indicate eight human deaths attributable to this cause. Symptoms of the bite include swelling, pain (due to the mechanics of the bite), loss of consciousness, vomiting, accelerated heart action, shortness of breath, vertigo, numbness, weakness, and swollen tongue and glands. Not all symptoms need, of course, necessarily appear in one victim.

The qualification of our "yes" in answer to the question, Are these animals dangerous? is this—you almost have to *try* to get bitten in order to become a victim. The Gila monster and its allies are not often encountered. They are peaceful desert animals and generally do not invade areas inhabited by man. They avoid man whenever possible, and almost always try to retreat rather than fight. They can't strike out like a snake, can't do any damage unless they get a good purchase, and can't bite through a shoe or a boot. It is a rare man who ever sees one outside of captivity (where they live well), and they represent no real threat to a normal, well-oriented human being. As a matter of fact, if you ever see one in the wild state you are more lucky than threatened.

# CHAPTER 11

# *Giant Snakes*

FELIX KOPSTEIN, a trained natural history observer, studied the reptile fauna of the East Indies, and knew it first hand. In a 1927 nature journal, he reported that a fourteen-year-old boy had been killed and swallowed by a Reticulated Python (*Python reticulatus*) approximately seventeen feet long. The story is probably true, if for no other reason, because Kopstein believed it. Very often, when logic is not apparently neglected, we can evaluate second-hand information only on the basis of source.

A great many other people have reported human deaths attributable to giant constricting snakes. Most of these tales were probably not true because the people reporting them were unable to establish any facts in connection with the alleged events. Tales so fanciful that they are downright shocking to the senses are repeated again and again. The literature of the great constrictors is not without its out-and-out lies. Some tales are so ridiculous one can but speculate that they were told originally in jest. Repeated time and again, they unfortunately gain currency until, with time and inevitable change, they emerge as fact.

A book was published in England in 1962 which describes "water" snakes three feet *round* and 140 feet long. A specimen (Anaconda) forty-five feet long according to the author, wrapped its tail around a submerged root and used its "head and neck coils" to drag a grazing cow into the water. A native porter is said to have severed the monster's head with *one bullet*. One might speculate that to sever the head of a forty-five-foot snake would require quite a bullet—a howitzer, for instance. The author, however, doesn't give you time to wonder how the porter managed to wield such artillery, because he has the severed head attacking him and his men. The head, he says, was "hideous" and "cat-like" (!) The snake's smell, according to this adventurer, is used to numb and hypnotize prey. The author manages to snap out of his odor-induced trance just in time, the severed head was only three feet away and closing in fast. Later on, he is induced to vomit by the touch of a boa constrictor's coils. At another point, the largest anaconda he ever saw wraps its tail around a tree and "whips" its coils at him. Again, Army Ordnance must have been handy because he decapitates the beast with that single shot. Another water serpent has a head three feet *wide*. Two baleful eyes as large as tennis balls, eighteen inches apart, appear. It must have been a

Boa Constrictor (*Constrictor constrictor*).     Roy Pinney.

particularly colorful reptile since these impressive orbs are described as violet blue, lit with streaks of scarlet fire!

This was not Marco Polo speaking, but an author in 1962 describing "personal adventures" [*sic*] in a book of non-fiction! In a book copyrighted in 1920, *Trapping Wild Animals in Malay Jungles* by Charles Mayer, the frontispiece is captioned, "The native screamed and the snake constricted suddenly, breaking nearly every bone in the man's body and crushing the life out of him." The claim is false! These words, in a book of ostensible fact, are pure fiction! Constrictors do *not* constrict suddenly. Some of their movements are quite rapid but the pressure applied by a coiling constrictor is a slow, inexorable process. Constrictors do *not* break "nearly every bone" in their victims' bodies; indeed, they seldom break any at all except by accident. They do *not* crush the life out of their prey.

The author has been unable to trace anyone who has witnessed the death of a human being in the coils of a giant snake. All of the information available is second-hand—at the very best. We shall have to tread lightly. It is a subject that has delighted the fictionalizers of natural history for centuries, and our path is fraught with danger, not from giant snakes but from people who have written about them.

Clifford H. Pope, in his excellent and reliable book, *The Giant Snakes,* numbers the true giants at six. He places them all in the family *Boidae*. It should be noted that approximately 85 per cent of the sixty to seventy members of the family fail to achieve a dozen feet at full growth. Other equally reliable specialists prefer to split the true giants into two families, *Boidae* and *Pythonidae*. The six giants named by Pope are:

Anaconda (*Eunectes murinus*)—South America—37–38 feet maximum.
Boa Constrictor (*Boa constrictor*)—South and Central America—18–19 feet maximum.
Indian Python (*Python molurus*)—India, Asia, East Indies—18–20 feet maximum.
Reticulated Python (*Python reticulatus*)—Tropical Asia—32–33 feet maximum.
Amethystine Python (*Python amethystinus*)—Australia to Philippine Islands— 22–25 feet maximum.
African Rock Python (*Python sebae*)—Africa—30–32 feet maximum.

The question of maximum length is a subject on which reams have been written. There is no end to the stories that have been told. The anaconda, particularly, has been said to reach astronomical proportions. In his extremely interesting book, *On the Track of Unknown Animals*, Dr. Bernard Heuvelmans recounts the attempts that have been made to capture, or even locate, the gigantic anacondas, reports of which have been filtering out of the South American forests for centuries.

Karl Weidmann with 14-foot live Anaconda (*Eunectes murinus*).
Karl Weidmann.

Major Percy Fawcett was on an assignment for the Royal Geographical Society of London when, in 1907, he shot an anaconda on the Rio Abuna. His claim was, "as far as it was possible to measure, a length of forty-five feet lay out of the water, and seventeen feet in it, making a total length of sixty-two feet." Other observers allow for 45 feet as maximum; some nineteen!

The anaconda is not the only one of the giants believed by many to achieve these huge sizes. Similar stories can be found for each of the others. Are they true? To the best of the author's knowledge, there is no natural factor in the snake's anatomy that would make it impossible for it to achieve these seemingly incredible lengths. On the other hand, there is no evidence that can really be accounted reliable to support claims that it does. It is all speculation. The author is certainly not privy to any secret information that would weigh in the argument, and will stay out of it until such time as *real* information is available. Knowing something about the photographic equipment and film speeds now available to the explorer, the author would prefer to see photographs. One thing is certain, if any explorer does encounter such a monster in a remote jungle swamp, photographs are about all we can expect to see. The weight of so large an animal would be such that it probably could not be transported, though the skin and skull could well be preserved. Skins alone are not to be trusted since they can be stretched to a remarkable degree before they are dried. A snake a dozen feet long will weigh between fifty and seventy-five pounds, depending upon species and condition. The pounds-per-foot factor increases with length as the girth increases. A seventy-five-foot snake would be a mighty load with which to contend overland, or down-river in a native canoe.

Are the true giants, at the maximum lengths given in this chapter, capable of killing a man? Depending on the man of course, a snake twenty feet long probably could, without too much trouble. Women or children could certainly be taken with even greater ease, and reports that seem reliable generally involve one or the other. The question of whether or not the giant snakes *can* kill a human being is not as important, however, as the question, *Will* they? Being able to do a thing and doing it are quite different.

The giant constrictors kill large prey, naturally enough, by constricting. They can give a vicious bite which, indeed, they generally do before coiling. Their incurved teeth and powerful jaws enable them to get a firm grip. The bite itself is non-venomous but does present problems of torn tissue and the danger of infection. *Constricting* does not mean *crushing*, as is so often contended. Every indication is that the constrictors do not normally crush their prey, they suffocate it. Once firmly around the victim's rib cage, the snake has only to wait. Each time the victim exhales, as it must to retain consciousness, the snake need only exert a slight increase in pressure. In good time, the victim is unable to draw in enough air to feed the brain the oxygen it requires. Once the victim has passed out the snake may continue the pressure until the heart stops, or may commence to swallow the still living but now inert animal. A really large snake firmly wound around a man could certainly exert the pressure necessary to kill him. It would require, quite probably, nowhere near a maximum effort. The big question in a hypothetical contest between a constrictor and a man would be the man's ability to stand up under the weight of the snake initially. If the man could remain standing, the snake might very well give up before getting a firm purchase. If, on the other hand, the man buckled under 250 or 300 pounds of snake, he would be hard put to defend himself against being suffocated. This is all rather academic, however, for although this may in fact have occurred from time to time, we still haven't answered the key question—*do* giant snakes attack man?

Snakes are short-sighted and are without ears. They can detect movement close-by, and almost certainly "hear" with their whole bodies. Even though they do not receive vibrations through the air as do the eared animals, they can feel vibrations carried by the ground with which they have such close contact. A snake is generally well aware of a man long before it sees him. Quite literally, it *feels* his approach. The pythons have facial or *labial* pits that are heat receptors. In a manner not unlike that of the poisonous pit vipers, the pythons can detect the presence of prey or enemies by the heat radiating from their bodies. By a system far more complex than our own, snakes "smell" the presence of other animals with keen accuracy. To say that they smell prey is not quite descriptive enough—they "smell-taste" the world around them. Their tongue, a device known as *Jacobson's Organ*, and their nasal passages play a combined part. This sense is very keen: it is chemical reception at its best.

This brief discussion of a snake's senses has as its purpose the point that, when a man approaches a giant snake, he does not generally do so unannounced except in rare and unusual circumstances. (Snakes do take to trees, of course, and a constrictor asleep on a branch would not get the vibrations of footsteps on the ground. A snake hanging from a limb could be surprised.) The chances are a snake on the ground will sense a man's approach far enough in advance to determine a course of action; flee, hold ground, or attack.

It seems fairly certain that some giant snakes have attacked human beings. It is equally certain that a very few people have been eaten after having been killed. These attacks, however, are most assuredly rare. They probably represent not so much a fair estimate of these animals' normal behavior as further evidence that, in the wilds, any combination of unfortunate circumstances is possible, sometimes with tragic results. Just as on the highways of the modern world gruesome mistakes can be made. These attacks were probably accidents at the outset.

There are some indications that snakes are a bit brighter than most of us have generally given them credit for; but they still function pretty close to the reflex level. If a snake sensed the approach of a man and failed to clear out before an encounter was forced upon it, it might very well strike out. Once it caught hold and felt the man's struggles, it might press home the attack by reflex rather than conscious intent. The snake's whole feeding mechanism is designed to respond to specific stimuli and a man could provide the necessary stimulation in these circumstances. The more violent the contest became, the more the snake might be stimulated to press the issue and seek the advantage. Compared to some of the animals to which the giants are known to give battle, man is a relatively easy mark. He does not have teeth or claws he can bring into play with any purpose beyond hysteria, and he is without hoofs and horns to interfere with swallowing, not that these matter much to the constrictors, it seems.

Schmidt and Inger (*Living Reptiles of the World*) refer to an "authentic" case of a Malay boy of fourteen falling prey to a snake on Salebabu Island, in the Taland group. He was killed and swallowed. (This is the Kopstein case referred to at the beginning of this chapter.) Herpetologist Arthur Loveridge, in a 1931 issue of the *Bulletin of the Antivenin Institute of America*, reported the death of a young mother on an island in Lake Victoria. She was found still in the coils of an African Rock Python (*Python Sebae*) about fourteen feet long. Although it probably killed her, it almost certainly could not have swallowed her. There have been other such reports, but very few from reliable sources. In no case

African Rock Python (*Python sebae*).
Transvaal Snake Park, South Africa.

known to the author was the attack witnessed by a knowledgeable observer, so the exact circumstances of the incidents remain clouded in mystery.

The giant snakes are not particularly rare, for the most part, and many live in close proximity to man—some within city limits of large urban centers like Bangkok, and along busy water fronts where the human traffic is very heavy. Pythons in the Orient and, reportedly, boas in South America are encouraged to take up residence under houses because they are a wonderful natural control on vermin.

While these stories of attacks do exist, there is no evidence to suggest that it is either normal or common behavior. Surely accidental encounters may have ended tragically, but they are evidently so rare that calling the giant snakes dangerous to man is stretching a point. All reliable observers report that the snake's first move is almost inevitably an effort toward escape. They either take off as fast as possible or freeze, instinctively taking advantage of their really excellent, and frequently quite beautiful, protective coloration. Frequently active at night, they may tend to bite when suddenly approached in the dark. If a few human beings have been unfortunate enough to encounter an aberrant individual, a snake whose escape route was cut off, or an animal who was for some reason short-tempered enough to seek an issue, we can pity the experience they must have had. These, almost certainly extremely rare occurrences, do not, however, indicate that the giants are naturally man-eaters, or even man-killers.

Before going on to discuss our next group of animals, it might be worthwhile to dispose of a few legends that have grown up around these animal giants. Although a snake may be able to strike from close quarters faster than a man can recoil, particularly if the man is really caught off guard, they cannot outspeed a man in an all-out race. It is difficult to imagine a large constrictor chasing a man across an open field, but if such a thing did occur, the man would win, hands down. It would take an exceptional swimmer, however, to outswim an anaconda. They move exceedingly fast in the water.

Further, these snakes do not have to anchor their tails in order to constrict. Wrap a small specimen around your arm and invite him to give you a playful squeeze, and you will see just how unnecessary an anchor post is.

The giant snakes are about as adept at milking cows as is the American Milk Snake. It is a laughably ridiculous legend but one that is still believed. The best way to disprove it is to ask the believer to milk a cow himself. After he has finished ask him to recall the pressure he had to apply and the tugging he had to do. Then, ask him what would have happened to the cow if each of his hands were lined with a hundred or so needle-sharp, incurved teeth. Unless you are dealing with a fool, he should concede the point.

No part of a giant snake's anatomy is poisonous at any time of the year. These animals are not immune to fire; cannot remain under water indefinitely; and they reproduce in a very normal reptilian way. The pythons lay eggs; and the boas, including the anaconda, give birth to living young.

The larger snakes will continue to fascinate man as they have always done. They are truly giant forms and, as such, carry a certain mystical aura about them. Although there will be no more of a basis for fear then than now, our great-great-grandchildren will still look at them in the zoo and recall, with delicious, tingling horror, tales of man-eating serpents. If your child asks you, as I once heard a little boy ask his father in the Reptile Wing at the Staten Island Zoo, "Do they just feed bad people to the snakes?" don't be upset. It is evidently an inevitable part of our folk-legend heritage.

# CHAPTER 12

# *Venomous Snakes: The Rattlers*

As SHOULD have become clear from the preceding chapter, snakes potentially dangerous to man fall into two groups—those that can cause mechanical damage and those that can cause chemical damage. The former are the boas and pythons; the latter, which are much more numerous and widespread, are also more diverse. These we will now investigate systematically. But first, it will be advantageous to place these creatures in some simple and comprehensive framework.

There are living today some 2,500 kinds of snakes, divided between thirteen families of varying size and importance—both from the naturalist's and our more specialized point of view. These may be listed as follows:

I. The Constrictors    (1) The *Boidae*, or Boas.

                             (2) The *Pythonidae*, or Pythons.

II. The Burrowers      (3) to (7) [Families of no interest to us.]

III. The Water Snakes  (8) The *Acrochordidae*, or True Aquatic Snakes.

IV. The Biters          (9) The *Colubridae* (including rear-fanged and some that constrict as well).

                        (10) The *Elapidae* (including Cobras and Corals).

                        (11) The *Hydrophidae*, or Sea-Snakes.

                        (12) The *Viperidae*, or Vipers and Adders.

                        (13) The *Crotalidae* or Pit Vipers and Rattlers.

The designation "biters" is entirely empirical in that all snakes "bite." These are thus grouped only to emphasize that it is among them that all the venomous species are included.

The order in which these are listed above may be best described as "standard practice" amongst herpetologists but that order may be reversed without in any way affecting its comprehension. And, for several reasons, we propose to do just this.

The Crotalids are, as regards the development and complexity of their envenomating mechanism, the most advanced. In fact, the families as listed above show a progressive development in this respect from the Colubrines through the others listed—and in that order—to the Crotalids; and the rattlers appear to be the most "advanced" and specialized of these. Thus, an explanation of the envenomating apparatus of this group will lead to a better understanding of that of the other groups, and will at the same time obviate a lot of verbiage.

Roger Conant, in his interesting, and very worth-while book, *A Field Guide to Reptiles and Amphibians*, places the rattlesnakes and close relatives in the sub-family *Crotalinae* (pit vipers) under the family *Viperidae* (vipers). He is certainly not alone in this, but Klauber[1] (along with Stejneger, Barbour, and a great many others) prefers to assign a separate family to the pit vipers, *Crotalidae*, and we shall follow this example in the initial identification of the subjects of this chapter.

There are six genera recognized in the family *Crotalidae*, as thus defined, although this, too, is open to discussion. These are:

| Genus | Members | Range |
|---|---|---|
| *Crotalus* | Rattlesnakes | North and South America |
| *Sistrurus* | Massasaugas and Pygmy Rattlesnakes | North America |
| *Lachesis* | Bushmaster | Central and South America |
| *Bothrops* * | New World Pit Vipers | Central and South America |
| *Trimeresurus* * | Asiatic Pit Vipers | Asia |
| *Agkistrodon* | Cottonmouth Water Moccasins, and Copperheads,† Old World Pit Vipers ‡ | North America, Southeast Europe and Asia |

* Sometimes grouped together as *Trimeresurus*.
† The Australian "Copperhead" is not related, but is an elapid snake, far more dangerous than this crotalid.
‡ Old World members of *Agkistrodon* usually have no other popular name than "Pit Viper." This can be rather confusing.

Although, as I say, there is room for discussion, we are on reasonably safe ground in stating that there are 30 existing species, subdivided into 66 subspecies of rattlesnakes—of two genera: *Crotalus* or *Sistrurus*. Of the two, *Crotalus* is by far the most important from a number of points of view. Sixty of the rattlesnakes are in this genus (as compared with 6 in *Sistrurus*); its members are spread over a much wider range; and they are generally larger, carry more venom, and have longer fangs.

One of the characteristics the two genera have in common is a definitive identification point for rattlesnakes. Of all the snakes that exist on this planet, only the rattlesnake has a true rattle. (No other snake has this device, and no snake is a rattlesnake unless it has one, unless *Crotalus catalinensis* might be an exception.) Here, at least, no confusion appears possible.

Snakes, because of their light bone structure, do not fossilize well. It is difficult to pin down the periods in which types first emerged, but C. W. Gilmore places the first venomous snakes in Europe somewhere

[1] Laurence M. Klauber's monumental and definitive two-volume work, *Rattlesnakes: Their Habits, Life Histories, and Influence on Mankind*, published in 1956, will be our arbiter in this chapter.

between eight and twenty million years ago (*Fossil Snakes of North America*). Rattlesnakes have been positively identified in deposits in North America between four and twelve million years old. This is enough to tell us that man never existed on this planet at a time when there weren't rattlesnakes. We can't, however, place the time when the two first met.

The chart in Appendix C lists the 66 recognized rattlesnakes now in existence, alphabetically by Latin name, gives a popular name for each, and provides a brief description of its range. It must be recognized that the descriptions of the ranges are sketchy. Frequently, only small isolated areas in the regions listed are today populated by the species or subspecies under discussion. A continuous population, blanketing the regions listed, is seldom the case because of varying geographical features and human habitation.

When you glance over this table, it is easy to see where the rattlesnake has developed most successfully. In all of South America, only 3 species or subspecies are presently known. Compare that vast continent's area of 7,035,357 square miles with Arizona's 113,909, and the fact that Arizona has 17 species and subspecies seems all the more astounding. Although this animal has been known in every state except two (Hawaii and Alaska), and has been exterminated, it is believed, in only two (Maine and Delaware), it is primarily an animal of the Southwest. Mexico's 35 mainland species and subspecies, and her additional insular variations, when coupled with Arizona's 17, New Mexico's 9, California's 10, and Texas' 10 pretty much places rattlesnake headquarters of the world in the southwestern portion of the North American continent.

The apparatus with which a rattlesnake inflicts injury consists of two highly specialized teeth, and their attendant mechanisms. Contrary to legends, which surprisingly still have currency among the ill-informed, the breath of the rattlesnake is harmless, as are its forked tongue and unique tail. Rattlesnakes cannot spit their venoms as can some cobras.

A rattlesnake cannot poison a suckling infant through its mother's milk by biting the mother, nor has a rattlesnake any hypnotic powers beyond that of causing hysteria in individuals with an unnatural fear. A garter snake can do as well, generally, in these cases. Categorically, the only way a rattlesnake can cause an injury is to puncture the skin with one or both of its fangs. What is involved is a bite or scratch, a stab, if you wish, but not a sting. No snake stings. That is left to bees, and a host of other creatures we discuss elsewhere in this book.

One strange belief is apparently well founded in fact. A rattlesnake can "bite" after it is quite dead. Reptiles, it seems, have prolonged reflex actions. James A. Oliver, Director of the American Museum of Natural History, reports that people have actually been bitten by snakes handled after they were dead. The reference is in a pamphlet he prepared for the New York Zoological Society entitled, "The Prevention and Treatment of Snakebite." This author has noted other reliable references to this rather strange fact.

The mechanism with which a snake can cause injury can readily be divided into two parts, (1) a system of venom production and storage, and (2) a system for the introduction of that venom into the tissues and circulatory system of the victim. We will discuss the latter part first.

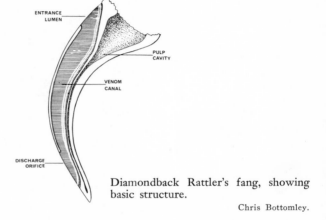

Diamondback Rattler's fang, showing basic structure.

Chris Bottomley.

Not all snakes have the same tooth system. There are the solid-toothed types without any fang differentiation known as Aglyphs. Snakes with *fangs* at the back of the mouth—that is, with enlarged and grooved posterior teeth—are called Opisthoglyphs. Here, the venom is chewed into a wound, as opposed to injected. Snakes with strongly differentiated fangs in the front of the mouth are either Proteroglyphs—snakes with permanently erected fangs—or Solenoglyphs—snakes with fangs that fold or rotate back to the roof of the mouth. Clearly, the most advanced and efficient biting mechanism belongs to the animals in the last of the four categories. They have their venom injectors in front where they can be most readily brought into play, and can accommodate longer fangs because they can fold them away. They actually carry fangs that are far too big for their mouths because they can only bring them forward when the lower jaw is close to 180 degrees from the upper. It should not be assumed, however, that the most efficient biting mechanism automatically indicates the deadliest bite. As we shall be noting, the most dangerous venom in the entire animal kingdom belongs to the third group, the front-fanged, permanently erect type, and not the viperine, folding-fang group. There are further refinements of these fang-type groupings, but they need not concern us in this survey.

The highly developed biting mechanism of the viperine snakes involves two modified maxillary teeth, and the means for swinging them downward. They move down with their protective sheaths from the roof of the animal's mouth, through an arc of roughly 90 degrees, to a position perpendicular to the upper jaw. The fangs are greatly elongated, curved inward and canaliculated, or equipped with an enclosed canal. As the animal's fangs penetrate the victim's tissues, the sheaths are pushed back up along the fangs.

One of the most remarkable things about the rattlesnake's fangs is that they are always present for the animal's needs. Although they are fragile and easily lost in action as well as by periodic shedding, the rattlesnake has immediate replacement provisions. In a system not unlike a cartridge clip in a semiautomatic pistol, the animal has as many as six additional fangs in various stages of development on each side of his head. As soon as one is lost, the most mature of the replacements goes through a few brief changes and the animal is again fully armed, as it was at the moment of birth, for action. There is an overlap in the schedule of change. In a letter to the author, Dr. Klauber points out that, for a short time, venom can be injected from both fangs on one side of the head. When the new one is fully operative, the old one drops out.

The fangs themselves curve back at an angle of 60 to 70 degrees. An entrance lumen at the top or back end, near where the fang joins its bony support, allows venom to enter a hollow canal down which it is forced. The venom does not come out the top of the fang, but rather through a discharge orifice slightly up from the point, and on the *front* of the fang, facing out from the animal's mouth. The fang has cutting edges also on the front to assist in effective penetration.

Of particular importance in determining the danger posed by a venomous snake is the size of the fang. If the fangs are very small and frail, the chances of the animal's breaking them on striking are increased, and the chances of its injecting its venom are reduced. Short-fanged animals are also hindered by even light clothing. Klauber reports fang lengths all the way up to $1\frac{1}{16}$ inch, and he estimates some specimens have $\frac{7}{8}$ inch of exposed, functional fang. However, rattlesnakes do not have the longest fangs in the world. African vipers (genus *Bitis*) undoubtedly hold the record. The Gaboon Viper (*Bitis gabonica*) probably outdoes all other species with fangs approaching two inches in length. However, fangs of $1\frac{1}{16}$ or $\frac{7}{8}$ of an inch in length, and even much smaller sizes, are capable of penetrating human tissue, even when protected by clothing, and reaching well-blooded tissue below the fat layers. Quite plainly, the rattlesnake's fangs are long enough to reach muscles, veins, and arteries.

Just how poisonous are these, America's best known and most frequently encountered, poisonous snakes?

Eastern Diamond-back Rattlesnake (*Crotalus adamanteus*).

Lee Ball.

The Wyeth Laboratories, a major producer of antivenin specific for the *Crotalidae*, published a very informative booklet in 1961 entitled "Antivenin (*Crotalidae*) Polyvalent." In discussing the Florida or Eastern Diamondback (*Crotalus adamanteus*), it refers to it as ". . . one of the most dangerous (rattlesnakes), ranks among the world's deadliest snakes." Discussing the Texas or Western Diamondback (*Crotalus atrox*), it says, "Bold and aggressive, it often crawls in the open and is commonly seen in cultivated areas, even in or near farm buildings. It is responsible for more serious and fatal accidents than any other North American snake."

James A. Oliver says in his booklet, "The Prevention and Treatment of Snakebite": "The Western Diamondback kills more people than any other snake in the United States. Babies can deliver a lethal bite."

Dr. Herbert L. Stahnke, director of the Poisonous Animals Research Laboratory at Arizona State University, says in his booklet, "The Treatment of Venomous Bites and Stings," ". . . This is due to the fact that nearly all venomous snake bites in the United States are inflicted by Pit Vipers, i.e., rattlesnakes, copperheads, and cottonmouth moccasins. These snakes are not only abundant and their habits and habitats conflict with those of man. . . . Serious tissue destruction can result from the bite of even the youngest pit viper." We could easily cite several hundred such references from equally reliable sources.

Information on rattlesnake venom is incomplete and much research

Western Diamondback (*Crotalus atrox*).

Roger A. Caras.

remains to be done. As closely related as different species are, there are apparently widespread variations among their venoms, and there is no one description that will accurately cover both genera, *Crotalus* and *Sistrurus*. Since laboratories like those of Wyeth are able to produce a polyvalent antivenin for all pit vipers, however, we can describe certain things they have in common. The variables between the venoms of different species may in part be a matter of amount, and not of kind. As the Wyeth booklet says, "Venoms are structurally complex substances; none has been completely analyzed."

It is generally accepted today that all pit viper venoms, or almost all, are both neurotoxins and hematoxins; viz., they attack both the nervous and the circulatory systems of the victim. It is also generally believed that each venom is predominantly one or the other, with the remaining characteristic being secondary. This is certainly true of the rattlesnakes.

The venom of snakes developed from saliva, and the venom-producing system grew out of salivary glands. Many species completely harmless to man have toxic qualities in their saliva linking venomous and non-venomous snakes. This all makes good sense since saliva plays a large part in the digestion of food in animals, and the venom of a poisonous snake is used, not only to kill prey, but also to begin the digestive process before it is swallowed. In fact, there appears to be no serious opposition to the statement that the venom of these animals is first and foremost a prey-killing and digestive substance, and only secondarily a defensive one. The evolutionary development of venom from saliva is linked initially with these primary functions. The entire complex of the snake's envenomizing apparatus was designed to get food and utilize it, and not to injure animals too large for it to feed on.

In appearance, venom is generally yellow in color (although some colorless samples are on record), and usually cloudy when first obtained. Since the cloudiness settles out if the venom is allowed to stand, we can assume that it is caused by cellular debris of some sort. It is usually described as odorless. It has a slightly sweet taste, but this is not very strong. Klauber says there is a slight tingling sensation on the lips when the venom is tasted. It should be noted again that no harm will generally come from tasting, or even swallowing venom as long as there are no open sores in the mouth, or in the digestive tract. (Cobra venom, on the other hand, *may* be injurious if swallowed.) Similarly, venom on unbroken skin is harmless although there is wisdom in the idea that it should be washed off as soon as possible. Venom is a poison but, like all poisons, it can be safely handled by people who know what they are doing.

Since venom is so complex a substance, and so difficult to analyze chemically, most researches have concentrated on breaking it down, not by chemical constituents, but rather by the effects it produces. Quantitative analysis usually involves a description of which effect on the victim

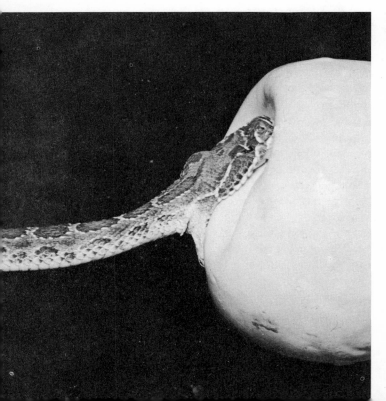

Rattlesnake-strike—the stab.

Walker Van Riper: Denver Museum of Natural History.

is most pronounced. Even a brief survey of the work that has been done in this field would far exceed not only the needs but the covers of this book. Keep in mind that a wide range exists even among the rattlesnakes; the venom of the South American Rattlesnake (*Crotalus durissus* and subspecies) is closer to the venom of the Indian cobra in effect than it is to that of the Florida or Texas diamondbacks.

What all this amounts to is that the venom of the rattlesnake is most definitely dangerous to man, or potentially dangerous in the event of individual encounter. Just as it is certain that some rattlesnakes can cause death by their bite, it is equally certain that some do not or may not. Since only the specialist can tell one rattlesnake from another with any certainty, the practical attitude in the field is to leave them all alone. Anyone can learn to tell the very different species apart—the massasauga from the Texas diamondback, for example—but since the color phases are so erratic, and since it is almost certain that the young of some species are more dangerous than the adult forms of others, the rule still applies. Reading about the use of the "T" or "Y" stick does not equip a person with sufficient knowledge to attempt to catch and handle a dangerous reptile. This should be left strictly to the experts. If you encounter a rattlesnake in the wild state, unless you really blunder into it, the chances are you will not be injured. Don't try to kill or capture it; leave it alone. It will soon go its own way, as relieved as you not to have had to face a showdown.

We have, then, an animal that is, at least in many of its forms, dangerous to man as an individual in direct contact. What of the statistical potential, how much of a threat is the rattlesnake?

Dr. Klauber estimates that the mortality rate from rattlesnake bite is about 1½ to 2 per cent. The U.S. Department of Health, Education, and Welfare provides the following statistics: deaths from rattlesnake bites amounted to, 1960—15, 1959—9, 1958—7, 1957—5. The states wherein these bites most often occur are, in order of incidence, Arizona, Florida, Georgia, Texas, and Alabama.

How great, then, is the nationwide danger from rattlesnakes? With approximately 1,500,000 deaths a year in the United States, five to fifteen deaths from any one cause is inconsequential. In Mexico, with a large rural population, much of it barefoot, the snakebite incidence is bound to be higher. If you live, work, or play in Arizona, Florida, Georgia, Texas, or Alabama, you have a better chance of being fatally injured by a rattlesnake than in any other states in the Union. Of course, there are parts of New York and Massachusetts where you are more apt to be bitten than in parts of the five states listed above. We are speaking now of statewide statistics, for whatever they may be worth. The five states that do lead the field probably do so because of the occurrence of the

Florida and Texas Diamondbacks (*Crotalus adamanteus* and *Crotalus atrox*), two of the most aggressive and dangerous of all the rattlesnakes. Neither Florida nor Georgia has anywhere near the variety of rattlesnakes that California has (three and five as compared to ten), and California is not on the top-five list.

If you are a man you have a much better (or worse!) chance of being bitten, and the reason for that is obvious: it is because of the places where you are most apt to work and play. If you are a child under seventy-five pounds in weight your chances of dying are much greater, although this is not to suggest that obesity is a practical defense against rattlesnake-caused fatality.

Klauber lists a number of other variables that influence the ratio of injuries to death:

1. Age, size, sex, vigor, and health of the victim.
2. Allergy complex; susceptibility to protein poisoning.
3. Emotional condition and nature of victim.
4. Site of the bite. (Fortunately, you have a better chance of being bitten on the extremities than near the vital organs.)
5. Nature of the bite: full, direct stroke, as opposed to glancing blow or scratch.
6. Protection afforded by clothing.
7. Number of bites; *occasionally* more than one is involved.
8. Length of time the snake holds on. Usually rattlesnakes hit and run, but there have been cases where they got hung up and even had to be pulled or shaken loose. Certainly, these cases are exceptional.
9. Extent of the anger or fear of the snake. While there is no truth to the old legend that a snake's *virulence* increases with his rage, it is true that a rattlesnake will not generally discharge all of its venom, which it needs for food-getting. If injured or violently excited, however, it might really let go and give all it has, or nearly all, much to the detriment of the victim.
10. Species and size of the snake. (We have already indicated that this is a major factor.)
11. The age of the snake is also a factor; very young and very old snakes are likely to be less virulent. However, this is relative.
12. Condition of the venom glands; full, partially depleted, etc.
13. Condition of the fangs.
14. Presence of various microorganisms in the snake's mouth; venom contains an antibactericidal constituent that can lead to serious and even fatal complications.
15. The kind of first aid, and eventual treatment given.

Klauber reports that, drop for drop, some rattlesnake venoms are sixty times (!) as powerful as others. Number 10 above would be the author's choice for the most important single consideration, though this is, of course, open to argument.

The medical text, *Principles of Internal Medicine*, states that "The minimum lethal dose of dried rattlesnake venom for man has been postulated to be 1 mg. per 6 pounds of body weight. The average Diamondback yields 220 mg. of venom, the Moccasin 150 mg., and the Copperhead 45 mg. Since these venoms are qualitatively similar, the larger quantity injected appears to account for the greater deadliness of the Diamondback." Of course, all rattlesnake venoms are not necessarily qualitatively similar, although the end result of a massive dosage might be. For the purposes of the practitioner, the statement would appear to be accurate enough. One other point, however: we can assume the three dosages given, 220, 150, and 45 mg., were measured from snakes artificially milked under laboratory conditions. If that assumption is correct, the information is slightly misleading since rarely would a snake evacuate its full supply on a single bite.

Dr. Herbert L. Stahnke, in his booklet, "The Treatment of Venomous Bites and Stings," describes and illustrates with actual case photographs terrible tissue destruction peculiar to essentially hematoxic types of Crotalid venom. This terrible localized destruction, on occasion requiring amputation, would not be typical of neurotoxins with their slight or absent localized effects.

What, then, can our conclusion be about the rattlesnake, and the danger it poses to man? Individually, the rattlesnake is a dangerous animal and one best avoided. Certain areas of the country realize more danger than others by a tremendous margin, due to large rattlesnake populations of indigenous species. Statistically, your chances of being bitten are very low almost everywhere, and non-existent in most places. The chances of your being killed by a rattlesnake are lower yet. If you are a calm person who takes normal precautions you are even less likely to get bitten, and less likely to be killed even if caught off guard and struck. Individually, the rattlesnake can be very dangerous; nationally, it isn't much of a health menace.

The rattlesnake, however, is not just a mass of statistics, nor is it simply an excuse for constructing a probability graph. The rattlesnake is an integral part of the natural economy of American wildlife. It is a durable, adaptable, and even a useful animal. It is an important cog in the machinery nature set up on this continent for the control of fast-breeding rodents. Without the rattlesnake, our natural balance in many parts of the United States would be quite different. Ironically, this dangerous animal helps keep many harmless animals harmless. Without the rattlesnake, many animals now harmless would be much more destructive and expensive to deal with.

The rattlesnake can probably survive just about everything that will happen on this continent in the foreseeable future except expanding

Handling Rattlesnake
specimen in the field.
National Museum of Canada.

urbanization and the resultant increase in suburban construction. This rapid spread of urban and suburban development has no natural limits other than the higher altitudes and the coastlines of the continent. Cliffsides and sand dunes that were once considered totally unfit for human habitation are today the well-springs of new architectural schools. Man's conquest of microscopic animals is leading to immense population expansion. To this growth, the rattlesnake must eventually bow. It is hunted, its natural prey is hunted and starved, and eventually it, like the mountain lion, Canada lynx, bear, and other species which do not sit well with man, will be a zoological curiosity. For the time being, however, it is here in quantity, and we might well heed the ancient admonition, *"Don't Tread On Me!"*

All of Canada, from the Arctic to the United States border, has only four species of venomous snakes, all of them rattlesnakes. Alberta has the Prairie Rattlesnake (*Crotalus viridis viridis*) in the southeastern sector; British Columbia has the Northern Pacific Rattlesnake (*C. viridis oreganus*) in the south-central and eastern areas; Ontario has the Eastern Massasauga (*Sistrurus catenatus catenatus*), the Timber Rattlesnake (*C. horridus horridus*), and both in the southern parts, and Saskatchewan has the Prairie Rattler in the southwest. Manitoba and Prince Edward Island each *may* have a species of rattlesnake in very limited populations. No venomous sea snakes are known to visit Canadian waters. Snake bite, as a problem, is negligible. The mortality rate is between one and two per year for the entire nation of 3,610,097 square miles. No other nation of even comparable size is so free from this problem.

There are more than forty species and subspecies of rattlesnakes in Mexico. The aggressive and dangerous Western Diamondback (*C. atrox*) occurs on the Baja California Peninsula, on San Pedro Mártir, Turner and Tiburon Islands, and in ten or eleven Mexican states. Although figures verifying this are not available, rattlesnakes alone are probably a much bigger health problem in Mexico than they are in the United States. Over-all snake-bite mortality appears to run ten times as high, but rural Mexicans have a larger variety of venomous species to contend with.

As we have seen, the rattlesnakes are not absent from South America, although they appear in nowhere near the variety found in Mexico and the United States. At the present writing, aside from *Crotalus unicolor,* the Aruba Island Rattlesnake (found only on tiny Aruba Island), only two subspecies are listed for all of South America: *C. durissus terrificus* and *C. d. vegrandis*. In a letter to the author, Dr. Klauber said that he is sure further taxonomic breakdowns of *C. d. terrificus* will be recognized once more work has been done on the group. The range of this rattlesnake in South America is considerable, Chile and possibly Ecuador being the only exceptions, and even Ecuador is not positively known to be free of them. They are known by many dozens of names because of the number of linguistic groups resident in small inhabited pockets in this vast area. Among the best known are: South American Diamondback, Rattlesnake, *Boicininga, Boiquira, Maracaboia, Cascavela,* and *Cascabel.*

As in parts of the United States and Mexico, the rattlesnake figures prominently in injury and death statistics attributable to venomous animals. Interestingly enough, the venom of the South American rattlesnakes is far closer to the venom of the cobras than it is to other rattlers; it is essentially neurotoxic. The animal is capable of administering a particularly lethal bite.

On December 3, 1775, Commander in Chief Esek Hopkins was piped aboard his flag-ship, the *ALFRED,* and took command of the fleet constructed by the new American Congress. Captain Dudley Saltonstall, commanding officer of the vessel, accepted a flag from his superior. The flag, a gift to Hopkins from a Colonel Gadsden, was hoisted at the main mast of the *ALFRED,* and the first of a long line of "rattlesnake flags" felt the pull of the wind.

The flag had a yellow field with a coiled rattlesnake in the center, and the words, "*Don't Tread On Me,*" at the bottom. On the same day, the United States Navy jack was raised on another ship in the fleet picturing a rattlesnake crawling across a field of thirteen stripes. A similar flag was the emblem of the South Carolina Navy. The Minutemen of Culpeper County in Virginia carried a flag showing a coiled rattlesnake with the

The Rattle.

National Museum of Canada.

additional legend, *"Liberty or Death."* The Massachusetts Navy had a rattlesnake coiled around a pine tree, and the words, *"An Appeal to God,"* before the ubiquitous, *"Don't Tread On Me."*

The rattlesnake, whether hoisted as a flag and leading British colonists in their battle against their king, or held alive and squirming between the teeth of a Hopi Indian as the symbol of lightning in the intense Hopi Snake Ceremony, has never been very far away from American folklore, symbology, and imagery. Ranging from southern Canada past our own southernmost boundaries deep into Central and South America, the rattlesnake, in its currently recognized 66 species and subspecies, is solidly implanted in the American ecological scene. Encountered in mountain crags, in deserts below sea level, and in steaming coastal swamps, this animal exists, or did exist before hunting and human invasion somewhat restricted its range, in every state within the continental limits of the United States. Alaska and Hawaii alone, of the fifty American states, have not known the readily distinguishable *whirrrr* of the rattlesnake's tail. Surrounded by legend, accredited with powers that bring it to the very threshold of deification, and scientifically studied more than any other group of reptiles, the rattlesnake appears to have a firm hold on popular fancy and full title to the role of American animal arch villain.

# CHAPTER 13

# *Venomous Snakes: The Other Crotalids and the True Vipers*

REVERTING to the Table on page 142, it will be seen that there are four other groups of Crotalids or Pit Vipers. The classification, let alone any true systematization, of these is one of the most difficult and in some respects unsatisfactory exercises in herpetology.

The Bushmaster (*Lachesis muta*) is the only species in its own genus of *Crotalidae*. It is the largest of all pit vipers, but fortunately is not particularly abundant in any part of its range. It inhabits abandoned burrows of mammals in hot, damp lowlands and jungles. It is found from Nicaragua south through all of Central and much of northern South America. Costa Rica, Panama, Colombia, Venezuela, the Guianas, northern Brazil, and Trinidad all play host to this impressive animal. *Surucucu, Mapepire Z'ananna* and *La Cascabel Muda* are some of its more common names. The last means "silent rattle," and since it is a native name we might assume it isn't based on the scientific relationship the creature actually does bear to the rattlesnake. It has the habit, as do other rattle-less pit vipers (and some harmless snakes), of rapidly vibrating its tail when disturbed. On a bed of dry leaves, the sound produced can sound much like the rattlesnake's specialized tail.

The bushmaster has the distinction of being the only egg-laying pit viper of the New World. The others give birth to living young. Lengths in excess of twelve feet have been reliably reported for this rasp-skinned, reddish-brown serpent, but nine to ten feet is closer to average. The *Shusupé*, as it is sometimes called, has particularly long fangs, one and three-eighths inches having been reported, with one to one and one-eighth inches probably being average for an adult specimen.

As to aggressiveness, the picture is confused. The American traveler, Leonard Clark (*The Rivers Ran East*), has the bushmaster "fatal to man in 5 minutes," and "it will follow a man and kill either by day or by night," not to mention "will continually strike until the victim is dead." Karl P. Schmidt, late Curator of Zoology Emeritus at the Chicago Natural History Museum, wrote an amusing piece called, "Anent the 'Dangerous' Bushmaster," for the August, 1957, issue of *Copeia*, the journal of the American Society of Ichthyologists and Herpetologists.

Bushmaster (*Lachesis muta*).

Courtesy of the American Museum of Natural History.

By amusing, the author means no disrespect because the story *is* amusing in the sense that it contradicts so effectively (and on such good authority) so much of what has been written about the bushmaster.

To the best of available knowledge, Leonard Clark lost his life on the Amazon in 1957, and since he can't defend his opinions, we won't take his observations to task. We will allow them to stand on their own merits as they face comparison. In his article, zoologist Schmidt cited a letter received from his friend, herpetologist Raymond E. Stadelman, dated April 17, 1957. Mr. Stadelman was formerly curator of a serpentarium in Honduras. He was an early contributor to the *Bulletin* of the now defunct Antivenin Institute of America. The letter concerns the capture of a bushmaster between eight and nine feet long in Colombia. An employee of the Villa Artega rubber station near Antioquia was bathing in a stream with his wife when he spotted the snake. Mistaking it for a harmless boa, he decided it would make a nice addition to the Stadelman collection. The (very) amateur collector tied a shoestring around the snake's neck (!) and together with his wife started to lead the bushmaster home on the improvised lead. Then the snake got stubborn about being dragged along like a dog in Central Park; the shoestring broke. While the man retied the fragile leash, his wife shoved and pushed from behind! The couple encountered an Indian who told them that their harmless "boa" was a dreaded bushmaster, and the wife left the scene. The husband picked the snake up with the help of another workman and carried it to the site of the Stadelman collection, nearly strangling the beast in the process.

Mr. Stadelman commented in his letter to Dr. Schmidt,

I have always had doubts about the famed aggressiveness of the Bushmaster, and believe this reputation is unwarranted. While I consider the Fer-de-lance to be very dangerous because it is nervous and apparently bites through fear, I think the Bushmaster just doesn't give much of a damn about anything. . . .

He goes on to describe how he frequently handled bushmasters without the snakes assuming a threatening attitude. Dr. Schmidt does point out at the end of the article that a pit viper with inch-long fangs is dangerous, whether aggressive or not.

Certainly, the bushmaster must be rated as dangerous to man. It has extremely long fangs, it carries a massive dose of venom and has caused deaths. We have discussed it at some length here because reliable, scientific reports list this snake as sluggish and not generally very aggressive. Folk legends, however, have it actually pursuing man. Somewhere between total indifference and constant murderous intent lies the truth. The nature of this truth determines how dangerous the animal is, its ability to kill being readily established. Bushmasters, like all other snakes, vary from specimen to specimen. Certainly, some individuals may be extremely combative while others are apparently quite docile when handled expertly. We can assume, based on the observations of really qualified individuals, that it is not the monster it is so often described as being. Left alone, it doesn't look for trouble.

It is with the remaining three genera of Crotalids that we encounter real problems. These problems are, however, of deep concern only to specialists so we may perhaps be granted the liberty of employing one technical simplification that makes the whole matter much easier for the layman interested only in knowing what snakes are dangerous and where they are to be encountered. This device is simply to revert to the old classification and combine the New World *Bothrops* with the Old World *Trimeresurus* for, if we do this, the scientific names that will be found in most of the literature will not be quite so misleading. Also, we can then say that the two genera (*Bothrops-Trimeresurus* and *Agkistrodon*) have both Old and New World representatives. We will take the latter first because it contains the remaining venomous snakes of our own continent.

These North American species are known, commonly, as the copperheads and the cottonmouths, and go as follows:

| Scientific Name | Common Name | Distribution |
|---|---|---|
| A. contortrix mokasen | Northern Copperhead | Massachusetts to Kansas, south to Alabama, west to Texas. |
| A. c. contortrix | Southern Copperhead | Virginia, Florida to Alabama, Texas north to Illinois and Missouri. |
| A. c. pictigaster | Trans-Pecos Copperhead | Trans-Pecos Texas. |
| A. c. laticinctus | Broad-banded Copperhead | Kansas, Oklahoma, Texas. |
| A. piscivorus piscivorus | Eastern Cottonmouth | Virginia to Key West and Alabama. |
| A. p. leucostoma | Western Cottonmouth | Illinois to Alabama, west to Kansas, Oklahoma, Texas, Missouri. |

The copperheads and cottonmouths are more closely related to each other than are some rattlesnakes. The cottonmouth is almost certainly the more dangerous. It is frequently referred to as the third most dangerous snake in the United States, statistically. Only the Eastern and Western diamondbacks cause more fatalities. Generally speaking, the cottonmouths are about as dangerous as most rattlesnakes of comparable size while the venom of the copperhead is weaker than that of the rattlesnake.

The genus *Agkistrodon* is represented in Mexico by the *Cantil* (*A. bilineatus*) which ranges from central Mexico south through Central America. It is highly toxic, but fortunately relatively rare.

Copperhead (*Agkistrodon c. mokasen*).

Courtesy of the American Museum of Natural History.

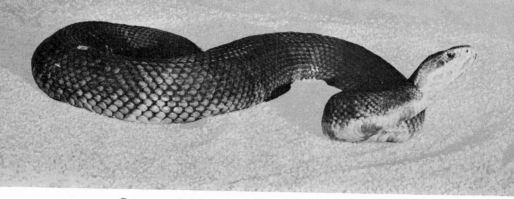

Cottonmouth Moccasin (*Agkistrodon piscivorus*).

Lee Ball.

Between ninety and one hundred snake bite deaths are reported for Japan each year. (A number of the sea snakes range that far north [*Lapemis, Laticauda, Pelamis*], but cases of injury or death to man from their attentions are rare in Japan as everywhere else.) The *Mamushi* or Pallas's Pit Viper (*Agkistrodon blomhoffii* or *halys*) is probably the chief villain in Japan. The *Mamushi* belongs to the same genus as the copperhead and cottonmouth of North America. The *Mamushi* ranges through a variety of terrains and is quite common. During the spring and summer months, large numbers are collected and shipped to big cities where they are displayed alive in drug store windows. A medicine is made from them that is used for a variety of complaints ranging from impotency to asthma. The author noted windows full of these animals in several Japanese cities. Some of the cases of snake bite reported probably come from the fact that the *Mamushi* is handled frequently and in large numbers.

There are eight other species of *Agkistrodon* in the Old World. Races of the species that contains the *Mamushi*, range from northern China to

Mexican Moccasin, or Cantil (*Agkistrodon bilineatus*).

Lee Ball.

extreme southeastern Russia; the other species are scattered over southeast Asia as far west as the Himalayas and south to the island of Ceylon, and to Malaya. These snakes are commonly called (in English, that is) simply pit vipers which is most misleading since the same general designation is given to the Old World representatives of the *Bothrops-Trimeresurus* genus, and even on occasion to the larger true vipers of the Middle East and Africa because they were once believed to live in pits!

Turning now to this other group or combined genus, we will again take the New World forms first. These are now commonly all called *Bothrops* by herpetologists, and the best known is undoubtedly the Fer-de-lance (*Bothrops atrox*). This is a much feared snake with very large venom glands, with powerful muscles to activate them, large fangs, and a rather active disposition. The venom is said to be fast-acting and to cause internal bleeding, both around the bite and also, in surprisingly short order, in other parts of the body. First aid is of course indicated but anti-venin is called for at the very earliest in the case of a bite from this snake. The species is widely distributed in the form of subspecies and local races from southern Mexico to Peru and east throughout northern South America to the West Indian island of Martinique where it has always been very prevalent and so became known to the first French colonists at a very early date.

The incidence of venomous snakes in the West Indies constitutes something of a mystery. Although surrounded on three sides by lands more than amply provided with snakes, they are strangely barren of venomous snakes. Trinidad and Tobago, islands that are really parts of South America, have the bushmaster, fer-de-lance, and a coral snake; the fer-de-

Fer-de-Lance (*Bothrops atrox*).
Courtesy of the American Museum of Natural History.

Central American Tree
Pit-Viper (*Bothrops
schlegeli*).

Chicago Natural History
Museum.

lance is also found on Martinique and St. Lucia. All the rest of the West
Indies are free of poisonous snakes.

This lack may indicate an early separation from the mainland. Where
geological evidence is otherwise, you have mainland species, *Bothrops*
and *Lachesis*. Rattlers, being more recent evolutionary products, perhaps
weren't around when they could have invaded the land that now makes
up these islands.

Some of the close-in coastal islands of the Caribbean undoubtedly have
acquired strays that floated across on vegetation carried down the rivers
from the highlands, but these are exceptions. To find hundreds of tropical
islands, some covered with dense jungle, free of these animals is a most
unusual situation.

The fer-de-lance is found not only on the two West Indian islands, Martinique and St. Lucia, but also from central Mexico south through Central America to northern South America. It is a particular problem to native laborers since it thrives on rats that normally infest sugar plantations. Its venom is haemolytic and even "babies" (born alive in litters reportedly as high as thirty or more) are highly dangerous. The same fer-de-lance is known in Costa Rica and Honduras as *Barba Amarilla* (yellow beard). Other names are *El Tercipela* (the Velvet One), *Barcin, Caissaca, Macagua, Guayacán,* and many more. Although more of a problem in Panama and some other areas than in Mexico, there can be little doubt that it is one of the more dangerous venomous animals. It achieves a length of eight feet (some reports say twelve), is a denizen of both moist and dry regions, forested as well as open country, and is universally dreaded throughout its range. Its nervous irritability is not the least factor contributing to its richly-deserved reputation as a bad citizen; it is a night "hunter." Ten other species of *Bothrops* occur in Mexico, but none match the fer-de-lance in disposition, virulence, or size.

It is an interesting if not a mysterious fact that the pit vipers of this group are clearly divided both in the New and Old Worlds into two distinct subgroups—arboreal species with prehensile tails and in most

Jararacussu (*Bothrops jararacucu*)

Harvard Institute for
Tropical Biology and
Medicine.

Tommygoff (*Bothrops mummifer*).

From *Living Treasure*.

cases displaying green coloration, on the one hand, and ground-dwelling forms, without prehensile tails and of various color combinations but in no case vivid green, on the other. Even more strange is it that some of the former on both sides of the Pacific have vivid red tails. There are some thirty-five forms in the New and twenty-five in the Old World.

Apart from the fer-de-lance the best known in the New World are probably the *Jararaca* (*B. jararaca*) and the *Jararacussu* (*B. jararacucu*) of Brazil both of which can exceed five feet in length and which can deliver strikes that can result in death. In some respects the most unpleasant form appears to be the Tommygoff or Jumping-Viper of Central America (*B. mummifer*), an exceedingly thick-bodied, short animal with a tiny tail held high off the ground. This snake can climb, though it is not prehensile-tailed, and its strike is so violent it can actually launch itself off a low branch or even, it is reported, the ground. It is possible that this species may develop the longest fangs for its size of any snake. Actual case histories of envenomation by this and the other tropical American *Bothrops* are sadly lacking but we must assume that they account for a large proportion of the considerable number of deaths caused by snakes in this area. And this is quite a serious problem as is demonstrated by the following table consisting of extracts or information from Swaroop and Grab, "Snakebite Mortality in the World":

*Argentina:* "it is believed that snake bite constitutes a problem of real importance in the rural sections of certain regions. . . ."

*Bolivia:* Statistics are apparently not available.

*Brazil:* "on the basis of the 1929 figures, it is estimated that there are 4,800 deaths from snake bite annually in Brazil. According to an indirect source, the number of annual deaths was estimated at about 2,000 in 1949."

*British Guiana:* Statistics for deaths from venomous animals (there were 15 from 1944–48) are not broken down as to type of animal.

*Chile:* "It is believed that there are no venomous snakes in Chile."

*Colombia:* From 1945 to 1949, there were 821 known deaths caused by venomous animals. It is not known how many of these were caused by snakes, but Swaroop and Grab observe: "a great variety of poisonous snakes are known to be present in Colombia, the most common species and the one causing the largest number of deaths being *B. atrox.*"

*Ecuador:* "From 1900 to 1946, 2,182 cases of snake bite were treated at the Luis Vernago Hospital, Guayaquil; of these 87 were fatal. Mortality data for snake bite for the country as a whole are not available."

*French Guiana:* No mortality figures. Bushmaster known to exist.

*Paraguay:* No available statistics.

*Peru:* Well-provided with venomous snakes, but no statistics available.

*Surinam:* No figures, but problem believed to be slight.

*Uruguay:* Fifteen known snake bite deaths from 1935–46. Largely *Bothrops,* it is believed.

*Venezuela:* During the three years, 1947–49, there were 1,295 snake bite cases reported, with 419 deaths, a mortality rate of nearly ⅓! [This figure is so inconsistent with those from the rest of South America that this author would tend to question it.]

Central America, 228,578 square miles of tropical, wildly mountainous territory with limited coastal lowlands, includes six republics: Guatemala, Honduras, El Salvador, Nicaragua, Costa Rica, and Panama, and the colony of British Honduras. Like Mexico, Central America has a wide variety of venomous snakes.

British Honduras reports a low incidence of snake bite, twenty-three from 1947 to 1951, with no fatalities included. This is in part accounted for by the very small population—under 70,000. Costa Rica has a considerably higher rate; El Salvador a reportedly low rate; no figures are available for Guatemala or Honduras; and Nicaragua is believed to have a low rate. Small populations and isolated, depressed areas, without medical records, in part account for sketchy, non-existent and reliably unreliable statistics. Yet, reportedly, snake bite is extremely prevalent both in the forested lowlands of the Caribbean coast of these countries and also on the dry coastal plains of the Pacific where Crotalids abound. The Tommygoff (*Bothrops mummifer*) is particularly troublesome in a number of areas. It is thought of locally as one of the world's most dangerously venomous snakes. Other Palm-Vipers, and certain Ground-Vipers (all *Bothrops*) contribute to the problem.

The genus *Bothrops* is very well represented in South America, although much work is left to be done in what appears to the non-specialist to be a perfect muddle. Most herpetologists apparently feel the genus should be broken down into several genera, at least. So far, no one has attempted this difficult project.

Among the best known *Bothrops* in South America, apart from the fer-de-lance, are a number of Palm-Vipers, Hognosed-Vipers, and Short-Tails. Particularly dangerous are Maximilian's Viper or Wied's Lance-head (*B. neuwiedii*), the *Urutu* or *Wutu* (*B. alternata*), the Snouted Lance-head (*B. ammodytoides*), the True Jararaca (*B. jararaca*), and the extremely dangerous and very aggressive *Jararacucu* (*B. jararacussa*). Schlegel's or Eyelash Viper, a prehensile-tailed creature, is probably the southernmost member of the genus, reaching well down toward the bottom of the continent. There are many, many more, and some of them figure rather prominently in the statistics of snake bite incidence. As it is with the rattlesnakes in the United States and Mexico, some are extremely dangerous and others are virtually harmless.

The remaining Crotalids are Old World forms and are now, as we have said, customarily all called *Trimeresurus*. They are distributed over a great triangle in eastern Asia, or what is better described as Orientalia, from the Ryukus west to the forested limits of the Himalayas and south to Ceylon and the greater Indonesian islands. Probably the most popularly known is the *Habu* (*T. flavoviridis*) of Okinawa, which became all too well known to Americans during World War II. This species appears to be extraordinarily abundant on both that and other islands of the group while subspecies are found in southern Japan. There is also an entirely different and much smaller species called the *Kufa* (*T. okinavensis*) found on the same island.

During military operations on Okinawa Shima during World War II, a twenty-year-old Marine private was lying in some bushes at the side of a tomb, peering down on Japanese soldiers below. He thought he felt a twig poke him in the cheek, and when he turned to see what it was, he was struck a second time below the left eye by a *Habu* (*Trimeresurus flavoviridis*), supposedly the most deadly snake in the Ryukyu Islands. This man and nine other victims of the *Habu* reported during the campaign were eventually returned to duty. The *Habu*, long feared as a particularly dangerous snake, is not known to have taken the life of a single American during the campaign when thousands and tens-of-thousands of G.I.'s poked into virtually every cave and brush pile on the 794-square-mile Pacific island.

While all the snakes of this genus are venomous, and many may be lethal to man when anti-venin and even simple first aid are unavailable, Schmidt and Inger note the very interesting fact that the arboreal, prehensile-tailed members of the Oriental group do not appear to be lethal or even seriously dangerous to man. They report, for instance, that Wagler's Viper (*T. wagleri*) of the greater East Indies is "very sluggish and gentle during the day, not at all prone to bite . . . is not dangerous to man, though it produces severe pain and local swelling. Venom relatively innocuous to man appears to characterize all of the arboreal pit-vipers of the Asiatic region."

In this and the preceding chapter we have noted nearly all of the venomous snakes of the Western Hemisphere. We have gone from Canada to southern Argentina, reviewed all the world's rattlesnakes, and many other pit vipers, and we did not find one animal whose bite means *inevitable* death. Taking the whole Western Hemisphere (from the Arctic to the Antarctic) we found snake bite a problem, for the most part, from Texas to Brazil. North and south of these two areas, snake bite diminishes rapidly as a statistical cause for concern. This "snake bite belt," we will find, carries on around the world. Venomous snakes are, indeed, dangerous to man, more often so up to 35 degrees of latitude north and south of the equator than anywhere else, but nowhere we have yet seen are snakes necessarily lethal when they do bite. What of the rest of the world?

The other large family of snakes, which have venom fangs that can be folded back, are the true vipers of the Old World. This is an extremely numerous group both in forms and individual populations. Only a very few have adopted the arboreal habitat but these, like the climbing pit vipers, have also developed prehensile tails. Most of the ground-dwelling forms have comparatively short tails, but some have exceedingly abbreviated ones. Their colors and color patterns vary in a bewildering manner and run the gamut of the earth colors, with all manner of dark and light patterns. Some of the desert forms are almost cream-colored and one and all are masters of camouflage.

Common European Viper (*Vipera berus*).
John Markham.

Since both systematic zoology and the scientific study of snake en-venomation were started in Europe, we may legitimately start our survey of the group in that subcontinent. Europe proper has a very limited variety of poisonous snakes. All are true vipers of the genus *Vipera*. The Common Viper (*V. berus*) ranges from the Pyrenees to 67 degrees north in Scandinavia and is almost certainly the northernmost, and most widely distributed, venomous land snake on earth. It is the only venomous snake in the British Isles and ranges from those Atlantic islands right across Eurasia north of the Desert Belt to Korea. The following table roughly capsules the venomous snakes of Europe:

## THE SNAKE BITE PROBLEM IN EUROPE

| Country | Partial List of Species | Extent of the Problem |
|---|---|---|
| Austria | *V. ammodytes* (Long-nosed Viper) | Very low. |
| Denmark | *V. berus* (Common Viper) | Seven deaths in 47 years—all victims 12 years old or younger. In all, 1,200 cases of snake bite. |
| England and Wales | *V. berus* | Seven deaths in the past 50 years. |
| Finland | *V. berus* | Very slight. |
| France | *V. berus* and *aspis* | Probably higher in the south of this country than in most other European areas. |
| Germany | *V. berus* | Very low. |
| Greece | *V. ammodytes meridionalis* | Not known. |
| Hungary | *V. berus* | Not known. |
| Italy | *V. berus* and *aspis* | May be slightly higher than most areas. |
| Netherlands | *V. berus* | Practically non-existent. |
| Norway | *V. berus* | Practically non-existent. |
| Portugal | *V. berus* and *latasti* | Not known. |
| Russia | *V. ammodytes* and *renardi* | Not known. |
| Spain | *V. berus* and *latasti* | About 5 deaths a year. |
| Sweden | *V. berus* | About 1,300 people bitten per year. Fifteen deaths from 1915 to 1944. |
| Switzerland | *V. berus* and *aspis* | Twenty-five deaths between 1881 and 1930. Between 5 and 10 bites per year. |
| Turkey | *V. a. meridionalis* | Not known. |
| Yugoslavia | *V. berus* and *aspis* | Not known. |

Europe, generally speaking, suffers less than most other temperate areas in the world. The death rate from accidents with venomous snakes, when compared with the population involved, is negligible. Some of the

Puff Adder (*Bitis arietans*).

C. A. W. Guggisberg.

vipers (*V. ammodytes*, for one) are reportedly more virulent than the ubiquitous Common Viper, but not enough more so to cause a problem of any significant proportions. Even one death, of course, is a problem, but in examining an area as large as Europe, and as heavily populated, snake bite cannot be called a matter of grave concern.

There are some thirty true vipers in Africa. The Puff-Adder (*Bitis arietans*) has a wide range and a dangerous, relatively slow-acting venom.[1] The Night Adder (*Causus rhombeatus*) is reportedly timid and slow to anger, but its habit of coming around human habitation at night results in many accidents. The Rhinoceros Viper (*B. nasicornis*) is said to be inoffensive for the most part. It does, however, have a particularly potent venom, and a wide range across the continent from Ghana to Kenya.

The Gaboon Viper (*B. gabonica*) is probably the one snake that comes closest to delivering the "sudden death" so often accredited to most venomous reptiles. It could be especially dangerous to man, and has two of the longest fangs known among the world's dangerous snakes. It has a massive head and, if it hit squarely, the fangs would be planted dangerously deep. It is altogether a very, very formidable animal. Happily, it has a mild disposition, and bites are not common.

Two Horned-Adders (*B. cornuta* and *caudalis*) are accredited with waspish dispositions and dangerous venom. The Berg Adder (*B. atropos*)

[1] The tragic death on January 28, 1964, of the director of the Salt Lake City [Utah] Zoo, from a Puff-Adder bite, shows the danger of handling these big vipers.

Night Adder (*Causus rhombeatus*).

Courtesy of the American Museum of Natural History.

of South Africa is also dangerous. Two Sand Vipers of North Africa (*Aspis cornuta* and *vipera*) and the Carpet or Saw-scaled Viper of East Africa (*Echis carinatus*) are common in desert areas. The carpet viper ranges from Africa through Arabia and Iran to India.

Writing from Pakistan to Dr. Laurence M. Klauber, Dr. Sherman A. Minton, Jr., said of the carpet viper:

The Gaboon Viper (*Bitis gabonica*).

Transvaal Snake Park, South Africa.

While not wishing to talk down *Echis* as a dangerous snake, I believe some of the factors that keep the fatality rate relatively high concern the human population at risk. The average snake-bite victim here is appreciably smaller than the average American or European, is to some extent malnourished and anaemic, and may well be suffering from chronic malaria and/or tuberculosis. The treatment he gets at a village dispensary may be positively harmful (e.g., permanganate injections). He may fare better at the hands of the local hakeem or snake charmer who will use his snake-stone, incantations, and herbal remedies. Even if the victim makes it to one of the relatively few modern hospitals, the best he can hope for is intelligent symptomatic and supportive treatment. Incidentally, the fatality rate in hospitalized cases here seems to be about 10% rather than the higher figures that have been reported particularly from parts of Africa.

Today, the headquarters of the true vipers is undoubtedly Africa, but this must not be taken to imply that the family originated there. The distribution of the various forms, or genera, of the family may perhaps best be understood if we regard the equatorial forest area of central and west Africa as the hub of their territory, and then consider a number of circular belts around this—belts incomplete only to the southwest which is, of course, occupied by the Atlantic. Within the hub are to be found such small-headed types as *Causus* and the great puff-adders. It also contains the burrowing *Atractaspis* which, though also having small heads that look more like those of non-venomous snakes, have particularly long fangs.

All around the deep forests lie, first, open woodlands; then savannahs; then semi-deserts; and finally the great expanses of true deserts that reach

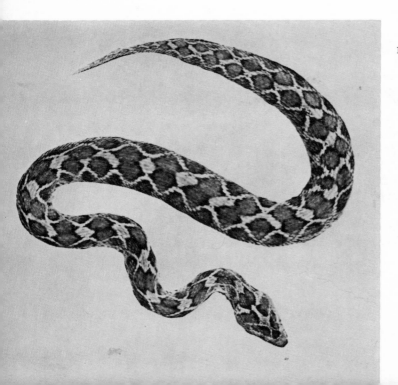

Saw-Scaled Viper
(*Echis carinatus*).
Dr. P. J. Deoras, Bombay.

from the Mauretanian coast on the west, to North Africa, the Near East, and thence northeast right across central Asia to China, east to India, south into Arabia, and southwest in a great curve through the Sudan and Ethiopia, to lower Somalia. This desert belt contains its own hosts of vipers. Outstanding among these are the horned vipers of the eastern Mediterranean, three particularly dangerous large species in Asia Minor and the Levant of which the Palestinian Viper (*V. palestinae*) seems to cause the most trouble to man, and Hind's Viper in East Africa. There are also dangerous forms in southern Russia, and in Iran and Pakistan. Jordan listed eighty-four snake bite deaths in the five years 1948–52, and Iraq listed twelve for the four years 1948–51. Iraq has the Blunt-nosed Viper (*Viper lebetina*), the Horned Viper (*Aspis cerates*), and the Saw-scaled Viper common further to the east. This last-named snake is one of the most dangerous in the world, from all indications, due to numbers, range, aggressiveness, and a toxic venom.

Beyond this arid belt, we have, to the north, the little adders of Europe and middle Asia, and, to the east, large tropical forms in India, Burma, the Indochinese peninsula, and several of the Indonesian islands. The most notable of these oriental forms is perhaps the *Daboia* or Russell's Viper (*V. russelli*), which is found all over the Indian peninsula and beyond to Siam and Java. It is dangerously venomous and of a savage disposition. It is one of Burma's archvillains and a constant threat to barefooted farm workers. It is found in great numbers in the Irrawaddy River valley. It is reported that even a very small specimen can inject twice the amount of venom required to dispatch a healthy full-grown man. Incidentally, this was Sherlock Holmes' famous "Speckled Band."

Probably the most venomous (for their size) of all the vipers, and the most potentially dangerous due to their abundance and habit of lying in depressions in paths in open, intensely hot places, are the Horned-Vipers of Egypt and Arabia, and the Saw-scaled Vipers, which latter range from North Africa to India and south to the island of Ceylon. The

The Tic-Polonga, Daboia or Russell's Viper (*Vipera russelli*).

Dr. P. J. Deoras, Bombay.

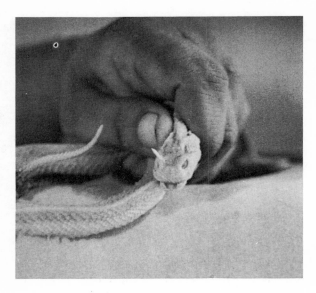

Persian Horned Viper
(*Pseudocerastes perse-cus*).

Dr. P. J. Deoras, Bombay.

saw-scales have exceptionally potent venom, are touchy, and have a lightning strike. The number of deaths caused by them cannot be assessed but, judging by their numbers in even limited areas of heavy population, it must be extremely high. The vipers, in fact, though creatures that normally lie and wait for prey, and which are sluggish compared to many other venomous snakes, constitute a real menace to man especially in the arid areas of the Old World where the human inhabitants do not wear thick, tough foot-coverings, or where they go barefoot.

# CHAPTER 14

# *Venomous Snakes: The Sea Snakes, Elapids, and Poisonous Colubrines*

THE remaining venomous snakes, as may be seen from the list given on page 141, fall among three great families. These are, first, the Sea snakes or Hydrophids; next the Elapids, which include the Cobras and the Coral Snakes and their allies; and third, the Colubrids, among which there are but few menaces—in fact, in the case of man, probably only two species. Although the second group contains the snake that all experts agree is potentially the most dangerous—the mighty king cobra—it appears that the real danger (of the venom itself) is in descending order from the Hydrophids to the Colubrids. The degree of "danger," "menace," and "potential danger" to man cannot be assessed by the same criteria. As we have constantly tried to point out, so many factors are involved that it is impossible and would be extremely dangerous to say that this, that, or the other snake species is the one most dangerous to man. Let us investigate these animals and endeavour to assess their potentialities —of various kinds.

About 5 P.M. on October 24, 1954, an eight-year-old Chinese boy was paddling in the gentle surf off Penang Island, Malaya. Although he felt no pain, he saw a snake fastened to his ankle. He showed the bite to his father, but was allowed to go back into the surf to play. By 6 P.M. he was feeling stiff and weak, by midnight he was passing blood in his urine. By 6 A.M. the following day, thirteen hours after being bitten, the boy was dead. On the same day, at the same beach, a twenty-six-year-old man was also bitten on the foot. He lived seventy-seven hours. Both were victims of a sea snake, an animal we shall discuss in detail.

Sea snakes, venomous creatures all, members of the family *Hydrophiidae*, are almost all residents of the western Pacific and Indian Oceans. The one exception is *Pelamis platurus*, the Yellow-bellied Sea snake, and this species reaches the western coast of Central America in not inconsiderable numbers. (Professor Loeb of UCLA reports seeing this animal as far north as San Diego.) Its range, from eastern Africa to western Central America, makes it the most widely distributed reptile in the world. Equipped with a particularly virulent nerve toxin, this snake has

Blue-Ringed Sea Snakes (*Hydrophis cyanocinctus*).

New York Zoological Society.

reportedly caused some human deaths. It must be noted, however, that considerable confusion exists on this point, and reports are consistently conflicting as we shall see.

The family *Hydrophiidae* includes fifteen genera, and approximately fifty species. Some members of the subfamily *Laticaudinae*, the more primitive sea snakes, do come ashore to lay eggs although they live most of their lives in the sea and eat fish exclusively. Members of the subfamily *Hydrophinae* have adapted to the point where they are totally marine, and, giving birth to living young, never venture out onto dry land. Indeed, they can't, for their ventral scales have been reduced to a degree where they cannot be used to move on land. Agile and swift in the sea, they flop and squirm ineffectually once removed from it.

According to Schmidt and Inger, they have also adapted to life in the sea in another strange way. They generally have an exceedingly slender neck and anterior half of the body, while their posterior end is much heavier, terminating in a flattened, vertical, paddle-like tail. Since these snakes hunt fish, which they obtain by means of their potent venom, they have to strike much the same way as any other venomous snake. Floating in a liquid medium, however, they can't obtain a purchase and have no fixed fulcrum. Nature has made the necessary adjustments and the heavy after-end supplies the inertia while the slender forward-end is designed to reduce the effects of resistance in the heavy medium of sea-water. All of these snakes are air breathers and will drown, as will any other lunged animal, if held under water beyond their limit. Like the whales and seals, the sea snakes are derived from land animals who forsook dry land to return to the easy life of the sea. They have not, however, been able to free themselves of the earth's atmosphere.

With the exception of *P. platurus*, these sea snakes are limited to the southwest Pacific and Indian Ocean areas. This one wanderer not only reaches Central and South America, but has been captured in Posieta Bay, Siberia! It is likely that the few specimens taken in the latter locale were carried there by the Tsushima branch of the Kurosiwo Current which flows northward into the Japan Sea. No other sea snake is known to travel far into deep waters, being, generally, coastal animals with a strong preference for river mouths, harbor and beach areas, and coral reefs. A few are occasionally seen somewhat further at sea, and some travel up brackish tidal rivers for short distances. One species, *Hydrophis semperi*, apparently got caught by a geological upheaval and dwells in fresh-water Lake Bombon on Luzon Island. *Laticauda crockeri* is also a lake-dweller being found in brackish Lake Tungano on Pennell Island in the Solomons. All others are strictly coastal animals.

As a group, these sea-going snakes are not large. Eight, nine, and ten foot specimens have been reported, but most species achieve nowhere near that size. Four to six feet is apparently about average.

According to Dr. Bruce W. Halstead, at least one species is known to have venom fifty times as potent as that of the king cobra. It is believed that all are venomous, although there exists a distinct difference of opinion as to how dangerous all of them are. They have venom glands located just below the eye. Their fangs are cobra-like, being permanently erect, hollow, and not very large. They are located at the front of the mouth.

Black Banded Sea Snake (*Laticauda colubrina*).

Australian News and Information Bureau.

There are many reports of these animals occurring in vast numbers at certain seasons. They evidently congregate for the breeding season, and reports exist of ships sailing through seas literally alive with them. Ivan Sanderson described to the author having such an experience in the Strait of Malacca in 1927 and the numbers of snakes involved apparently were of astronomical proportions. It is reported that they are particularly aggressive during the breeding season.

The "United States Navy Diving Manual" (NAVSHIPS 250-538) has a hazard table for marine life: one plus means minimum danger, and four plus means maximum. Collectively, sea snakes are rated three plus. Under the column marked "Behavior" is the comment, "Boldness varies." Despite the fact that these snakes are venomous, often dangerously so, and even though they are plentiful in some parts of their range, bites are not too common. The determining factor appears to be aggressiveness and, although reports on this characteristic vary, the relatively few cases reported would tend to support the idea that they are more retiring than pugnacious. Most snakes prefer to give ground rather than take on a foe as large as a man and the sea snake has a better chance to retreat before a showdown is forced on it than has a land form. A swift whisk of its paddle-like tail with a single side-to-side movement, and the serpent is gone. This would appear to be rather characteristic behavior except during the breeding season when competition is high and might lead to a general reluctance to surrender to any intruder.

Most accidents reported with these animals are tied in with fishing activities. They apparently hunt by night, and have been known to take bait and suddenly appear at the gunwales much to the chagrin of some poor angler. They are very often taken, and sometimes in large numbers, in nets. Over a hundred were taken in a single seine-haul off Luzon. Some fishing peoples, it is reported, refuse to report or discuss accidents with these animals on superstitious grounds and good statistics aren't available. Many of the areas inhabited by the *Hydrophinae* are remote and underdeveloped. It is impossible to get a reliable population count, much less a reasonable estimate of snake bite mortality. This, however, would appear to be a fair consensus: they are often extremely venomous, they do on occasion bite, although they are not generally aggressive. It would be best to leave the water when they are around, and they certainly shouldn't be handled by anyone who isn't an expert. They have a limited economic value since some are hunted for their skins, from which a good grade of leather is made; they are bottled in chunks, and sold as an aphrodisiac and a general medicine, and they are smoked on bamboo skewers and used in Japan and parts of the Ryukyu Islands as food. In such places, they are highly esteemed as a delicacy.

Dr. H. A. Reid of the General Hospital in Penang, Malaya, has consented to the use of the following extract of a case history of a sea snake bite which appeared in his paper, "Three Fatal Cases of Sea Snakebite," in *Venoms*, the 1956 symposium of the American Association for the Advancement of Science:

A Chinese fisherman, aged 54, was admitted to the Penang General Hospital on November 24, 1952, in a semi-paralyzed state. Eight days previously, he had returned from fishing off the west coast of Penang Island about 4 A.M., and, while kneeling down on the seashore sorting his nets, he felt a bite on the left knee. With the aid of a torch, he found that he had been bitten by a snake which he killed with a stick and threw back into the sea. It was about 2 ft. long and black and white in color with a flat tail. He noticed two teeth marks with small clots of blood at the spot where he had been bitten. He returned to his house and during the following few days the left, then the right leg, and finally the whole body became progressively weaker. He was eventually found by Security Forces operating in that area and carried by chair about 2 miles to transport by which he was brought to Penang General Hospital.

On admission bite marks were observed above the left knee. Intelligence, speech, and memory were noted as normal. All the limbs were weak and painful, and he was unable to sit up.

The following day, November 25, 1952, he was quite conscious though restless. At times he appeared mentally alert, answering questions reasonably, but mostly he seemed confused and uncooperative. He then complained bitterly and constantly of thirst. The pupils were small, equal, and reacted to light. Eye movements were normal. There was generalized loss of power and tone in all limbs. He could move somewhat feebly but was unable to lift his head off the pillow or sit up in bed. Involuntary movements were not seen. All tendon reflexes including the jaw jerk were absent. Abdominal reflexes were not obtained, plantar responses were flexor, and he was incontinent of urine and feces. No reliable estimation of sensation could be made but he responded to pinprick on the face and elsewhere, and no gross hyperesthesia was observed. Two pairs of puncture wounds were seen above the left knee, 5 mm. and 4 mm. apart respectively. There was no swelling, bruising, or tenderness, and the marks might well have been made by a hypodermic needle. The remaining physical examination was not remarkable; blood pressure 100/65, respiratory rate and fundi normal. The urine was normal apart from a trace of albumin. No abnormal color was seen. Cerebrospinal fluid was normal.

During the next two days, his condition remained essentially unchanged. He was restless and noisy, constantly complaining of thirst despite intragastric drip of 5 pints milk daily. His respiratory rate and rhythm appeared to be within normal limits. He died in the early morning of November 28, 1952, 4 days after admission and 12 days after the bite.

The same paper presents two other cases, both involving bathers. They were both bitten on the same day at the same beach. The first, a boy of eight lived for thirteen hours. The second, a man of twenty-six lived for seventy-seven hours. Evidently, cases of bathers being bitten are almost unheard of. These two cases are the first fatal cases involving bathers on record, and it may be more than a coincidence that they occurred at the same place on the same day. Dr. Reid does not draw this conclusion in his paper and I must be held responsible for it; *possibly* it was aberrant behavior on the part of a single animal. The bites are reported as having been administered about two hours apart. The adult was the first victim (3 P.M.), and the child the second. A small boy would have less tolerance, generally speaking, than an adult and could have been killed even by a snake that had delivered a lethal bite only two hours earlier, assuming that sea snakes, like land snakes, do not tend to discharge their full load unless wildly agitated. This, however, is pure speculation, and I repeat, must be laid at my door and not Dr. Reid's.

It is interesting to note that the bite of the sea snake is virtually pain-less and very slow acting. The lack of reports of accidents may be due to the failure of victims to associate the two, or even know that they have been bitten. Here, again, however, this is speculation, albeit a reason-able projection of known factors.

Turning now to the Elapids, we come face to face with the group of animals which, as a whole, probably do represent more potential danger to man (as a whole) than any other on earth. I would stress that this does not mean that they are any more aggressive, any more venomous, or any more lethal than many other kinds of animals; it is more that they happen to be extremely prevalent throughout very extensive areas where humans abound and where they are particularly prone to be in a position to encounter the animals. Also, the very same areas lack modern medical facilities to a large extent and in several places they are rife with superstition, which is inimical to both prevention and cure of this conflict.

Although the greatest potential menace to man by snakes is in areas where there are most people; and although the Elapid snakes take first place as this menace, their headquarters, though surely not their place of origin, turns out to be Australia. This continent has more kinds of venom-ous than nonvenomous snakes, and no less than eighty-five different kinds of Elapids are found there. These land-dwelling snakes are close relatives of the Cobras, with fixed, relatively short fangs in the front of their upper jaws. According to D. M. Cochran, the larger Australian snakes are *outstanding for their abundance, insolence, and high toxicity*.

As long ago as 1894, in Melbourne, Australia, Dr. George Britton Halford wrote:

A gentleman residing in South Yarra . . . rang me up at about midnight in May, 1868. He told me he had been bitten by a snake, that he did not want my advice, only that he wished to know if it was a poisonous snake or not. With that, he opened a parcel and let the snake, which had been cut in halves, fall upon the carpet. The fall made it, although dead, wriggle about a little. I saw the punctures on his arm, examined the head of the snake, and found it to be that of a vigorous Tiger snake. Presently he asked leave to go on the verandah, where I heard him vomiting, and an hour or so afterwards, at his home, he coughed up into his cambric handkerchief, bloodcolored sputum. I felt sure he would die, which he did, twelve hours after the bite. His intelligence remained nearly to the last. The devitalised blood . . . was no longer capable of carrying on the processes of life. It was as if one were looking at St. Paul's Cathedral, and seeing it from some mysterious cause tumbling into dust. Such were my thoughts watching the passing away of this fine man.

On June 13, 1960, *Life* magazine carried an article about a twenty-two-year-old snake-handler in California who was bitten by a Tiger Snake (*Notechis scutatus*). The article says the young man was "the first person outside of Australia ever bitten by the rare tiger snake, deadliest of all land serpents." It is not exactly certain that this creature is the deadliest of all venomous snakes (and it is not rare in Australia), but Swaroop and Grab point out:

It has an extremely toxic venom . . . is one of the most aggressive reptiles found in Australia . . . is reported to be responsible for a high proportion of the deaths from snake bite in the country.

Of the more than eighty-five varieties of venomous snakes that occur in Australia, F. G. Morgan of the Commonwealth Serum Laboratories

Australian Tiger Snake (*Notechis scutatus*).
Australian News and Information Bureau.

Australian Death Adder (*Acanthophis antarcticus*).
Australian News and Information Bureau.

pins the appellation "most deadly" not on the tiger snake, but on the *Taipan* (*Oxyuranus scutellatus*). In a paper he did on this serpent for *Venoms*, Morgan describes it as a large, active, highly dangerous snake "capable of injecting at a bite an enormous dose of highly potent neurotoxic venom."

In his paper, Morgan describes the unfortunate case of a young man from Sydney named Kevin C. Budden. While visiting Queensland in July, 1950, Budden collected a *Taipan* for research purposes. He was carrying the specimen to his car when "the snake managed to bite him on the thumb and hung on, biting savagely, being removed only with great difficulty by the victim." Budden still managed to save his specimen, but he died the next day from the bite.

The *Taipan* is reported as rarely encountered since it is scarce, shy, and quick to escape. It grows to a length of over ten feet.

Morgan lists the Death Adder (*Acanthophis antarcticus*), the Tiger Snake, the (Australian) Copperhead (*Denisonia superba*), the Common Brown Snake (*Demansia textilis*), and the Red-bellied Black Snake (*Pseudechis prophyriacus*) as the main contributors, along with the *Taipan*, to Australia's snake bite mortality. Swaroop and Grab agree. They describe the death adder as especially active and dangerous.

It should again be pointed out that the Australian copperhead has nothing whatsoever to do with the American snake of the same name. They are not at all related. To the lay reader who may object to the use of Latin names following the popular name of each animal, as it appears for the first time in this text, this example will demonstrate the necessity of that generally accepted practice. Here is the case of two English-speaking nations on opposite sides of the world. They both have venomous snakes known throughout their respective ranges by the same name, "copperhead." The snakes have nothing to do with each other. Without the refinement of scientific names, confusion would be supreme!

Interestingly enough, although 60 per cent of Australia's land snakes are venomous, and Elapids, very few are deadly to man. From 1942 through 1950, there were only fifty-six snake bite deaths reported in Australia. This figure is incomplete, almost certainly, since, under Australian law, these deaths are not ordered to be recorded. (In addition to its venomous land snakes, Australia plays host in its coastal waters to twenty-seven different species of the sea snakes.)

Australia is frequently described in pulp literature as the home of the deadliest snakes in the world. This well may be the case, but when these treasuries of inaccurate herpetological lore go on to describe Australian snakes as creatures whose bite no man can survive, they pass over into pure fiction. Reliable reports in the Medical Journal of Australia (Ferguson 1926, and Tidswell 1906; both quoted by Fairley in 1929) give the following fatality rates:

## SOME FATALITY DATA—AUSTRALIAN VENOMOUS SNAKES

| Animal | Victims | Deaths | Fatality Rate |
|---|---|---|---|
| Death Adder | 10 | 5 | 50.0% |
| Tiger Snake | 45 | 18 | 40.0 |
| Brown Snake | 70 | 6 | 8.6 |
| Red-bellied Black Snake | 125 | 1 | .8 |

No doubt availability of antivenin and improved medical techniques would make the death-rate even lower today.

The very dangerous death adder of Australia is found in New Guinea and in the Moluccas. A number of relatives of the brown snake, including the *Taipan*, also occur in New Guinea along with great numbers of sea snakes along the coasts. New Zealand is free of venomous snakes, as are Norfolk and Nauru Islands. The snakes listed as most deadly for Papua and for New Guinea are the death adder and the brown snake. Records for these very underdeveloped areas are too scattered to have any real meaning. Although scientists working on New Guinea report that the area is anything but crawling with snakes, there are a number of highly dangerous species, and a lot of barefoot people. Another factor that might contribute to a rather high incidence of snake bite (and we do not *know* that this is the case) is the fact that the natives are badly starved for protein, and snakes are esteemed as food. Rather than being avoided, they are hunted. In British Papua alone from 1949 to 1952, 118 persons were admitted to hospitals for snake bite of whom nine died. In the same three-year period in New Guinea, 123 people were hospitalized, with no deaths recorded. The hospitalization of a native on this island, however, is very much the exception, rather than the rule.

The Fiji Islands have no recorded snake bite mortalities although sea snakes appear in coastal waters. Eastern Samoa is free of this problem, and the 2,140 individual islands of the Pacific Island Territories have no dangerous species.

The second group of Elapids, both in numbers and breadth of distribution, may perhaps best be called the Coral Snakes. Their headquarters is in the Oriental or southeast Asian region, but they are also strongly represented in the New World. There are two genera in North America, and some forty species of various genera in tropical America.

All the snakes we have discussed so far as residents of the United States have been members of the family *Crotalidae*, the pit vipers. There are two species of snakes in the United States that are related to the cobras, and quite removed from the viperine groups. The coral snakes are *proteroglyphs*, that is, having strongly differentiated fangs in the front of the upper jaw which are permanently erect. These fangs are of necessity much shorter than the fangs of the vipers and pit vipers since they must fit into the snake's mouth when it is closed without being able to fold away. This fang system is more primitive than the viperine system, but efficient enough to cause considerable damage. Fortunately, the highly venomous American Elapids are small, and generally very retiring animals.

### NORTH AMERICAN *ELAPIDAE*—THE CORAL SNAKES

| Scientific Name | Common Name | Distribution |
|---|---|---|
| *Micrurus f. fulvius* | Southeastern Coral Snake | Florida north to North Carolina, west to Mississippi River. |
| *M. f. barbouri* | South Florida Coral Snake | Southern Florida. |
| *M. f. tenere* | Texas Coral Snake | Arkansas to Southern Texas. |
| *Micruroides euryxanthus* * | Sonoran Coral Snake | Southern Arizona, possibly New Mexico and West Texas. |

* Not considered a dangerous species.

Cases of snake bite involving the coral snakes are extremely rare, and almost inevitably result from people handling specimens. Coral snakes are so small, rarely much over two feet long (although a record specimen just half an inch under four feet is on record), that it has to chew to get a firm purchase and penetration with its small fangs. Elapid snakes, such as corals, unlike the vipers and pit vipers, do not have enlarged heads, but are proportionate throughout their entire length. A very small snake has a very small head. It would be *almost* impossible for an average-sized coral snake to "strike" and penetrate clothing. People have been bitten, however, and the venom is a particularly dangerous neurotoxin. The effects are widespread over the body rather than localized, and although death is neither inevitable nor immediate, as so often reported, the bite of these snakes is very dangerous.

Coral Snake (*Micrurus nigrocinctus*).
Courtesy of the American Museum of Natural History.

Coral snakes can readily be listed among the deadly venomous animals of the world, but cannot be considered much of a health menace. If you spent your whole life within the geographical boundaries of their range, death by their bite would still be one of the least likely climaxes to your career. Your chances of even seeing one would be very slim since they are quite retiring and seldom encountered. And even if you came running home all out of breath announcing that you had just seen "the American cobra," the chances are you would be mistaken. The Scarlet Kingsnake (*Lampropeltis doliata*) and various of its subspecies, mimic the corals to an extraordinary degree, and since part of their range coincides with that of the Southeastern and South Florida Coral Snakes, there can be little doubt that confusion often results. Of course, it works both ways, and mistaking a coral snake for a harmless scarlet kingsnake would be a dangerous error to make. The kingsnake ranges further north than the corals and reports of coral snakes from Tennessee and Kentucky are apparently products of this confusion. The easiest way to tell them apart is the order of color; if the red is bordered by black, it's harmless; if the red is bordered by yellow or white, it's a coral. Order: black-red-black-yellow (or white) equals harmless; black-yellow (or white)-red-yellow-black equals coral snake.

In a word, the American members of the cobra family are among the most colorful and deadly animals on the continent, but also the least likely venomous reptiles to cause the average citizen any concern. If you don't go looking for them or pick them up, the chances are many uncounted thousands to one against your ever becoming a statistic.

*Micrurus,* the genus that gives North America its few unoffending coral snakes, reaches full flower in South America. There are more than forty species and subspecies of *"Coralitos"* on the continent. *M. spixi* of Brazil is the most impressive. It is the giant among coral snakes and specimens measuring over five feet have been taken. Even so none of the group represents much of a threat to man when compared with the pit vipers. They do occasionally appear in the statistics as having delivered a lethal bite, but, as in North America, they are seldom involved unless handled carelessly, sat upon directly, or trod upon by someone with bare feet.

There are a group of especially slender coral snakes separated into another genus (*Leptomicrurus*) which occur from Peru to Colombia. Like all coral snakes, the venom is essentially neurotoxic, very potent, but seldom involved in human deaths.

The situation in southeast Asia is somewhat different. Both the mainland and the islands are inhabited by a large number of different snakes belonging to this group. All develop venom, but the incidence of humans being bitten by them is extremely low and only very few cases are on record. One such caused by a species of *Maticora* is on record and produced very strange intermittent symptoms, but was not fatal.

The next group of elapids—though not necessarily their nearest relatives—are the kraits. Colonel William A. Noble of the Salvation Army, for forty-one years a medical missionary in India, told the author in a

The Banded Krait (*Bungarus fasciatus*).

Addiss & Crofut.

King Cobras (*Ophiophagus hannah*) courting.

New York Zoological Society.

personal interview in April, 1962, that the natives of Madras State in southern India called the Krait (pronounced "Krite") (*Bungarus caeruleus*) the "Seven-Stepper," believing that, if bitten, a man can take only seven steps before dying. This belief is not true, although the krait carries a particularly potent venom. Legends of almost instantaneous death from one snake or another are found almost everywhere venomous snakes are known. No such tale is true, although some venoms certainly act more swiftly than others.

Two highly venomous kraits, the Common (*Bungarus candidus*) and the Banded (*B. fasciatus*), are very common in Burma, but their fortunately passive disposition keeps the mortality rate low. Actually, it is the incidence rate that is low, and the mortality rate high—much higher than among cobra bites, for the first of the two species named. These snakes

Common, or Indian, Cobra (*Naja naja*).                    Lee Ball.

are really quite rare and, therefore, seldom a problem, but their neuro-toxic venom is highly dangerous.

The two remaining groups of elapids are more closely related. These are the famous cobras and mambas. The former are spread all over tropi-cal Asia and Africa, the latter are confined to Africa. Among cobras, there is one species that stands out in every respect, and which is held in awe by all who know it or have heard of it. This is the great King Cobra (*Ophiophagus hannah*) which may grow to almost twenty feet in length. The venom is potent and, due to the size of the animal alone, massive, but fortunately this snake is not too common and is said to be rather retiring. It may, however, raise its forebody if approached and present a most menacing appearance; and that it will attack humans appears to be authen-ticated, although the circumstances are often obscure.

There are a few different kinds of other cobras in Asia, the best known being the famous Indian or Common species (*Naja naja*) the stock in trade of oriental snake charmers and the central figure of countless stories ranging from true to false to utterly absurd. (The incidence of bites and deaths caused by this species is discussed in the next chapter.) The species is represented in the Near East by the very closely related *Naja haje* which is the classical asp of Egypt and is used in that and surrounding countries by local snake charmers. This can also be a deadly aggressor, but it is far less numerous and its distribution more "spotty," while the human population where it occurs is vastly smaller than in south and southeast Asia.

There are many other kinds of cobras in Africa, most notable among which are probably the Spitting Cobras (*Naja nicricollis* and *Hemachatus haemachates*). These snakes can hit a man's face with remarkable ac-curacy at ten or more feet, and temporarily blind him. The pain is re-portedly severe, but permanent injury is not generally the result. There are also Tree Cobras in many parts of tropical Africa—*Pseudohaje guenthieri* and *goldi*.

The other African cobras, including the Black (*N. melanoleuca*) and the Egyptian (*N. haje*), do not spit. The Egyptian is the most widely distributed cobra on the vast continent. The Cape Cobra (*N. nivea*) and several others have a more limited range. The Water Cobra (*Boulenger-ina annulata*) is known from the Cameroons, the Congos, and Lake Tanganyika.

Closely related to the cobras, but without the ability to raise "hoods," are the Mambas. During the past century these snakes, some of which may grow to fourteen feet in length, have become almost, if not more, notorious in the Old World than are the cobras. In the western world their reputation has long since surpassed that of our rattlers or even the once dreaded fer-de-lance. It is true, moreover, that the mambas are

Snake charmer in Marrakesh, Morocco.

Indian Cobra—"hood" expanded.

Erich Sochurek.

Ringhals, or Ring-Necked Spitting Cobra (*Haemachatus haemachates*).
Transvaal Snake Park, South Africa.

exceedingly active, agile, fast, and often aggressive snakes; and it may perhaps be said that, if any story of a snake deliberately attacking a man be true, it is more likely to have been a mamba than any other—the *Taipan*, fer-de-lance, and king cobra not excluded. Their venom is known to be very potent indeed, they have considerable fangs, and, what is more important, the teeth in the front of the lower jaw are much exaggerated so that if they do land a strike they tend to impale and hang on to their victims, so giving free rein to the envenomation process. It is, however, their agility and speed combined with their climbing abilities, and the fact that they delight in long grass and other thick ground cover, that makes them so dangerous. Not only may you literally run into or kick them in such an environment, you may well panic if one comes sailing *over* the ground cover, and it is then that you are in most danger, for they tend to strike at moving objects in their path.

Writing in the December, 1956, issue of *African Wild Life*, J. A. W. Bennetts tells of his father's dispatching a Black Mamba (*Dendroaspis polylepis*) with a shotgun on his farm on the south coast of Natal. The

Egyptian Cobra (*Naja haje*).

Transvaal Snake Park, South Africa.

snake, measuring over fourteen feet in length and between three and four inches in diameter, had reportedly killed several natives. Legends about this particular snake had been known for over twenty years at the time the elder Bennetts killed it.

The last major group of snakes to develop venom are the family *Colubridae*, among which a number of forms have fangs on the back or rear of their jaws through which poison can be injected into their food as they start to swallow it. Rear-fanged snakes or *opisthoglyphs* are found in the Orient, Africa, South, Central, and North America. In the last are the Lyre Snakes and some others; in South America such genera as

Green Mamba (*Dendroaspis angusticeps*), showing fangs.

Transvaal Snake Park, South Africa.

Boomslang (*Dispholidus typus*).

The Rev. P. Smit.

*Oxybelis, Pseudoboa,* and others. By no stretch of the imagination can these be considered a threat to man, though we may speculate that accidents could occur if the animals were handled carelessly. The author has not encountered a single case where a rear-fanged snake caused a human death in the Western Hemisphere. However, the situation in Africa is different.

On that continent there are at least two rear-fanged snakes known to cause human deaths. The first is the Bird Snake (*Thelotornis kirtlandi*) and the other is the notorious *Boomslang* (*Dispholidus typus*), of South Africa in particular. This is an inhabitant of open country and varies in color from various browns to bright green. It has a habit of inflating its neck when aroused, and may then bite viciously, but it is, on the whole, a retiring beast. The venom appears to be potent, but reaction to it may be much delayed.

# CHAPTER 15

## Snakes: How Dangerous Are They?

THERE can be no argument with the statement that, today, of all animals that are potentially dangerous to man, the snakes as a whole are the most dangerous. This is, when you come to consider the matter, odd to say the least, for one could hardly imagine two terrestrial forms of creature more distant in appearance and habits, or, one would have thought, less likely to come into contact. Yet, throughout the temperate and tropical areas of all the world, the two forms do constantly come into contact and, the more people there are, the more such contacts seem to occur. It might be considered unnecessary to point out that it is the envenomation mechanism of the snakes that brings this situation about; but it *is* necessary to restate the fact, for snakes are no more aggressive than any other animal and, as I hope you have noted and will continue to note, no animals are truly aggressive unless sick, molested, injured, or unless you infringe on their territory or what they consider to be their privacy. There are exceptions such as the curious matter of so-called "man-eaters" and "rogues" but no animal today hunts man for food deliberately and none customarily molests you except, perhaps, certain fish and crocodilians.

Since snakes do constitute the greatest single menace to man, I consider it worthwhile trying to assess this menace. This is an exceedingly difficult thing to do, due to several diverse factors.

Case histories, comments and editorial observations are available by the thousands. Pulp magazines and medical journals, military manuals and health organization reports, books, booklets, pamphlets, and scientific reports exist in bewildering quantity. Man, quite obviously, has always been deeply concerned with venomous snakes. As remote as a venomous snake may seem to a city-dweller, people in many parts of the world are daily faced with the reality of their existence. Just as the reader may look both ways before crossing a street, as a matter of course, other people must take comparable precautions before reaching into a cupboard, putting on their shoes, or stopping to pick a flower. Just how much of a reality the venomous snake is can be judged from the fact that the best available statistics put international snake bite mortality at between 30,000 and 40,000 per year! We will consider these figures (by Swaroop and Grab) in this chapter.

1. About 200 of the 2,500 currently recognized species of snakes are dangerous to man. It can be assumed that all of the 200 are capable of killing a healthy, full-grown man, but the mortality rate shows a tremendous spread. With some snakes, the bite is extremely unlikely to cause death (there are *no* deaths recorded for a number of species); in others it is almost a likelihood. There is no known snake the bite of which is certain to cause death, nor is there any snake whose bite causes immediate death except under exceptional conditions.

2. The factors that determine the extent of the effects felt by the victim have been dealt with in the chapter on rattlesnakes. There is a long list of factors all tied in with (a) the health and condition of the snake, (b) the health and condition of the victim, and (c) the circumstances of the bite itself.

3. To cause death, the bite of a snake must deliver a lethal substance into the tissues of a victim in such a way that it will be distributed to the vital organs. Most truly venomous snakes are capable of doing this under the right conditions.

4. The number of people bitten each year cannot even be guessed. The majority of the victims are in remote and underdeveloped areas where no records are kept. The number of deaths each year is roughly placed between 30,000 and 40,000. No refinements of this problematical figure are presently possible, but enough is known to state that snake bite is a major problem.

5. The sea snakes, about which so much has been written, are decidedly dangerous upon contact, but contact is so unlikely that they represent a minimum threat. The snake bite mortality figure for the world is the result of contact with terrestrial animals.

6. Many areas of the world have a population of venomous snakes, but no real health problem. Areas like Canada, the United States, and most of Europe are representative of this fortunate condition. Relatively few countries are entirely free of venomous serpents.

7. In a few areas (India, Burma, Mexico, Brazil, and possibly parts of Africa) snake bite is a major health problem. Unfortunately, there is a disproportionate percentage of deaths among children. There are several reasons for this: (a) children are more apt to go charging off into dangerous or potentially dangerous situations without thinking, (b) children are generally less observant and less likely to recall identification points, (c) children's curiosity is apt to get the better of their common sense, and (d) children have less body weight and therefore generally less resistance to the effects of the venom.

8. Available statistics indicate that more men are bitten than women, the ratio is probably close to 4 to 1. The reasons for this are apparent: men generally work and play outdoors more than women. In under-

developed areas where women are engaged in agriculture, this ratio probably doesn't hold up.

9. No snake always attacks, no snake is always deadly, and no venomous snake has the power to do anything but bite, that is, sink its fangs and inject a noxious substance. If a venomous snake can't bite you, it can't harm you, except in a very few cases where it can temporarily impair your sight by spitting or in the extremely rare cases involving constrictors. This statement is categoric!

So where does this leave us? Despite these remarks which, on analysis, amount almost to obvious truths or even platitudes, we are still left with the inescapable fact that a very large number of people are bitten by snakes every year all over the world and that a not inconsiderable number of them die as a result.

We have now (I hope) learned which are the venomous snakes and where they live, albeit very sketchily since it would take many volumes to describe their appearance, habits, and distribution in detail. But what of the other side of the coin? What is known of the result of the presence of these animals in various parts of the world—in terms of human envenomation, suffering, and death? Here the picture becomes, perhaps, even more hazy because we really still know so little of what is actually going on in the world, while modern medical practice has still to penetrate the major part of it and medical statisticians are still way behind that procedure. For some countries we have statistics that we assume to be reliable; for others we have educated estimates; others still, educated guesses; and others again mere guesses or no facts at all. Let me therefore review what is known—or, rather, published—on this facet of life. I will start out with tropical America, then proceed to the Oriental region, and, finally, to Africa, assuming that Europe and North America have already been adequately dealt with.

Mexico has its share of venomous snakes, and the resulting mortality rate is considerably higher than in the United States. According to Swaroop and Grab, whose statistics we will be using throughout this chapter, snake bite mortality in Mexico for 1940 and 1941 ran to 157 and 219 respectively. That accounts for only 9 per cent of the total deaths caused by venomous animals. Scorpions killed 1,627 and 1,810 Mexicans in the same two years. Statistics, however, are not complete and these figures can do no more than indicate the probable nature of the problem.

All five genera of venomous snakes found in the United States (not counting rear-fanged snakes) are also found in Mexico, *Crotalus*, *Sistrurus*, *Agkistrodon*, *Micrurus*, and *Micruroides*.

This is not a complete list for Mexico, but does clearly demonstrate that, with its wide variety of rattlesnakes, its moccasin (the *Cantil*), a selection of *Bothrops* pit vipers, and about a dozen species of coral snakes, this country has more than its share of venomous snakes; and, as a consequence, an unfortunate number of snake bite mortalities.

South America has more unexplored territory than any other inhabited continent. Only Antarctica exceeds this vast continent in blank areas on the map. Darkest Africa is bright and sunny by comparison. Certainly, all of the reptiles have not yet been collected and identified. Many areas are exceedingly remote and statistics on snake bite incidence and mortality are simply not to be had. This much is known: those parts of South America that have been thoroughly examined by qualified zoologists have yielded a rich variety of venomous snakes. In all of South America, Chile alone (it is believed), is free of these animals. What of their threat to man?

As is the case everywhere in the world where there are venomous serpents, there are so many variables involved in assessing the danger that we must restrict ourselves to approximate and generalized observations. Certainly, there are some species that appear more frequently on the statistical tables (like the Eastern and Western diamondbacks in the United States, the various cobras in Asia, etc.), and in South America there are the fer-de-lance, and the *Jararacucu*.

Turning next to the west, let us consider the situation in what is customarily called the Far East, and start beyond Japan. In this area, all existing families of venomous snakes are represented and often by a very large variety of species and incredible numbers of individuals.

There are, of course, no readily available statistics from mainland China, but the area is known to have something of a problem. Kraits, cobras, including the king cobra, pit vipers, and true vipers are known to occur. Projecting the general Asiatic picture to its logical conclusion, the snake bite incidence and, correspondingly the death rate, may be high in some few parts of China, notably the warm south.

The island colony of Hong Kong has at least two of the venomous sea snakes off-shore: the four-foot *Acalpytophis peronii*, and *Hydrophis cyanocinctus*, which achieves a length of over six feet. As might be expected, bites from these two animals are rare, but can be quite serious when they do occur. It is estimated that about one hundred cases of snake bite occur each year in Hong Kong (including its mainland New Territories) although this figure is not reliable as a statistic. The population is predominantly Chinese and these people often treat such problems at home with native remedies. Between August, 1951, and July, 1952, twenty cases were reported in Hong Kong's largest government hospital, the Queen Mary. It is that figure, plus the estimates of other hospitals and cases not seen at all, that were used to project the estimate of one hundred by Swaroop and Grab. A Green Tree Viper, often called Bamboo Snake (*Trimeresurus albolabris*), a close relative of the Central and South American *Bothrops* pit vipers, causes most of the cases of snake bite in Hong Kong. *Naja naja,* the Common Cobra, is another snake found in the colony.

The king cobra and several other cobras are found in the Philippine Islands. Two Coral Snakes (*Doliophis bilineatus* and *D. philippinus*) are found, but bites are rare and deaths rarer still. Wagler's Pit Viper (*T. wagleri*), a stout, short animal (about three feet is average) is found on some of the islands in the group. It is not considered very dangerous. *Aipysurus, Hydrophis, Laticauda,* and *Pelamis* sea snakes are found in Philippine waters, and are hunted for their skins and for export to Japan as food. Figures are not available, but possibly the active hunting of these animals may result in some bites. However, that is speculation.

Java and Sumatra have large venomous snake populations with Viperids, and Elapids in abundance. Most interestingly, snake bite does not appear to be much of a problem.

There is reportedly a very low incidence of snake bite in Borneo (including Sarawak, Brunei, and other states therein) although the common cobra and king cobra and a viper abound in some areas. A wide variety of sea snakes are found in the surrounding waters and have been reported in astounding numbers during certain seasons. The Red-headed Krait (*Bungarus flaviceps*), marked with scarlet patches and six feet in length, occurs but few cases of its biting man are known. Sarawak, particularly, is known to have large numbers of venomous snakes.

Indonesia has its share of venomous snakes. A variety of kraits are common, and the very dangerous king cobra is responsible for a number of deaths each year.

The Malay Peninsula has its share of kraits, cobras (including the king), coral snakes, sea snakes and pit vipers, but the death rate is low. The average is probably lower than ten per year.

Thailand, too, has the common cobra, the king cobra, Russell's viper, and kraits. *Calliophis* and *Doliophis* Coral Snakes, although not contributing to the death rate, are found, as well as a number of *Trimeresurus* Pit Vipers. The common green or bamboo viper is most often seen, though not particularly dangerous. Over a thousand people were killed between 1946 and 1950 in Thailand by these animals.

Herpetologist Carl Kauffeld pointed out the following interesting facts in a note written after reading a rough draft of this chapter:

The reptiles of Sarawak, the rest of Borneo, and all the greater Sundas, along with the Philippines, are extremely well-known, and we know that all the dangerous venomous snakes of the Asiatic mainland, and then some, abound on these islands.

For a very long time, efficient colonial Dutch government prevailed on these islands. Java is one of the most densely populated spots on earth and 90% of the population is agrarian. How come then snake bite is so rare? This has been pointed out more than once as a reason for questioning the Indian statistics on snake bite. There is something decidedly fishy about the Indian reports. They exceed anything on earth, yet we have an almost identical situation in Java and where officialdom has had its finger on native health problems for years, with negligible incidence of snake bites and mortalities.

Burma is one of those unfortunate areas where there are large numbers and many species of truly dangerous snakes. The death rate is said to be exceedingly high. From 1935 to 1940, there were 12,733 reported deaths. These figures are so extraordinarily high that some question must be raised. For an area with a population of just over fourteen and a half million, the reported snake bite mortality rate is almost impossible to accept.

Two species of Cobra (*Naja*), the Spectacled and the Monocellate or Burmese, are probably responsible for a good many deaths. Both animals deliver large doses of a dangerous neurotoxin. The tremendously impressive King Cobra (*Ophiophagus hannah*), also known as the Hamadryad, is also found in the deep Burmese jungles.

The beautiful island of Ceylon is another area with a high death rate. Three of the dangerous forms found in Burma, Russell's viper, the common cobra, and the common krait, cause all of the trouble. Deaths from these occur at an average rate of three hundred per year.

No country on earth, if we accept available figures, comes even close to matching India for snake bite mortality. Every year, anywhere from one-half to two-thirds of the world's victims reportedly come from this one over-crowded country. The estimate is frequently put at *20,000 deaths per year!* While it will be a long time before a better figure will be available, this figure contains so many unknowns that it is little more than a guess. Some of the predictable error factors are: (1) most snake bites will occur in rural areas where medical facilities and medical records often range from crude to non-existent, (2) in very underdeveloped areas, the importance of statistical information is impossible to convey, and reports given to visiting medical teams will be avoided, falsified, or exaggerated. A number of sources suggest that snake bite is a convenient explanation for an awkward death, and quite possibly some crimes in rural areas are covered up with this device.

Some cases are reported and authenticated and Swaroop and Grab state that, "Before August 1947, snake bite was responsible for about 15,000 deaths each year. . . ." Dr. P. J. Deoras of the Haffkine Institute in Bombay says in his booklet "Snakes: How to Know Them," "in the former Bombay State alone 1,300 persons died of snake bite in 1955." Clearly, snake bite in India is a problem of considerable magnitude.

Of the 2,500 species of snakes in the world, India has 400, and of these,

80 are venomous, although only about a dozen are seriously dangerous to man. Various species and subspecies of cobra, various kraits, Russell's viper and an *Echis* viper apparently account for most of the accidents. Death rate statistics from these bites are difficult to come by, but if an average of 10 per cent can be accepted (and it is a reasonable figure), about two hundred thousand people a year are bitten in India. In one table of statistics, the fatality rate for the cobra was given as 4.8 per cent, for the krait, 88.9 per cent (!), and for the Russell's viper, 8.3 per cent.

M. L. Ahuja and Gurkirpal Singh, in their paper "Snakebite in India" (in *Venoms*) give the number of bites per year at 300,000 with an overall mortality of 9.5 per cent. The highest mortality occurs among children under ten years of age. Men suffer more than women from this accident in a ratio of four to one, but that is incidence and not mortality.

### INDIA'S DANGEROUS SNAKES

| | |
|---|---|
| King Cobra | *Naja hannah* |
| Cobra | *Naja naja* |
| Krait | *Bungarus caeruleus* |
| Russell's Viper | *Vipera russelli* |
| Saw-scaled Viper | *Echis carinatus* |
| Triangular-headed Horned Viper | *Pseudocerastes persicus* |
| Himalayan Pit Viper | *Agkistrodon himalayanus* |
| Green Pit Viper | *Trimeresurus malabaricus* |
| Bamboo Pit Viper | *T. gramineus* |
| Coral Snake | *Callophis beddomei* |
| Sea Snake | *Enhydrina schistoma* |
| Sea Snake | *Hydrophis spiralis* |

Major C. H. Simpson has written to the author relating personal experiences with snakes and kindly granted permission to quote from his letter. Speaking of venomous snakes in general, he says:

> I have had only one case of a fatal snake bite on my estate, this was a girl who was plucking tea leaves, she trod on a krait, which bit her on her toe. I sent her as fast as possible to the nearest hospital with antivenene, but she died before reaching it.
>
> There have been many cases of bites from snakes which were not fatal. I myself have been bitten by a pit-viper, and a ratsnake, with hardly any effect. It is usually said the king cobras will attack on sight, but my experience is otherwise, I have killed over 20, and in no case was there an attack by the snake. But a king cobra will not run if it sees a human approaching, unlike all other snakes, which do run.

Nothing can convey the experience of meeting a venomous snake so well as a well-related personal adventure. Major Simpson is particularly adept at this, and I think the following two excerpts from one of his letters give a more accurate impression of the venomous snake in India than a volume full of statistics:

I was one night sitting up on a rock to shoot wild pigs which were eating my crops, and had made a mattress of grass to recline on. After dark, I heard a faint rustle on the edge of the grass, and thinking a field rat was after my sandwiches I raised my hand to give it a smack. Then I realized that the rustling sound indicated a lengthy cause, so I froze with my arm up, while a long cold body slid over one bare knee and under the other and away. I was reminded that there had often been a cobra seen in that spot. However, the snake went off, and I copied its example, caring little if the pigs did have a feast in my corn patch.

I was driving a patch of jungle for a sambhur stag, and I took post in a dry watercourse to await the expected arrival of the stag. I became aware of a rustling in the dry leaves lining the water-course, and saw to my horror, that it was caused by a very large king cobra (Hamadryad), which was coming along methodically stirring the heaps of leaves in the hollows. The line it was taking would bring it within a few feet of me. So I quietly covered it with my rifle, not wanting to fire unless it was absolutely necessary, as the stag would then be warned. Although my movements were slow and silent, the snake saw me and raised about two feet of its body from the ground and looked at me. I was quiet and tried to make my friendly feeling felt by it. In a few seconds it lowered its head and continued hunting in the leaves, passed me with only a casual glance, and went on down for about twenty yards. Here it found what it was looking for, a large rat snake, and then I saw at what speed it could travel, for although the rat snake had a start, it overhauled it and caught it in a few seconds, had it attacked me, I do not think I could have shot it, it was too quick.

Africa, as I have tried to indicate, has a wide variety of dangerous species, although the relatively small population in many areas keeps snake bite from being the health problem it is in India and Burma. The African snakes occur in just about every kind of terrain, leaving only the high snowcapped mountains and the heart of the burning desert wastes free. There are terrestrial, aquatic, and arboreal species.

There just are not any reliable figures on snake bite incidence and mortality for Africa as a whole. Some few areas have been subject to rather intensive study, but these are very much the exceptions. As we note statistics here and there, we must keep in mind that these figures represent only cases reported. There are still vast areas virtually untouched by anything resembling modern medicine. It is difficult to find out what people there are doing, much less snakes. Any figures we do find can only represent a part of the whole. Europeans who have spent years in these regions, however, report that snake bite is not a major problem.

Egypt reported 170 deaths between 1944 and 1948. The large, barefoot population probably suffers at a higher rate than 34 deaths a year since both the grassy and the desert regions have a collection of cobras and vipers. Suicide with venomous snakes goes well back in Egyptian history, and the symbology of the region has apparently always included the venomous snakes. Libya has a cobra and a couple of sand vipers, but probably not much of a problem in the overall. Much of the area where the snakes are found is uninhabited. Six to eight deaths a year were officially registered for a number of years. Ethiopia doesn't seem to be too badly troubled although there are cobras and true vipers in the less mountainous parts of the country.

Uganda, Kenya, and Tanganyika have a full complement of typical African species, and something of a snake bite problem in some areas: 12 deaths out of 554 cases were reported in 1950. Southern Rhodesia has a wide and interesting selection of venomous snakes, but poor statistical records.

The Republic of South Africa has no records of any consequence for native populations, but from 1934 to 1938, 57 Europeans died of snake bite. To the adders, cobras, and mambas can be added the *Ringhals* Cobra (*Haemachatus haemachates*) and a few other species with restricted range. The *Boomslang* is particularly common. This snake carries a virulent poison and although it is a rear-fanged animal, it is decidedly dangerous to man. It is one of the very few snakes of this type that does constitute a real threat, as stated earlier.

Zanzibar has few dangerous snakes and no cases reported in recent years. The following areas all have a variety of dangerous species but few reliable records: British Somaliland, Basutoland, and Swaziland.

Mozambique has the full range: cobras, mambas, and true vipers. There are occasional fatalities among fishermen from the Sea Snake *Pelamis platurus*.

The islands of Madagascar, the Comoro Archipelago, and Mauritius are free of poisonous snakes. The sea snakes are found off-shore, but no cases of attack on man are known in recent years.

Portuguese Guinea reported 6 deaths in 1952. This is a fractional record. Cobras, vipers, *Boomslangs* and a couple of mambas are present.

Angola, another area with fractional statistics, has a rather impressive number of potentially dangerous species. The puff-adder, Gaboon viper, and the green night-adder (*Causus resimus*) occupy the area along with several of the cobras and the very much feared mambas.

Gabon, particularly, has a minor problem with the two dangerous cobras, the black and the water. The latter might occasionally be a threat to fishermen attending their nets and traps. It frequents the edges of lakes and uses small caves among the rocks in shallow water.

French Equatorial Africa formerly consisted of three territories: Middle Congo, Gabon, Ubangi-Chari-Tchad. Today, they are autonomous republics in the French community. Some 959,256 square miles are involved with an estimated population (1936) of 3,418,066. The area runs from dense forest to desert; there are a number of mountain ranges, and many lakes and rivers. In hospitals, from 1947 to 1951, 155 people died from snake bite. The mamba and the puff-adder caused many of these deaths. The Gaboon viper and the spitting cobra are problems in the savannah country. The colorfully marked rhinoceros viper is common in the forests. The night adder is common around human dwellings.

Nigeria has a rather large population (31,171,000) in vast, frequently underdeveloped areas. Snake bite cases *may* be comparatively high in some regions. To the usual African complement of true vipers, cobras (spitting and non-spitting varieties), and mambas can be added the Burrowing Vipers (*Atractaspis*) and several other venomous species which are harmful but probably not lethal to man.

Ghana is yet another region with a wide selection of truly dangerous snakes and useless statistics. The saw-scaled viper and a wide variety of cobras are responsible for a number of accidents in this country.

French West Africa is formed of areas known or formerly known as Ivory Coast, Niger, and Senegal. Statistics for the region are extremely fractional. Between 1948 and 1951, 83 deaths were reported in hospitals. For the most part, during those years, records weren't kept. Of the four years, only in 1951 were records, even sketchy records, available for all the regions. The night adder abounds, the rear-fanged *Boomslang* is common and the spitting cobra is often seen. The Egyptian cobra, the black, and one or two other members of the hooded tribe add to the local problem.[1]

The forested regions of French West Africa have a number of vipers: the Gaboon, rhinoceros, and puff-adder are among the species often reported.

That concludes our review of the venomous snakes of the world. As to just how dangerous to man they really are, remember that all the other dangerous animals we discuss in this book, marine and terrestrial, *combined*, come nowhere near causing the suffering and death for which the snakes are responsible. Snakes almost certainly kill more people in a year than sharks do in a century, more people in a month than man-eating

---

[1] The hood of a cobra, by the way, appears when the animal spreads a number of its ribs outward and stretches the skin. It has nothing to do with the creature's head. Cobras are so often photographed with the hood spread that some people believe they always look that way, while in fact they generally don't. The cobra spreads its impressive hood in defensive posture, and while expressing interest in its mate. There are other stimuli, certainly, that can prompt the cobra to put on a show, but generally it looks like a rather dull, sleek, harmless snake.

cats do in a hundred years, and more people in a day than rogue elephants have since time began. No area in the world is crawling with venomous snakes intent upon killing man despite the nightmarish proportions indicated by some of the projected statistics reported in this chapter, but venomous snakes are still the most dangerous animals to man, as a whole, in the world. It is therefore difficult at first glance to put the situation in perspective. Venomous snakes are a critical part of nature in balance. The more of these forms that occur in a region, the more rodents are destroyed, for rodents constitute a major item in the diet of the majority of species. If the venomous snakes of the world should suddenly vanish, the rodent population would run wild and possibly, in the long run, through the spread of disease and the destruction of crops, cause much more suffering than the snakes ever could. When venomous snakes invade populated areas, then, of course, they must be eliminated. However, it is a decided mistake to think of them all as man's inveterate enemies. Unlike the situation with so many other potentially dangerous animals, the argument for conservation is not so much aesthetic or scientific as economic. Snakes, venomous as well as harmless, are of great importance in maintaining the balance and order of the natural world.

The United States Army Field Manual, "Jungle Operations" (FM 31-30, 1960) says, on page fifteen:

There is altogether too much fear of snakes on the part of the soldier without jungle experience. The wide spread fear of "the snake infested jungle" is an entirely imaginary picture. Poisonous snakes will be encountered in most of the jungles of the world, but not as frequently as pictured. The soldier's inherent fear of snakes reduces his efficiency in the jungle to a great extent. It is important to remember that relatively few people die from poisonous snake bites.

This puts it very succinctly.

# CHAPTER 16

# *Crocodilians*

THE ancient order of reptiles known as the *Crocodilia* encompasses all the living alligators, crocodiles, caimans, and gavials, and many closely related, extinct forms known from numerous fossil finds. The order contains some of the most persistently dangerous animals in the world, animals that are *by nature* man-eaters. With the possible exception of a few sharks, I know of no other animals that are normally so disposed; and men, of course, don't live in the sea.

Allowing for the usual quibbles among systematists as to nomenclature, the following list covers all of the presently recognized species:

## WESTERN HEMISPHERE

| Species | Range | Maximum Recorded Length (Feet) |
|---------|-------|-------------------------------|
| American Alligator (*Alligator mississippiensis*) | Southern United States | 19–20 |
| American Crocodile (*Crocodylus acutus*) | Southern U.S., Central America, West Indies, Northern South America | 23 |
| Orinoco Crocodile (*C. intermedius*) | Orinoco complex | 23 |
| Morelet's Crocodile (*C. moreleti*) | Mexico and Guatemala | 8 |
| Cuban Crocodile (*C. rhombifer*) | Cuba | 12 |
| Smooth-fronted Caiman (*Paleosuchus palpebrosus*) | Amazon Basin | 4–5 |
| Dwarf Caiman (*P. trigonatus*) | Amazon Basin | 4 |
| Black Caiman (*Melanosuchus niger*) | Amazon Basin and adjacent territory | 15 |
| Spectacled Caiman (*Caiman crocodilus crocodilus*) | Amazon Basin | 8–9 |
| Central American Caiman (*C. crocodilus fuscus*) | Central America and Northern South America | 6 |
| Broad-nosed Caiman (*C. latirostris*) | Eastern Brazil | 6–7 |
| Paraguayan Caiman (*C. yacare*) | Paraguay River and tributaries | 8 |

202

EASTERN HEMISPHERE

| Species | Range | Maximum Recorded Length (Feet) |
|---|---|---|
| Gavial (*Gavialis gangeticus*) | India | 21–22 |
| False Gavial (*Tomistoma schlegeli*) | Malay Peninsula and East Indies | 16 |
| Chinese Alligator (*Alligator sinensis*) | Eastern China | 5 |
| Congo Dwarf Crocodile (*Osteolaemus tetraspis*) | Upper Congo | 3–4 |
| West African Dwarf Crocodile (*Osteolaemus* sp.) | West Africa | 6 |
| African or Nile Crocodile (*Crocodylus niloticus*) | Africa and Madagascar | 16 * |
| African Slender-snouted Crocodile (*C. cataphractus*) | Congo Basin | 8 |
| Salt-water Crocodile (*C. porosus*) | SE. Asia to Australia | 20 |
| Philippine Crocodile (*C. mindorensis*) | Philippine Islands | 8 |
| Australian Crocodile (*C. johnstoni*) | Northern Australia | 8 |
| New Guinea Crocodile (*C. novae-guineae*) | New Guinea | 9–10 |
| Siamese Crocodile (*C. siamensis*) | SE. Asia and Java | 12 |
| Mugger Crocodile (*C. palustris*) | India and Ceylon | 13 |

* Some records indicate that this figure may be as large as 26 feet. It is very much an open question.

If we accept the above breakdown (suggested by Schmidt and Inger, and modified after conversations with Kauffeld), we find an order with eight living genera and twenty-five species, about evenly divided between the Old World and the New. The genera *Alligator* and *Crocodylus* are found in both hemispheres, while *Caiman*, *Melanosuchus*, and *Paleosuchus* are only in the New, and *Gavialis*, *Tomistoma*, and *Osteolaemus*, only in the Old. We have, then, two genera world-wide, and three exclusive to each half of the world.

As the above list indicates, the largest living crocodilians may not exceed twenty-three to twenty-five feet. There are strong arguments to the contrary, however. Fossil remains, often indistinguishable from contemporary species, or nearly so, show that these animals once grew to a much greater size. A skull in the American Museum of Natural History is over six feet long, and undoubtedly belonged to an animal fifty feet or more in length. Occasional reports of crocodiles "as big as submarines," while obviously hyperbole, may, when coupled with the fossil record, suggest that some specimens exist today far larger than the presently known record lengths. For our purposes, such matters are academic, because a man-eater fifteen feet long is as dangerous as a thirty-foot specimen.

The crocodilians are true remnants of the age of reptiles, and monsters like *Phobosuchus* (of the six-foot skull) undoubtedly hunted young dinosaurs. All crocodilians are egg-layers, exclusively eaters of flesh, well adapted to life in the water as well as on land, and very primitive. They are witless brutes with a high reproductive rate. Despite their penchant for eating their own young, they respond to protection, and the American alligator has increased rapidly in recent years now that hunting is forbidden.

Most, if not all species hunt prey too large to swallow, and, since they cannot chew, they have to tear it apart. This is a particularly gruesome aspect of their behavior. They grasp a limb of their prey and rotate rapidly on their own axis, dismembering their victim with great efficiency. Sometimes they wait to drown the victim before starting the dismembering; sometimes they do not. Reportedly, they may "store" food, viz., wedge a large victim into rocks or vegetation under water for a few days until the body softens and becomes easier to pull apart. I do not know whether this last recorded behavioral characteristic is true or not, but it is so often reported it is recorded here as a possibility.

Claims of great longevity among crocodilians are unsubstantiated. Specimens reportedly hundreds (and even thousands) of years old are significantly rigged as tourist attractions. Records are very incomplete, but it appears certain that some alligators, at least, pass fifty years. The crocodilians apparently have no maximum size beyond that dictated by age, since they continue to grow as long as they live. Admittedly, the rate of growth toward the end of their lives is slow, but a very old specimen is a very large one.

Which species are dangerous to man, and under what circumstances?

Schmidt and Inger report: "The African crocodile . . . attacks human beings in some areas and not in others. This is somewhat mysterious, or at least has not been explained satisfactorily." They go on to describe how native villages in some areas find it necessary to build stockades to protect women going for water or to wash their clothes at the river's edge. Other villages live in peace with the same species. Larger specimens, they suggest, do become habitual man-eaters.

The Salt-Water Crocodile (*C. porosus*) of India and the East Indies is probably even better known as a man-eater, and authentic reports are readily available demonstrating attacks on man. Since specimens of these

Saltwater Crocodile (*Crocodilus porosus*).
Courtesy of the American Museum of Natural History.

animals can approach a ton or more in weight, an attack is a very serious matter. Philip J. Darlington, Jr., the entomologist, served in New Guinea during World War II in the Army Medical Corps. He was seriously injured by a ten-foot specimen that caught him by the arms. When young Michael Rockefeller tragically disappeared off the southern coast of New Guinea, the salt-water crocodile became a subject of discussion in every newspaper in the country. I attended a meeting of the Explorers Club in New York shortly thereafter and listened to endless discussion by men with experience in the field summarizing the salt-water crocodile as one of the most dangerous animals in the world. A subsequent issue of the club's *Explorers Newsletter* (January 1962, Vol. II, No. 6) reported these observations:

At that time, the disappearance of young Michael Rockefeller was making headlines of the papers, and someone asked Dr. Gilliard, who probably knows New Guinea better than any of our other members (and possibly as well as his own back yard), his opinion of the chances of the early rescue of young Rockefeller, a fine youngster and promising anthropologist. Dr. Gilliard, in his always very charming, unassuming, and yet very learned manner, made most interesting comments and expressed his personal concern.

He stated that, as distinguished from the fresh water crocodiles of the rivers of the hinterland of the region which are found as high as 5,000 feet above sea level and are not very large in size, the monstrous salt water crocodiles, of the shore, are among the most vicious animals in the world—fearless and blood-thirsty—in fact, far more deadly than the sharks investing these waters. Dr. Gilliard also stated that he considered them indeed a cause of great danger as far as young Michael was concerned and did not reflect much optimism.

Noel Monkman was trapping specimens in northern Australia for a zoo when he had to go over the side to repair some damage done to his boat by a submerged log. Evidently his shirt billowed out behind him in the current, and it was suddenly grabbed by a salt-water crocodile and Monkman was jerked to the bottom. He was barely able to rip himself free of the shirt and make it to shore.

Writing of the Great Barrier Reef and its inhabitants, and the salt-water crocodile in particular, Dr. Paul Zahl said: "Even if these monsters had not killed and eaten many men in Australia and the East Indies, their size and fearsome dentition would set them apart as objects of dread." He suggests that the species in question is the bulkiest of living reptiles, and reaches thirty-three feet!

In her book, *Six-Legged Snakes in New Guinea*, Evelyn Cheesman reports an episode in 1939 when a group of natives gathered to dispatch a sixteen-foot crocodile found hiding under a river bank overhang, suspecting it of being a man-eater. Inside the creature they found the torso of an adult male villager who had vanished from the river's edge the day before when he had gone there to wash some fish. The man's limbs were never found.

However, no account of the salt-water crocodile matches that given by Bruce Wright in his *Wildlife Sketches, Near and Far*.

In the winter of 1944–45, British troops had over 1,000 Japanese infantrymen hemmed in at the edge of a mangrove swamp on Ramree Island, off the west coast of Burma, in the Bay of Bengal. From the air, the eighteen miles between the southern inshore edge of the island and the mainland of Burma appears to be solid vegetation. A trip through it by boat, however, reveals that there is no dry land, just miles of muck and waste-deep water inhabited by the great *Crocodylus porosus*. The Japanese commander expected units of the Imperial Fleet to rescue them but the Royal Navy intervened and the Japanese were cut off. Aerial reconnaissance by the British revealed that the Japanese were streaming into the impassable swamps on foot in an effort to escape capture by British troops swarming across the solid part of Ramree Island. British units were dispatched in canvas boats with mortars and machine guns mounted on railroad ties, and they paddled into the open water leads in an effort to contain the doomed Japanese units. By February 19, 1945, the route to the mainland had been effectively sealed and the Japanese were locked up inside the swamp. Heavy gun-fire from both sides ensued, and, in Wright's own words:

The din of the barrage had caused all crocodiles within miles to slide into the water and lie with only their eyes above, watchfully alert. When it subsided the ebbing tide brought to them more strongly and in greater volume than they had ever known it before the scent and taste that aroused them as nothing else could—the smell of blood. Silently each snout turned into the current, and the great tails began to weave from side to side.

As the tide slipped out from between the island and the mainland, it left hundreds of both wounded and uninjured Japanese troops mired knee-deep in water and muck. The crocodiles moved in about nightfall. Wright goes on to describe a night of pure hell, as dead, wounded, and unwounded men alike were grabbed by the crocodiles. The uproar of thrashing as the great animals "spun" to dismember their prey was clearly audible to the British anchored just outside the swamp. The screams of the Japanese soldiers continued throughout the night.

Of the 1,000 men who stumbled into the swamp, just twenty survived. Some of course fell to gun-fire, some drowned, and others perhaps died of yet other causes, but there can be little doubt that this night, February 19–20, 1945, revealed one of the most deliberate and wholesale attacks upon man by any large animals at any time that is on record and fully authenticated.

Had the story come from a source other than Bruce Wright, I would be tempted to discount it. Bruce Wright, however, is a highly trained and skilled naturalist. He was there at Ramree, and there can be no question that this story is true.

The caimans of South and Central America grow to great size, and take an immense toll of domestic cattle. During the dry period, Novem-

Caimans (*Caiman crocodilus*). Karl Weidmann.

Nile Crocodile (*Crocodilus niloticus*).

C. A. W. Guggisberg.

ber–December, hundreds of caimans congregate in small pools and the cowboys of the Amazon delta kill them in great numbers. Reports vary as to ferocity and danger to man, but some accidents at least have probably occurred. The huge Black Caiman (*Melanosuchus niger*), achieving a length of over fifteen feet, is more often accused of attacks on man than other species. They are often seen in great numbers sunning themselves on river banks and in muddy streams in the dense jungle. They move with startling speed on land, and appear to be far more active than the American alligator found to their north. However, I know of no actual attacks on man by an unmolested caiman.

Hornaday rated the Nile Crocodile (*C. niloticus*) as second only to the Salt-Water in danger to man. He cites William Harvey Brown as saying people have been pulled from boats in Angola. Lest geographical confusion arise from references to Nile crocodiles and Angola, the Nile and the African crocodile are the same animal, and it is found all over the continent south of the desert. James F. Barclay, who travels the world over making films on missionary work, told me a story about crocodiles in Ethiopia. An advance unit moved into that country recently to scout film locations for a forthcoming production and attended a baptismal ceremony. They watched guards, posted on high ground near the river for the duration of the ceremony, shoot crocodiles as they closed in on the crowds of worshippers being baptized in the stream. It was evidently a very normal day in the life of the congregation, and it is hoped that it will be recorded on film when the production unit arrives on location.

Emil Ludwig described the Nile crocodile as: "Hated with genuine passion by the natives, and even by the dog, who realizes the danger; it is the enemy of all animals and all men . . . it drags man and beast into

American Alligator (*Alligator mississippiensis*).

Courtesy of the American Museum of Natural History.

the river." Kermit Roosevelt shot a twelve-foot crocodile in East Africa, and found, among other things, the claws of a cheetah in its stomach. Apparently, anything that moves, except the very largest species, hippopotamus, elephant, etc., is a potential meal for the great saurians. Reports of man-eating come from all over Africa, and date back to ancient times. It is impossible to estimate the number of people who have been killed, but certainly it is enormous.

Virtually all reliable reporters have the alligators as less active and aggressive than the crocodiles. As with the giant Gavial (*Gavialis gangeticus*) of India, there are no authentic records of man-eating by American alligators. Attacks, certainly, are known and have been widely publicized. A small girl was grabbed by a gator in Florida in the early 1950's, but was saved; in April, 1950, another girl was severely bitten on the legs; and in 1949, two large males were trapped and removed from the Okefenokee Wildlife Refuge because they had begun stalking the fishermen and visiting tourists.[1] (The Chinese alligator only grows to about five feet and hence is harmless.)

In the 1930's, a hunter shot a large American Crocodile (*C. acutus*) near Biscayne Bay, Florida. Thinking the animal dead, the man kicked the fifteen-footer which lunged at him and caught him in the mid-section. The man died of the injuries inflicted by the teeth. It is the only known death attributable, in the United States, to the American crocodile.

Young caimans of several species are imported into Florida each year and sold to tourists as alligators, the U.S. native species being protected. These caimans, set free by disgruntled recipients who find them to be

[1] "Alligators and Crocodiles in Florida," Florida Game and Fresh Water Fish Commission.

something less than ideal pets, may be establishing a population here and, in a few years, the United States may, as a result, find itself with a more broadly diversified saurian population than in the past. There are persistent stories, sworn to by many, that these "alligators" brought or sent from Florida resorts have established themselves in the sewers of New York where they feed on rats. I have never noticed any, but then I am seldom in the sewers; and I have not been able to obtain any verification of these assertions.

There is no question that some of the twenty-five currently recognized species of crocodilians are extremely dangerous to man. The great salt-water crocodile is probably at the top of the list, with the African or Nile form second; and several others of the genus *Crocodylus* are not too far behind. Other species, like the American alligator and crocodile, the gavial and several others, apparently seldom attack man and must be adjudged harmless unless molested. Any large crocodilian, however, is capable of inflicting serious injury with its large teeth and formidable jaws, and by lashing out with its powerful tail. These animals, one and all, are primitive with a very low level of intelligence. They are interesting to watch, certainly deserving of protection where they are not a menace, but are best left alone. They are remnants of life as it once was on this planet, and an important part of our wildlife heritage.

# PART IV

## The Amphibians

# CHAPTER 17

# *Frogs, Toads, and Salamanders*

BECAUSE they occupy a position half-way between aquatic and land animals, the amphibians form a class that, to the average person, is mostly shrouded in mystery and generally blurred by abundant misinformation. Salamanders emerge from flames, toads and frogs are spontaneously generated in a variety of natural conditions, and specimens of both get mixed into all manner of broths and brews, sometimes to revitalize the human reproductive process, or to poison a foe. While it is true, as we shall discuss here, that the chemical properties of the skins of some amphibia are quite remarkable, fictional beliefs concerning the group as a whole are overpoweringly absurd.

The class *Amphibia* contains the descendants of the first group of vertebrate animals to emerge from an aquatic environment and spend most of their adult life on land. Fossils date back at least 280 million years, and the class is undoubtedly older than that.[1] Today, there are more than 3,000 species, spread all over the tropical, subtropical, and warm temperate zones.[2] The amphibians are probably the least harmful class of vertebrate animals on this planet. They do not compete with man for food, they destroy nothing, and they neither transport nor transmit any known diseases to man. No known species has been demonstrated to have a venomous bite, although some few are poisonous in another and unique way. They are extremely beneficial in that they consume great quantities of noxious insects.

Amphibians, as a class, consist of: the Coecilians (pronounced see-sil-ians) (order *Gymnophiona*), tropical, subterranean, primitive, and legless; the Salamanders (order *Caudata*), secretive animals, most of them small; and the Frogs and Toads (order *Salientia*), certainly the best known of all. While the range of form and structure from the coecilians to the frogs is great, all amphibians are relatively primitive creatures with a very low level of intelligence. They are creatures of instinct and reflex.

The coecilians can be ignored for our purposes here, although they are an interesting group of primitive animals. They are not known to be venomous, are not reported as significantly poisonous, and no grounds exist for considering any dangerous to man.

---

[1] Fossil salamanders have been found in Greenland in strata believed to be Devonian.
[2] One salamander occurs as far north as southern Alaska.

Giant Salamander (*Megalobatrachus japonicus*).
From *Cold-Blooded Vertebrates*, Smithsonian Institution Series.

The salamanders are mostly terrestrial but some are aquatic. Some are eaten by man, but they are of little economic importance. The giant forms (family *Cryptobranchidae*) reach five feet in length (*Megalobatrachus japonicus*) and reportedly can give a vicious bite when handled carelessly. The story of a zoologist requiring several stitches after being bitten by one recently came to the author from a reliable source. However, these non-venomous, generally non-poisonous (some few have a very mildly poisonous skin secretion), exceedingly shy creatures can hardly be considered a threat to man. Conceivably, a Japanese fisherman collecting the huge *Megalobatrachus* for the market (they are esteemed as food) might be bitten, but the animals are not aggressive.

The frogs and toads form the largest living order of amphibians. Some bite viciously and some are extremely poisonous.[3] Unknown numbers of human beings may have been killed by frogs, *indirectly*. The natives of certain Central and South American areas make a poison from frogs of several species. Some researchers have expressed the opinion that these skin-secreted poisons may prove to be among the most lethal animal-produced substances in the world. The fact that these substances are highly poisonous has been known to science for many years, but no definitive answer as to the degree of the toxicity is as yet available.

The vast majority of the frogs and toads are completely harmless, but a few species if handled cause a fearful rash not unlike a burn. Members of several genera can give a very bad bite indeed if carelessly handled. The *Ceratophrys*, the toad-shaped "horned" frogs, are South American species found in forested swamps. They are generally aggressive and feed on other frogs. Bell's Ceratophrys (*Ceratophrys ornata*) is very

[3] Not, however, venomous.

Colombian Horned Frog
(*Ceratophrys calcarata*).
Robert S. Simmons.

prone to bite. The Colombian Horned Frog (*Ceratophrys calcarata*) is particularly aggressive and apparently quite reckless in assaulting much larger animals. Contrary to local legends, it is not venomous, just extremely touchy. A Brazilian relative (*C. varia*) is reportedly similarly inclined. They are a bizarre group of irritable but harmless beasts.

The skin of nearly all amphibians secretes some poison but this protective device (it discourages other animals from eating them) is very much more highly developed in some forms, and reaches a peak, it is believed, in the tropical American families *Atelopodidae* and *Dendrobatidae.* Some frogs, and a number of toads (notably the genus *Bufo*) have large glands located behind the eyes that secrete a milky fluid. This does not exude but has to be squeezed from these glands through a number of small pores, and is poisonous. The poison involved is an extremely complex chemical, and, when extracted and processed, is deadly to animals up to the size of a cat or dog. Presumably, a massive dose of this foreign protein could be harmful to man as well.

The North American Pickerel Frog (*Rana palustris*) is covered with a poison deadly to other frog species on contact! The mucous glands

A Dendrobatid Frog
(*Dendrobates* sp.).
Courtesy of the American
Museum of Natural History.

of all frogs secrete a lubricant for the skin that is more or less dangerous to small animals. Other glands, also located in the skin, secrete a wide variety of other poisons that seem to have a similar effect: this effect is like digitalis, speeding up the heart action, until it stops. Convulsions and a variety of other symptoms are noted in smaller animals when kept with this attractively-spotted frog.

A number of South and Central American frogs of the families *Atelopodidae* and *Dendrobatidae* are, as has been said, probably the most poisonous in the world, and the latter family—known as the "Arrow-Poison Frogs"—is apparently the worse of the two. Notably poisonous are the following species:

| | |
|---|---|
| Zatek's Frog | *Atelopus zateki*—Panama. |
| Flat-Spined Atelopus | *A. planispina*—Ecuador. |
| Boulenger's Arrow-Poison Frog | *A. boulengeri*—Peru and Ecuador. |
| Two-Toned Arrow-Poison Frog | *Phyllobates bicolor*—South America. |
| Yellow-Spotted Frog | *Dendrobates flavopictus*—Brazil. |
| Golden Arrow-Poison Frog | *D. auratus*—Central America. |
| Three-Striped Arrow-Poison Frog | *D. trivittatus*—South America. |

There are many more, and some probably still unknown.

South American Indians impale the poisonous species on sticks and roast them over a fire. The poison drops secreted as the skin contracts are collected and fermented. Arrows are dipped in the resultant concoction and used in hunting. It is decidedly deadly against smaller animals but the danger to larger species, including man, is not clearly defined. Some sources refer to it as harmless against man; others say that it is deadly. For years, reports have been coming out of Central and South America of species that not only provide an arrow-poison lethal to man but that are extremely dangerous to handle while alive. The number of these reports is quite astounding, but, for the moment, the author does not know of a species, a victim (*by name*), a place, or a date of any such occurrence.

If these stories are true, as told, then it may turn out that certain amphibians do indeed produce the most potent biotoxin in the whole animal kingdom. For the moment, however, the matter must rest as unsubstantiated. Research is in progress on these problems, and this is not all academic, for such a biotoxin would have great interest for the pharmaceutical houses. Important medical discoveries may be waiting in the skin of a frog.

However, to sum up, aside from a few poisonous species, and a few giant frogs ("One will fill the bottom of a bucket," I was once told by a noted herpetologist at Harvard) which can bite quite effectively, the amphibians of the world, as a group, are more colorful and musical than dangerous.

# PART V

## The Fishes

# CHAPTER 18

# *Sharks*

IN THIS CHAPTER we will examine the record of the most dreaded creatures in the world, fishes of the subclass *Elasmobranchii*, the sharks.

In 1848, R. M. Ballantyne reported in his book, *Hudson's Bay*,[1] that
an Indian had set out along the coast of the Gulf of St. Lawrence in a
small canoe. His wife and their several small children were with him.
A large shark began battering their frail craft and brought it to the
point where it was about to break up. In desperation the Indian took his
youngest child, an infant of a few months, and threw him into the
water. While the shark was devouring the child, the Indian managed to
get the rest of his family ashore in the sinking craft.

At 4:30 P.M. on July 27, 1958, eight-year-old Douglas J. Lawton was
wading in less than four feet of murky water off Longboat Key, Sarasota,
Florida. He was not ten feet from shore when his terrified screams
brought his twelve-year-old brother, who was in the water with him,
and his parents and some friends, who were on the beach, to his rescue.
They found a five-foot Tiger Shark (*Galeocerdo*) hanging onto the
inside of the boy's left leg. The shark continued to bite and hang on until
it was literally torn and beaten off its hysterical victim. Dr. J. O. Ferguson
amputated the leg that same evening at Sarasota's Memorial Hospital.

On June 14, 1959, thirty-three-year-old Robert L. Pamperin was diving
for abalone in twenty-five feet of clear water about two hundred feet
north of Alligator Rock, La Jolla, California. He suddenly rose to the
surface, screamed for help, and then disappeared. His friend and companion dove after him and saw the top half of his body protruding
from a shark's jaws. The animal's length was estimated at twenty feet
and it was able to engulf the man whole. The body was never recovered.

Between July and September of 1959, a six-foot shark killed five, and
injured thirty victims at Machagon near the mouth of the Devi River,
India.

On November 26, 1959, thirteen-year-old Mauama Mari swam beneath
a native house set on pilings at Kaparoka, Papua, New Guinea. The child
succumbed to shock and loss of blood when a shark tore off his right leg.

In October, 1943, a fourteen-foot Leopard Shark (*Negaprion*) was

[1] As repeated by Bruce S. Wright in his *Wildlife Sketches, Near and Far*.

219

caught and brought ashore at Miami Beach. When it was opened, a man's hand, portions of a forearm, leg, and pelvis were found in its stomach. The F.B.I. identified the victim from fingerprints. He was Clyde Kelly Ormond, a member of the Armed Forces on a tanker that had collided off the Florida coast six days before. No one will ever know if Ormond was fortunate enough to have drowned before he was eaten.

Why is it necessary to retell these tales? Because, from reports such as these, it is hoped some understandable pattern of the shark's behavior will one day emerge.

Sharks have been described as "beasts without a bone in their bodies or a brain in their heads." This is almost true. A shark does not have a single bone in its body. Its skeleton is composed entirely of cartilage and the animal as a whole is exceedingly primitive. Ancestors of the sharks date back to the Devonian period of the mid-Paleozoic era, nearly a quarter of a billion years. As for brains, suffice it to say that those of the sharks are small and relatively poorly developed by modern standards of vertebrate animals. It has been estimated that about two-thirds of the brain's total mass and capacity are given over to the one sense of smell.

Although the group is still imperfectly known, there are at least 300 species of shark recognized today. They range in size, at maturity, from 6 inches to an estimated 50 feet. Teeth identical to those of the Great White Shark (*Carcharodon*) have been dredged up that were over 5 inches long. A conservative estimate would put the shark who lost such a tooth in the neighborhood of 100 feet in length. The teeth involved are not fossils, but recent ones. To the best of the author's knowledge, no one has ever recorded the sighting of a white shark anywhere near 100 feet long. There is evidence that they might exist, however, and there is no reason to make categorical statements either way. Twenty-footers have been taken and a 100-footer could be really no more dangerous to a man in the water than his cousin, one-fifth that size. The great white shark, known in some places as the death shark, is the most dreaded of known man-eaters.

The sharks currently thought of as being the biggest in the world, the 50-foot Whale (*Rhincodon*) and 40-foot Basking Sharks (*Cetorhinus*), are inoffensive plankton strainers, harmless to man. They are relatively rare and retiring, but when spotted floating placidly along only inches beneath the surface of the sea are an easy mark for a man with a harpoon. Presumably, they could do damage to a boat if they thrashed around after being stuck, but there is no conceivable ground for considering them dangerous to man. Swimmers have grabbed onto their fins and been towed along. Small boats have cruised along beside them for hours and excellent motion-picture footage has been taken of them both from above and below the surface. Like the baleen whales, these sharks cruise along like

Common Hammerhead Shark (*Sphyrna zygaena*).
Courtesy of the U.S. Department of the Interior.

massive vacuum cleaners filtering life-giving, high-protein plankton from the sea.

The Bureau of Commercial Fisheries of the Fish and Wildlife Service gives these maximum sizes in Fish and Wildlife Circular 119—"Sharks, Skates, Rays, and Chimaeras":

| Species | Maximum Length Measured U.S. Coast | Maximum Length Recorded World | Traditional Maximum Size Literature |
|---|---|---|---|
| Basking Shark *Cetorhinus maximus* | 32 ft. 2 in. | 45 ft. | 40–50 ft. |
| Whale Shark *Rhincodon typus* | 38 ft. | 45 ft. | 45–50 ft. |
| Great White Shark *Carcharodon carcharias* | 18 ft. 2 in. | 21 ft. | 36 ft. 6 in. |

These figures have been challenged, and with a tendency to upgrade them, particularly in the case of the great white shark.

Great Hammerheads (*Sphyrna tubes*) and Thresher Sharks (*Alopias vulpinus*) have been taken off U.S. coasts 18 feet long. Tiger Sharks (*Galeocerdo cuvieri*) nearly 14 feet long, 15½-foot Sixgill Sharks (*Hexanchus* sp.), and 16½-foot Greenland Sharks (*Somniosus microcephalus*) have also been caught along the U.S. coastline.

The skates, rays, sawfish, and the chimaeras, which are strange-looking creatures tapering sharply from a broad head to a threadlike tail, are closely related to the sharks. Of these forms, certain rays alone are believed dangerous to man, by reason of venom or electricity, and are treated in other chapters. The others are harmless. Some giant rays attain a length of 17 feet and a "wing-spread" of 22 feet. They characteristically propel their massive forms into the air and crash back onto the surface in monumental belly flops. The reason for this behavior is not known, but it is frequently suggested that they do it to rid themselves of parasites that are known to trouble them. Again, a presumption could be made that they might land on a swimmer, diver, or small boat and do great damage, but this far-fetched hypothesis is about the only danger these inoffensive species might pose to man. The giant rays, or Mantas, are spectacular but harmless plankton-feeding animals.

It is often suggested that a 20-foot sawfish could slice a man in half with his toothed beak. Perhaps this is so. I have been told it has happened in the coastal fisheries of the Guianas. I could locate no specific cases, although the matter was investigated.

Sharks are marine creatures for the most part. Some species do invade rivers, and some seek fresh water in which to give birth to their young. One species, the Lake Nicaragua or fresh water Bull Shark (*Carcharhinus leucas*), believed very dangerous to man, lives land-locked in Lake Nicaragua, 3,089 square miles of water, as much as 200 feet deep and 135 feet above sea level. This may be the only true fresh-water shark, although there are reports of a New Guinea species.

Sharks are typically, but by no means exclusively, tropical and subtropical fishes. The Greenland and Pacific Sleeper Sharks (*Somniosus*), at least, range into very cold seas. The hammerhead, tiger and great white shark are fairly common in Canadian waters during July and August. On July 9, 1953, a shark attacked a boat that was tending lobster traps off Cape Breton Island, Nova Scotia. It bit a two-inch hole in the wooden craft and sank it. John McLeod survived, but John Burns drowned. His body was found untouched sometime later. The attack took place less than twenty degrees south of the Arctic Circle. On April 3, 1940, the warden of a bird sanctuary on Canada's Basque Island was stalked by a shark while ice floes still littered the surface of the sea. He had shot some small animals to use as fox bait and the blood was dripping into the water. He escaped unharmed, but the tall dark dorsal fin of a shark threading its way between ice floes is not the typical picture in most people's minds. It is not, however, an uncommon sight.

The often-heard statement that the water has to be 70 degrees or warmer for a shark to attack man is *not* true. It is true that the vast majority of shark attacks do occur in waters above 70 degrees, but this is so because most sharks, excepting the very-deep-water species, live most of their lives in warmer waters, and it is in the warmer waters that you are most likely to find swimmers. The two together give us both our statistics and the misconception that warm seas are the only seas in which a man must fear the shark.

A great many sharks, just how many is not known, live in the deeper parts of the ocean. Catches have been made at over nine thousand feet and there is no reason to believe that this is anywhere near the limit. These deep-water sharks are not a threat to man for very obvious reasons. It is in the littoral, or surface zones of the sea that the trouble begins.

However inadequate the shark may be intellectually, there is nothing wrong with its senses. Its ability to home in on prey from great distances is nothing short of uncanny. The area of the brain generally associated with the thought process is completely lacking in sharks and any learning they do is on the reflex level. Their sense of smell is believed to be very well developed, but the actual value of their eyesight is still a matter of discussion. Their sense of taste is believed to be very important in the location of prey and they are equipped to taste with organs located all over their heads and parts of their bodies as well. Their use of this sense is imperfectly understood. Another puzzling sensory function is the shark's hearing. They are apparently extremely sensitive to some water-borne vibrations and tests are being made that may help define the role this plays in their behavior toward man. They may "hear" with the lateral line that extends the length of their bodies as well as with organs in their heads. Actually, along their bodies they don't "hear," but have a sensitivity to vibration.

The shark is a beautifully-designed predator. It is a killing machine with a voracious appetite. However much it may be feared and hated, it is just plain silly to think of it as "cruel" and "heartless." Sharks have no emotions, as such, and it only clouds the issue to try to pin human qualities on an animal. They do what they must to stay alive, and it is in this context that we must examine their behavior and relate it to ourselves. We know enough as thinking human beings not to touch the spinning blade of a buzz saw or plunge our hands into a roaring fire. Let's see if we can learn enough to stay out from between the shark's well-armed jaws. One thing is certain, it doesn't matter a bit to the shark whether or not we like the idea of being eaten. To a shark, lunch is lunch.

Psychologically speaking, that is what is so horrifying about any man-eating animal. As human beings we have come to rely heavily on the quality of mercy, however often it has been strained. In one's mind is the reserve idea that if things get too bad, we can always humble ourselves, beg for mercy and be spared. Instinctively, we know that no such plan will work with a mute, carnivorous beast. We have no reserve, nothing to fall back on. If we are caught by such an animal, tears will mean nothing. It is a nightmare of terrifying proportions. This unconscious knowledge colors much of our thinking, and only a clinical approach can give any real perspective to these animals. This is a major reason that so much of the layman's experience and observation of shark attack are of little or no value to the scientist. They are too colored by hidden fear and too often by conscious revulsion.

Man has long been concerned with his relationship with the shark. From earliest times, in one place or another, there have been commercial shark fisheries. Sharks are still fished for their hides, some of which make a good quality leather, once the sharply pointed placoid scales are removed. Some make excellent eating, and, reportedly, some Mako (*Isurus*) and Blue Shark (*Prionace*) is still marketed as swordfish in the United States. [At the time of this writing, the author has about forty pounds of Blue Shark steak in his freezer, and it does, indeed, taste very much like swordfish.] The liver of the shark, a very large organ, is rich in vitamins A and D, and was an important source for the pharmaceutical houses before synthetics were developed. It is still collected for this purpose in some areas, although, as reported elsewhere in this book, it can be poisonous to eat.

However important the shark-fishing industry may be or may have been, on a world-wide basis, man's major interest in the animal has been defensive. Recreation takes man into and on the sea, and man's surface and airborne craft sometimes fail him and expose him to the dangers the shark represents. Sharks, too, are damaging to the fishing industry. Anyone who has tried to fish an area where scimitar-shaped fins are cleaving the surface can tell you of the effect this animal has on the habits of other fish. Our efforts to understand this animal are only just now really moving into high gear.

Reports of devastating attacks by swarms of sharks on shipwreck victims and downed fliers led to great efforts during World War II. The U.S. Naval Research Laboratory, stepping in where others left off, helped to develop a shark repellent consisting of 80 per cent dark, water-soluble dyes, and 20 per cent copper acetate. Original authorization for the experiments came from the Bureau of Aeronautics. Tests went on for years, and even though a large tea-bag-like device containing the repellent, designed for attachment to life-preservers and vests, is still being

Counter-shark cage.

From *The Silent World,* courtesy Columbia Pictures Corp.

issued, reports vary as to its effectiveness. In other parts of the world, beaches have been uselessly bordered with perforated pipes emitting streams of bubbles. Anti-submarine nets have been tried, in some cases with a good degree of success. Australia and South Africa, particularly, have made extensive efforts to protect their great and beautiful public swimming areas. Meshing with regularly-attended nets has dramatically reduced shark populations, and attacks in meshed areas are relatively rare. Nothing, however, really works against the individual shark near a swimmer. Sharks still swim through clouds of dissolved repellent, sport almost playfully in streams of bubbles, navigate nets at high tide, and investigate experimental sonic devices. Nothing is presently known that can guarantee the safety of a man in the water when hungry sharks are near.

In 1958, the American Institute of Biological Sciences (AIBS) and the Office of Naval Research sponsored a conference of experts from Japan, Australia, South Africa, and the United States, at Tulane University. The Shark Research Panel resulted from this conference and today acts as a clearing house for information on shark attacks and behavior submitted from all over the world. The Panel also expedites research recommendations. It consists of three dedicated men: Leonard Schultz, Stewart Springer, and Perry W. Gilbert. The Lerner Marine Laboratory in Bimini is a field station of the American Museum of Natural History, and the Office of Naval Research has provided specially constructed shark pens where captive specimens can be studied in close detail by scientists of the Panel. The senses, response mechanisms, attack patterns, and feeding habits of the different species are under study. Volumes have been written about these experiments and about the data collected by the Panel from sources far removed from Bimini's crystal-clear waters. It is only a matter of time, one hopes, before man does find an effective deterrent to shark attack. Its development will probably result from the work of the Shark Research Panel and the scientists who serve as consultants to it.

What makes the large shark such a dangerous animal? First of all, he *is* tough. The author has fought a ten-foot Blue Shark (*Prionace*) for over an hour and a half, brought it to gaff, shot it through the head several times with a large-bore pistol, and had it hung up out of the water. Over two hours later, it was still alive! Peter Ianuzzi, a fellow enthusiast in marine affairs, caught a large blue after a stiff fight, which the author shot through the gills with a soft-point bullet from a .303 British carbine. Two hours later, out of the water, the shark was alive. Dragging a shark backwards through the water is supposed to drown it. The author saw a 350-pound mako fight like a demon after being dragged backwards for over four hours, at speeds up to ten knots. The sharks are tough and tenacious animals. They have the vitality of all primitive organisms.

A second factor making many sharks dangerous to man is the limited visibility generally involved. Most people who have been attacked have been partially submerged, with their heads above the surface. It is true that calm water around coral formations is amazingly clear, but, for the most part, the shark's attack is a silent and secret affair. On some occasions, the tell-tale fin circles the victim and closes in slowly, giving away the shark's intent. Too often, however, the attack is sudden, swift, and unexpected. In the final analysis, it is the shark and not the man who is at home in the water. Experts, like members of the diving teams of Jacques-Yves Cousteau, have the presence of mind and self-confidence in the water to fend off sharks without panic. But few swimmers, surf riders, and ship-wreck victims have the opportunity to develop such aquatic savoir-faire. When the average man in the water sees an attacking or nosy shark—if he sees it—he panics. A panicky human being has no defense against a graceful marauder with 350,000,000 years of experience behind him. A shark attacks when instinctive behavioral patterns are triggered. It takes all of man's self-confidence to contend with the situation.

Perhaps the greatest difficulty in dealing with sharks arises from their unpredictability. You can't tell what they're going to do, or when they're going to do it. A U.S. Navy survival manual for fliers, called "Shark Sense," refers to them as having one-cylinder minds. This is true, as we have seen. The amusing manual goes on to describe the shark as a kind of subaquatic maverick who specializes in doing the unexpected. The pamphlet waxes poetic with,

> How strange, the tiger of the sea;
> He runs from you and dines on me.

Quite simply, most generalizations about shark behavior have proven to be valueless. Some sharks are driven off by shark repellent (in some areas) while others ignore it. Some sharks flee from streams of bubbles emitted by divers, while others frolic in them. Some sharks turn tail when an intended victim thrashes the water, or beats the surface with his hands or an oar. Other sharks bore right in, ignoring the fuss, or perhaps attracted by it. Skin-divers have reported driving off sharks by yelling

Dr. Perry W. Gilbert with an anesthetized Mako Shark (*Isurus oxyrinchus*).

Courtesy of Dr. Gilbert.

underwater, but you can't depend on it. To date, none of these differences in behavior can be explained by species, sex, size, water temperature, or time of day. Reports of shark attack and shark behavior cross all lines. Our understanding of their behavior and our ability to predict their actions will come only from our knowledge of the physics and chemistry of their senses, and that knowledge is being developed (hopefully) at this time.

One of the most nightmarish aspects of shark behavior is the so-called "feeding frenzy." It is known that blood and certain other substances attract sharks from great distances. They are known to be able to home in on blood and fish oil from at least a quarter of a mile. When a number of sharks close in, a pattern of behavior may be triggered that can only be described as manic. They bite and tear at anything, including themselves and each other. Throw tin cans into the water and they will be gobbled up. Reports exist of sharks being ripped open by gaff hooks during a feeding frenzy and turning around to eat their own entrails. It is evident that nothing could survive such an onslaught. The lack of survivors from downed aircraft and sunken ships almost certainly results from behavior of this kind, in some instances. Sharks are known to be attracted by explosions in or on the water. No repellent is of use during these frenzied mass attacks.

Blue Shark (*Prionace glauca*) attacking a hooked shark.

C. M. Caras.

The author had read of this mass-feeding pattern a number of times and set out to witness it first hand. With three friends, I chartered the shark-fishing boat of Frank Mundus of Montauk, New York. Mundus has earned a world-wide reputation as a shark fisherman. The forty-five-foot *Cricket II* sailed from the tip of Long Island at 6:30 A.M. on Saturday, September 22, 1962. The plan was to drift with the current, periodically ladling chopped-up fish, or "chum," over the side. Drifting away and sinking at the same time, the chum would pave a neat path of fish oil from the sea bottom to the boat. The mate never had a chance to start the chumming. Within 30 seconds after the engine was cut, a 10-foot blue shark passed beneath our stern. A minute or so later it was followed by three or four others. Within ten minutes, we had about twenty big Blue Sharks (*Prionace glauca*) circling the boat. Before we gave out from exhaustion, we took five, on 50-pound test line, totaling nearly 1,300 pounds. Some fought for over an hour, while others were brought to gaff in a matter of a few minutes. As the sharks were brought in close enough to gaff and lasso, others closed in so rapidly that it was impossible to tell which shark was on the line and which were trying to eat it. As the diesel winch pulled the captured specimens out of the water, others grabbed hold and were pulled clear of the surface as they hung on and shook loose huge chunks of meat from their still-living hunting partners. Six of us aboard the boat leaned over the side and beat sharks on the head with gaff hooks, chum ladles, rifle butts, and anything else that could be used as a club. I shot several through the head at a range of a foot and a half with a 9 mm. pistol as they tore at our hard-won prizes. One that was hit between the eyes went over backwards and started to sink with a few convulsive flicks of its tail. Before the water it splashed landed on the deck, two other sharks closed in on it. Frank Mundus, who is evidently braver than the rest of us, leaned over and grabbed one by the tail. Infuriated, it struck out at another shark that brushed against it. Mundus stabbed one in the face, drawing blood and condemning it to be eaten alive. A shark that had been caught, gaffed and roped, grabbed another and started to tear out a chunk of meat while it was being dragged backward around the boat to where the pulley and winch could lift it out of the water. This was an unusual experience where all of the sharks were large—mostly around ten feet long. It was easy, but uncomfortable, to picture what would have happened to anyone who fell overboard at such a time.

It is often suggested that, except for "feeding frenzies," most shark attacks are attributable to rogue individuals. One shark, so the theory goes, will move into an area and attacks on man will continue until the animal is caught or moves off. There is evidence to support this theory, or at least indicate that it is true in some cases. Some individual sharks may be much more disposed to attack man than others of the same species. One well-known episode makes a good case for this theory. Ten-year-old Lester Stillwell was swimming in Matawan Creek, twenty miles from the ocean behind Sandy Hook, New Jersey, on July 12, 1916. He was seen being attacked by what was apparently an 8½-foot White Shark (*Carcharodon*). Stanley Fisher attempted to save the boy but was attacked himself in three or four feet of water. Stillwell was lost, but his body was later recovered. Fisher was rushed to the hospital, but died while being carried into surgery. Twelve-year-old John Dunn was swimming about half a mile downstream from Fisher and Stillwell, with his brother and several friends. They heard of the attack and rushed to get out of the water. John Dunn was not quite fast enough and his leg was barely saved at the hospital. Three people were attacked in a matter of minutes by what was, from all appearances, one shark. The shark itself was atypical, since it was so far from the ocean and in rather shallow water. The word *rogue* would seem to fit such an individual. Just how many shark attacks can be attributed to these lone marauders is not, however, known.

Great White Shark (*Carcharodon carcharias*).
Courtesy of Miami Seaquarium.

Sharks can injure man not only with their teeth but by rubbing against exposed skin. Densely distributed over a shark are placoid scales, or dermal denticles. These consist of dentine over a pulp cavity. If the lacerations they can cause are not in themselves disabling, they can cause the victim to bleed, triggering attack behavior in the same and other sharks. Whether or not sharks deliberately rub up against potential victims for any reason is not known. There have been suggestions made that they do.

Sharks, like most reportedly dangerous animals, have a number of legends developed around them. When an animal, like a shark, is truly potentially dangerous, misinformation ceases to be amusing; it can be downright dangerous. As we have pointed out, sharks do not need 70-degree water in which to attack. Although many more men than women have been attacked, sharks are no respecters of sex, and women are certainly attacked. Sharks do *not* have to roll over on their backs to bite. Although most species known or believed to be dangerous have their mouths underneath and set well back from their snouts, all are perfectly capable of getting their snouts up and out of the way; hence it is sheer folly to presume that a shark in a normal swimming position is harmless. Also sharks can and do attack at night. Sharks can and do attack in bright sunlight, on stormy and rainy days; and they do not need water ten feet deep to be dangerous. A freshly caught shark, high and dry, can bite your head off.

Sharks are fish, although they are admittedly far removed from the mainstream of development of the world's bony fishes. No littoral species of shark is blind and they are not led around by pilot fish. Pilot Fish (*Naucrates*, etc.) are free-loaders who clean up the scraps that the shark, a messy eater at best, leaves behind. Nor is the pilot fish immune to attack if it gets too near the shark's jaws.

There can be little doubt that large sharks do attack boats, and sink some. In our chapter on the killer whale are several references to attacks by sharks so large that whales and not fishes were blamed. In each case, careful examination has demonstrated that a shark was the offending animal. A large shark can smash a small boat with its great bulk, tip over a boat by placing part of its weight on the gunnels, or simply tear one apart with its teeth. Just how big a boat has to be before it is immune to attack depends simply on how big the shark is. It is certain that the Great White Shark does attack both men and boats. Here again, however, there is no way of knowing whether attacks of this kind are apt to be made by any large shark of a dangerous species, or only by an aberrant individual. Indeed, there may be something crudely equivalent to insanity among certain sharks that makes them individually far more aggres-

*WHAT NOT TO DO!* Australian spear-fishing champion Ben Cropp closes in for a kill on a Whaler Shark (*Galeolamna* sp.). The kill will be made with a hypodermic gun and strychnine nitrate. This practice is *not recommended*.

Australian News and Information Bureau.

sive than the norm. Higher forms of animal life—elephants, big cats, and bears, among others—are known to vary greatly in their individual attitude and disposition. This may be true of sharks as well. The answer may come when the chemistry and mechanics of the "feeding frenzy" are better understood. There is a great deal still to be learned about these dangerous and interesting animals.

Writers of fiction, and even many so-called nonfiction writers, have accused just about all sharks of being man-eaters. This, of course, is baseless. Probably not more than 10 per cent of the currently recognized species have ever been implicated in attacks on man. Even some species that have been involved in human injuries, such as the Nurse Shark (*Ginglymostoma cirratum*), are not demonstrably true man-eaters. Almost always, attacks by these sharks have been brought about by divers and spear fishermen disturbing the normally peaceful animal and getting nipped for their pains. Not by any stretch of the imagination are all sharks dangerous to man. Most are not.

As silly as it may be to hear someone accuse all sharks of being man-eaters, at least it isn't a dangerous claim. At the opposite end of the spectrum, however, we have quite a different situation. In recent years, the lure of the sea and the freedom to it given by self-contained under-water breathing apparatus has brought thousands of novices into the surf with cameras and spears. The skin-diver has come into his own. He follows in the wake of his ideals, the expert diving teams of France and Italy. Unfortunately, these novices are very often not as serious about their sport as were their forerunners. If anything, they treat their new-found freedom beneath the sea a little too matter-of-factly; though this is not true of all skin-divers by any means. Many are keen sportsmen with a decidedly scientific bent. Excellent work has been done, and is being done, by serious-minded skin-divers assisting in rescue and salvage work, submarine archaeology, and biological surveys. There are, though, an unfortunate number who seem to feel an uncontrollable urge to prove that there is nothing dangerous in the sea. The "I Kissed a Man-Eating Shark" kind of article litters the pages of the world's pulp magazines. In these monuments to literary mediocrity, the distinguishing feature seems to be that the line separating fact from fiction has been totally obliterated. The articles themselves are really amusing and harmless, but collectively they may one day bring about a lot of damage. There is a growing cult of uneducated skin-divers whose common denominator is disrespect—disrespect for the very real hazards of their sport. Once again, these "Saturday Experts" on everything aquatic are not to be confused with the thousands of fine, serious-minded sportsmen who are putting their new-found skill to work on constructive projects. The claim, so often heard, that all sharks are cowards and of no danger to a man in the sea, is as patently ridiculous as the counter-claim that all are dangerous. The difference is that the former claim may very well lead some new adherents of the sport down a marine garden path to destruction.

What sharks *are* dangerous to man? Somewhere between twenty and thirty species have been authentically implicated. Information is far from complete and a thoroughly reliable and authoritative list cannot be compiled at this time. Too often, even where it can be demonstrated that an attack has taken place, there is no way to determine the species. Even victims who survive are generally understandably uncertain about what they have seen.

The following table represents data collected from a number of sources. The species listed have been known to attack. Those species followed by an asterisk are *believed* to be the ones most often implicated, and are therefore probably the most dangerous. There is no significance to the order in which they appear. Halstead notes these four families as being, in the order given, most dangerous: *Isuridae*—Mackerel Sharks, *Carcharhinidae*—Requiem Sharks, *Carchariidae*—Sand Sharks, and *Sphyrnidae*—Hammerhead Sharks.

## SHARKS KNOWN TO BE DANGEROUS TO MAN

| Common Name | Scientific Name | Remarks |
| --- | --- | --- |
| Great White or Man-Eater * | *Carcharodon carcharias* | Oceanic—probably most dangerous single species. |
| Mako * | *Isurus oxyrinchus* and other species | Oceanic—notable game fish, large and fast. |
| Porbeagle | *Lamna nasus* | Continental. |
| Tiger * | *Galeocerdo cuvieri* | Coastal and oceanic—global—particularly dangerous. |
| Lemon | *Negaprion brevirostris* | Coastal—Atlantic. |
| Lake Nicaragua | *Carcharhinus [leucas] nicaraguensis* | Lake Nicaragua only—only known fresh-water shark. |
| Dusky | *Carcharhinus obscurus* | Atlantic—probably minimum danger. |
| White-Tipped * | *Pterolaminops longimanus* | Atlantic and Mediterranean—oceanic. |
| Sand | *Carcharias taurus* | Global—coastal—probably minimum danger. |
| Bull | *Carcharhinus* sp. | Coastal, ascends rivers. |
| Gray Nurse | *Carcharias arenarius* | Australia. |
| Ganges River * | *Carcharias gangeticus* | Indian Ocean to Japan—aggressive—ascends rivers. |
| Hammerhead * | *Sphyrna* sp. | Oceanic and coastal—global—unpredictable. |
| Whaler | *Galeolamna macrurus* and others | Australia. |
| Great Black-Tipped | *Carcharhinus maculipinnis* | Follows fishing craft—some attacks known. |
| Zambezi | *Carcharhinus zambezensis* | South Africa—coastal—responsible for most attacks in Durban area. |
| Nurse | *Ginglymostoma cirratum* | Not to be confused with Australia's Gray Nurse—harmless unless provoked. |
| Blue | *Prionace glauca* | Coastal and oceanic—sometimes found in large concentrations. |

There are some conflicting, confusing, and sometimes confounding reports, opinions, and legends about at least another dozen kinds of sharks. We purposefully say *kinds* here instead of *species* because the matter of species is particularly confusing. Some species of shark in one part of the world are known to be dangerous while related species elsewhere are believed harmless. Common names (more often encountered in literature than scientific names) are very confusing. The Blue Shark

(*Prionace*) of the eastern coast of North America is not the Blue Shark (*Isurus*) of Australia. The shark known to Australians as the Blue or Blue Pointer is called Mako in other places, and Mackerel in still others. The Mackerel Shark (properly *Lamna*) is any number of different animals depending upon where you live. To top it all off, the scientists are not all agreed on family and generic breakdowns, or on subspecific designations. Not all species of sharks, it is safe to assume, have even been scientifically examined.

How many human victims do sharks claim each year? No answer is possible, although the figures compiled by the Shark Research Panel come as close to being complete as any can. Primitive people fishing and

Great Blue Shark (*Prionace glauca*).
Courtesy of the Harvard Museum of Comparative Zoology.

diving off remote oceanic islands might very well fall victim to sharks without reports ever reaching beyond the coral reef that surrounds the atoll. Native people from isolated coastal zones of Africa, India, the Malay Peninsula, South America, and other areas do not keep records, and do not necessarily pass information about mortality along to people who do. The Shark Research Panel reports that during 1959 there were 36 unprovoked and 3 provoked attacks known. Approximately a third of these were fatal. Coppleson reports that, between 1919 and 1949, there were 77 attacks in Australian waters: 42 occurred in the surf, 31 in harbors, rivers, and estuaries, and 4 on swimmers far offshore, or in the open ocean. The 77 do *not* include 33 on pearl divers between 1926 and 1938, or several attacks at Darwin and along the north coast of Australia. Forty-seven attacks between 1913 and 1959 are reported for Florida waters by the Florida Board of Conservation. There are reports of 87 attacks for all U.S. waters between 1907 and 1960. The list is almost certainly incomplete. The number of attacks is small when compared with the number of swimmers in the water every sunny day, or the number of small boats that set out each year. As most researchers point out, however, the death or injury caused by a shark attack is particularly gruesome. The victims of these attacks must know terror in its most extreme form. Few more horrible deaths can be imagined than being eaten alive.

Shark attacks most often occur between 11:00 A.M. and 6:00 P.M., the peak bathing hours on the world's beaches. Of all recorded attacks, 94.3 per cent occurred between sunrise and sunset. Still, it is probably more dangerous to swim at night than during the day. The Shark Research Panel estimates that the number of swimmers at night is less than 5 per cent of the daytime total. However, 5.7 per cent of the known attacks have occurred after dark. Peak months are summer months for two reasons, migrating fish moving north, plus more people exposed during the warmer season. In the final analysis, dangerous sharks probably attack when they are particularly hungry, when there is a victim handy, and when the attack mechanism, whatever it is, is triggered.

Sand Shark (*Carcharias taurus*).
Courtesy of the Harvard Museum of Comparative Zoology.

There are all kinds of free advice on what to do when a shark starts nosing around. Hitting him on the nose, sticking your finger in his eye, yelling, staying still, splashing and kicking, swimming calmly, grabbing his fins and riding him, or charging him and playing "chicken" have all been suggested. In individual cases some of these tactics undoubtedly have worked. Still, nothing can be depended on. A shark intent on attack is apparently insensible to pain and is apt to maintain the initiative no matter what you do. The best advice is still the most obvious: get out of the water as quickly as possible. If this is not possible, keep as calm as you can under the conditions and *keep facing the animal*. It is usually wise to stay under the water as much of the time as possible and do whatever you can to fend the marauder off without drawing blood, yours or his. If an injury has been sustained, everything should be done to stop the bleeding, since blood in the water is likely to attract other sharks. Many people have managed to survive actual attacks, and many more have been able to chase off inquisitive sharks before the attack began, but too little is known about these animals to permit any really reliable generalizations. If you are in the water when a dangerous shark approaches, you are in grave peril. Whether or not he does attack will be more up to him than you. The Shark Research Panel does offer this advice, however:

1. Always swim with a companion. Do not become a lone target.

2. Stay out of the water if dangerous sharks are known or suspected of being in the area.

3. Do not enter or remain in the water with a bleeding wound.

4. Avoid swimming in water where underwater visibility is poor. Avoid swimming at night.

If skin-diving:

1. Never dive alone.

2. *Do not molest a shark.* To provoke even a small and seemingly harmless one is to invite trouble.

3. Remove speared fish from the water *immediately*. Do not tow them around.

4. If a shark starts to circle you, a common prelude to attack, get out of the water using a rhythmic beat. Do not cause undue disturbance. Stay submerged until the last moment if wearing SCUBA.

5. If a shark moves in before you can retreat, do not panic but try to keep the shark in view. *Try* releasing bubbles, *try* charging it, *try* clubbing it on the snout. *Try* to avoid hitting it with bare skin. *Try* shouting, underwater.

If you are a survivor of an air or sea disaster:

1. Do not strip. Clothing can be protection against a shark's rough skin.

2. Get wounded survivors out of the water onto a raft or float if possible.

3. Remain quiet; conserve energy.

4. If swimming is necessary, use rhythmic strokes.

5. Do not hang arms or legs over the side of a raft.

6. Do not jettison blood or garbage.

7. Do not fish when sharks are around. Abandon hooked fish if a shark comes near.

8. Use shark repellent if available. It sometimes works.

9. If in a group in the water, form a tight circle facing outwards. Hit sharks on the snout if they move in, but with bare hands only as a last resort.

Sleek and powerful, insensitive, insensible, and efficient, the great marauding sharks are among the world's most dangerous animals. They kill nowhere near the number of people that snakes do, only a fraction as many as are killed by lightning, and fewer in ten years, world-wide, than die in motor accidents in the United States on a single 4th of July or Labor Day weekend.

Nevertheless, care and watchfulness are indicated when exposed to any danger of attack.

# CHAPTER 19

# *Skates and Rays*

OF ALL THE FISH that swim in the seas and oceans of the world, no others are responsible for so many injuries to man as the stingrays. Estimates for the United States alone range from 750 (Findlay E. Russell) to about 1,500 (Bruce W. Halstead) victims per year.

Rays of many kinds are very common inshore inhabitants of all tropical, subtropical, and most temperate seas. Only one of the seven families of so-called stingrays is found regularly in fresh water, the others being marine forms that only occasionally enter brackish and sweet water. One of the factors involved in the great number of human injuries is that the stingrays are mostly shallow-water animals. Some deep-water species are known, but most of the stingrays of the world can be found in waters where humans might seek diversion or have to wade for a living.

Stingrays are found along almost all of the coastline of the United States, all of Central, and most of South America. Europe as far north as central Scandinavia, all of the Mediterranean, all of Africa, and the Indian Ocean play host to these animals. The Pacific coast of Asia as far north as central Japan, and all the coasts of Australia and the Pacific Islands are infested with them. A belt of stingrays runs around the world, and the number of human injuries must run into many, many thousands each year. Unfortunately, the world is not compensated for this misery by the enjoyment of stingray flesh. They are seldom eaten and are rated by most commercial fishermen as "junk fish." When man finally has enough sense to use the high protein "flour" available from the otherwise useless "junk fish," the stingray may well repay mankind, and be eaten by the ton.

The rays are elasmobranchs, closely related to the sharks. Like the sharks, they don't have true bones, and are extremely primitive. They have been swimming about the world's varying coastlines for hundreds of millions of years.

The seven families known to contain dangerous species[1] are given by Halstead as:

| | | | |
|---|---|---|---|
| *Dasyatidae* | True Stingrays | *Myliobatidae* | Eagle or Bat Rays |
| | or Whiprays | *Rhinopteridae* | Cow-Nosed Rays |
| *Potamotrygonidae* | River Rays | *Mobulidae* | Devil Rays or Mantas |
| *Gymnuridae* | Butterfly Rays | *Urolophidae* | Round Stingrays |

[1] Not all species of these seven families are necessarily dangerous, however.

238

Sting Ray (*Dasyatis centroura*).
Courtesy of the Harvard Museum of Comparative Zoology.

Round Sting Ray (*Urolophus jamaicensis*).
Courtesy of the Harvard Museum of Comparative Zoology.

Rays feed on worms, crustaceans, and molluscs, and can generally be found partially, or almost wholly submerged in sandy or muddy bottoms where they excavate for their living prey. None of these primitive creatures are known to be vicious or prone to attack man. Almost every case ever reported involved the victim stepping on or attempting to handle a specimen. Although the victim may not realize it, he has to be the aggressor in order to get stung. The insidious aspect of the whole business is that such aggression by man is almost always unintentional. Accidents with stingrays are generally all but unavoidable.

In all stingrays, the animal's weapon is in its tail, and the unwary wader who treads on the animal triggers reflexes that bring the tail up and forward in a powerful slashing motion. The stingray is the only truly venomous fish that causes extensive tissue injury in addition to injecting a toxic substance. Lacerations five to seven inches long are not unusual, and many is the stingray victim who has had to have his foot sewn up after an encounter.

In his excellent guidebook, *Dangerous Marine Animals*, Dr. B. W. Halstead breaks the stingrays' envenomizing apparatus down into four main types:

| *Type* | *Found In* | *Description* |
|---|---|---|
| Gymnurid | Butterfly Rays (*Gymnura*) | Not well developed. Close to base of short tail. Not very effective weapon. |
| Myliobatid | Bat or Eagle Rays (*Myliobatis, Aetobatis, Rhinoptera*) | Large; situated at base of whip-like tail. Can be effectively used. |
| Dasyatid | True Stingrays (*Dasyatis, Potamotrygon*) | Very well developed. Set far out on whiplike tail—most dangerous type. |
| Urolophid | Round Stingrays (*Urolophus*) | Dangerous. Set in short powerful tail. |

All of the stinging organs are located on the top, or dorsal aspect of the tail, and all are essentially the same kind of device. There is a rough, barbed spine or spines enclosed in a sheath of skin. Although two or more on some species are known to exist, one is the usual number. The sheath of skin is known as the integumentary sheath, and it evidently covers the spine until it is brought into play. The spine is hard, but it is not true bone; it is properly identified as *vasodentine*.

On the underside of the spine, running its length, are a series of shallow furrows, the ventrolateral-glandular grooves, lined with soft, spongy tissue. It is this tissue, and perhaps parts of the integumentary sheath, that produce the venom.

The venom consists of soluble proteins, and ten different amino-acids have been found in the chemical analysis of the substance. The immediate effect of the venom (and the often gross injury occasioned by the introduction of it) is pain; throbbing, sharp or shooting pain, and it evidently can be extreme in degree. Eventually the venom can affect the heart and circulation, as well as the respiratory, nervous, and urinary systems of the victim. Frequently, portions of the sheath are left in the wound, and it is not uncommon for the barbed spine to break off and remain lodged in the victim. The removal of these foreign bodies, particularly the spine which cannot be just drawn out with forceps, is painful and necessarily increases the size of the wound. Swelling and discoloration generally accompany the injury, and may last for several weeks. Weakness, nausea, and extreme nervousness are usual complaints. Cramps and violent pain can occur, and, rarely, death. Dr. F. E. Russell reports that two out of 1,097 reported cases along the coastlines of the United States in a five-year period died. Sixty-two of 232 cases examined by physicians were hospitalized.

An additional problem can arise from the fact that the tetanus bacillus, *Clostridium tetani*, may be injected into the wound along with the venom. The introduction of this bacillus and related bacilli isn't too much of a problem in relatively sophisticated societies where a tetanus booster is

A South American River Sting Ray (*Potamotrygon histrix*).

From the collection of Dr. Harold W. McCormick

given as a matter of course for injuries of this general type. In under-developed areas where proper medical facilities are lacking, the tetanus factor can cause more deaths than the venom itself. Russell and Lewis report that not all stingray spines contain the venom-producing tissue. Some stings, then, produce nothing more than a stab or slashing cut. As painful as this may be, and as prone to secondary infection, it is not as troublesome a prospect as the injection of a substance dangerous to the body life-system.

Although the South American fresh-water stingray (*Potamotrygon motoro*) is reportedly extremely dangerous, as are a number of other species throughout the world, death from an encounter with one of these tropical fishes is rarely reported, due to low populations in their areas. However, all stingrays have been recognized as dangerous since the time of ancient civilizations. In early American history, Captain John Smith got badly stung in Chesapeake Bay, in June of 1608. Yet deaths are not often recorded.[2] The animals themselves are not aggressive unless molested, and would certainly rather (if we can infer they are capable of choice) avoid man than become involved. Still, it remains an undeniable fact that accidents with them are frequently difficult to avoid, and will continue to occur as long as man fishes, swims, collects sea shells, or just plain wades. They are dangerous animals in that they do cause a great many injuries, an enormous amount of pain, expense, and wasted manpower, and some deaths, from time to time. The best defense against them is the power of observation. In areas where they are believed to exist, it is a good idea to carry a stick and probe ahead as you walk in the water. If you touch one, the chances are it will scoot out of the way.

If you do see a stingray, and have no immediate business with it, leave it alone unless you want to hasten it on its way with some long implement, other than your naked toe. If you accidentally net or hook one, beware of the tail! The hand, arm, and even face and neck of the fisherman, are as susceptible to that slashing serrated barb as the foot of the wader. Injury can be particularly dangerous for children whose small bodies react to the effects of the venom more rapidly and more completely than those of adults. Even without intent, the stingray, although seldom deadly, can be dangerous to man.

[2] In February, 1945, thirty-three-year-old Arthur Biggins, an Australian army sergeant, died at St. Kilda City Baths, Victoria, when a stingray drove its spine into his heart. It has been substantiated, but is certainly a freak accident. A Miss Jessie M. Laing of New Zealand died the same way. Both cases are reported in the supplement to the *Bulletin of the Post Graduate Committee in Medicine* of the University of Sydney, March, 1963.

# CHAPTER 20

# *Venomous Fish*

A CLEAR DISTINCTION must be made between *poisonous* and *venomous* fish. The two words are generally interchangeable in common usage, but the practice can be thoroughly confusing when we have two distinctly different phenomena to discuss. For our purposes, *venomous* refers to the ability (by an animal) to introduce a noxious substance by means of a special device; while *poisonous* refers to animals whose very substance or parts thereof are dangerous to man as food. In other words, a toadstool may be poisonous, whereas an arrow dipped in poison is venomous.

There are numbers of fish in tropical, subtropical, and even temperate waters equipped to administer a toxic substance on contact. We have discussed some of these, the stingrays, in the last chapter. They are described separately because injuries caused by them are much more common than by any of the others, and contact with them is much more likely.

The forms we will discuss in this chapter use their venomous devices in self-defense, at least so far as humans are concerned. Categorically, none of these forms attack humans with these devices unless threatened at close quarters. Aggression in their direction, however, is met with a startlingly effective defense measure. The devices are not used in food-getting as far as is known. The venoms involved vary greatly in toxicity; most are merely painful while others can be lethal.

The introduction of a highly toxic venom into human tissue constitutes a medical emergency of the first magnitude. Effective antivenins for fish venoms are not generally available, and proper first-aid measures are not always easy to determine. Injury by many forms under discussion in this chapter is an agonizingly painful affair. A man can be rendered either unconscious, or at least sufficiently shocked as to be totally disabled while still in the water. The only preventative is recognition. Before entering the water where these forms are found, it behooves the individual to learn the appearance and habits of indigenous species, and give them wide berth. Some, like the Stonefish (*Synanceja* sp.), are difficult to avoid because of their incredible powers of camouflage. Others broadcast their presence by their generally bizarre appearance. But, contrary to one ridiculous fable, these forms are just as dangerous out of the water as in. If netted or hooked, they should be treated with the utmost respect. Handling one in a boat can be just as hazardous as stepping or sitting on one in the water.

Writing in *Animal Kingdom* in November, 1960, James W. Atz said:

The Stonefishes are the world's most venomous fishes. Such categorical statements are seldom safe to make when dealing with such biological variables as the strength of animal poisons and the health and immunity of creatures subjected to them, but there is no question that Stonefishes are in a class by themselves.

After reviewing the available evidence, we would tend to answer Dr. Atz, "Hear! Hear!" There can be little doubt but that the stonefishes are the most venomous fishes presently known.

There are three species of true Stonefish currently recognized, *Synanceja verrucosa, S. horrida,* and *S. trachynis.* These particularly grotesque-looking creatures range from the east coast of Africa, east to the mid-Pacific. They are very common and found as far north as the Red Sea and as far south as Australia. They are shallow-water bottom dwellers, although few people get to see them, not even their victims. Wherever they are known, they are greatly feared.

Stonefish (*Synanceja verrucosa*).

Courtesy of Prof. J. L. B. Smith.

The stonefishes have none of the sleek grace of other fishes. The head is broad and quite flat, the body sharply tapered, and the tail blunt. They don't have normal piscine scales, but are of a warty texture, covered with a layer of slime. All of this supreme ugliness has a definite purpose, however, since a stonefish (6 to 12 inches) in its natural surroundings—coral and rocky bottoms—is all but completely invisible. Your chances of seeing one under foot as you wade in even the most shallow of waters are practically non-existent. Add to perfect camouflage a reluctance to move that amounts to inertia, and you have an animal virtually impossible to detect. Even a great fuss in the water inches away will fail to disturb one beyond inducing it to erect its venomous spines. They remain frozen and invisible until it is too late—for their victim.

The stonefishes administer their extremely dangerous venom by direct contact through the spines in their fins. They don't squirt anything, and they don't taint the water around them. There are thirteen spines along the back, three in the anal fins, and one in each pelvic fin. All the animal has to do is erect its spines and wait. Each spine has two sacs well toward the tip, which secrete the virulent substance when pressure is applied to the tip of the spine. The fluid flows along grooves into the wound—the insertion of the spine having stripped back a sheathing that covers the whole apparatus. Most injuries to humans result from a brush with the dorsal spines, almost invariably resulting from stepping on a specimen. Occasionally one is kicked, bringing the anal or pelvic spines into play. Since stonefish were around and undoubtedly venomous before man evolved, the device is apparently protection against other sea creatures. The stonefishes do not use their envenomizing apparatus to procure food. For that process they rely on camouflage. They lie waiting until a likely meal happens along. Literally faster than the human eye can see, they lunge forward, snapping the prey up in their cavernous mouths. Even other fish, it seems, can't spot a stonefish amid coral rubble.

Stonefish can live out of water for surprising lengths of time, and survive. Dr. Saul Wiener reports that specimens have survived as much as ten hours out of their natural environment. They have evidently developed a secondary respiratory system to cover their needs when exposed in small pools at low tide. These facts would indicate that even apparently dead specimens encountered high and dry along the shore should be handled with extreme care, or not at all. This would be particularly true if the encounter took place below the high-water mark.

Certain writers have attempted to deny the danger of the stonefish, citing cases where people have been jabbed and suffered no ill effects beyond a slight puncture wound. These cases are undoubtedly true, since examination of captured specimens will reveal an inevitable percentage of *dry* spines, i.e., spines without venom sacs. Whether certain individual animals fail to develop sacs for all of their spines, or whether these *dry* spines are the results of previous encounters is not clear. One thing is certain, many, and probably most stonefish carry a full, bristling array, and it would be hazardous in the extreme to be careless with one of these creatures. (No doubt also, some reports of stonefishes were cases of mistaken identity.)

All reports of injuries from these creatures emphasize one aspect, pain. Extreme, agonizing, sometimes maddening pain is apparently the first sign of an encounter, and it can last for as much as twelve hours. There are reports of victims rolling around on the beach screaming and frothing at the mouth. People attempting to help victims have been bitten by them and struck violently.

Writing in *The Medical Journal of Australia*, August 16, 1958, Dr. S. Wiener says: ". . . . excruciating pain dominates the clinical picture in the early stages." C. C. Ralph in 1943 (*Victorian Naturalist*) wrote of a patient "screaming and half mad with agony," and morphine did not help the man! Writing in *Copeia* in 1951, Dr. J. L. B. Smith said:

Pain starts almost at once and rapidly becomes intolerable. Within ten to fifteen minutes the victim either collapses or becomes delirious and maniacal, raving and thrashing about in a boat or on the ground. If stabbed whilst wading, it generally takes three or four men to hold him and get him to shore without drowning. The intense agony lasts from 8 to 12 hours, after which it gradually diminishes, but the victim is weak and exhausted.

Those who die generally do so within a time assessed at about six hours. Swelling starts soon after the stab and continues to increase for "some days." Legs may attain elephantine proportions. Some victims are able to walk after 3 weeks, but mostly it is said to be "a long time" before the limb is usable. Often large blisters form and sloughing of large areas of skin occurs. Sometimes the dark pigment is destroyed and the skin of the blistered area remains light pink. Stabs in fingers and toes have led to the loss of those digits which turn black and "fall off." Some persons are still sick as long as a year afterwards.

Six years later, writing in the same journal, Professor Smith told of two rapid fatalities:

In March, 1956 an Indian youth of 15, well-built and athletic, was swimming there (Pont Larus, Mahé, Seychelles) and came towards the rocks. As he trod he felt a stab in the sole of his foot. He pulled himself up, sat on the rock and then saw three punctures. By this time intense pain had developed at the site of the punctures, which spread rapidly up the leg to the body. In a short time he was in agony and showing signs of collapse. Alarmed by his appearance the others managed to find a pirogue in which he was taken to shore. By this time he had turned blue and was frothing at the mouth. He was at once put in a car that set out for the hospital, but he died on the way there.

According to the medical officer who examined the body, this was greatly cyanosed, and the apparent cause of death was a cardiac or respiratory poison that had been injected. His medical attendant reported that he had not suffered from heart trouble.

At Pinda, Mozambique, on the 23rd September, 1956, two men went out in a canoe to the margin of the reef, close on 5 miles from land, and near low tide went wading, hunting for fishes with spears. The elder soon noted that the other had collapsed in the water. Hastening over, he found his companion almost delirious, but able to say that he had been stabbed in the foot by a "sherowa" (*Synanceja*). Others came to help; the wounded man, now unconscious, was carried to the nearest canoe, and the stonefish was found and killed, cut open and the gall-bladder extracted, for the natives believe this, swallowed, to be an antidote to the poison. The victim was by then unconscious and well within an hour was dead.

I examined the corpse later. There was only one stab in the front of the second toe of the right foot. It was close on ¾″ deep and went along the bone. The man must have kicked against the stonefish from behind. There was neither discoloration nor swelling in the toe or foot and from the rapidity with which he succumbed the toxin may well have been injected directly into a blood vessel. The victim was between 30 and 40 years of age and apparently, as well as from enquiry, strong and in good health.

Bulletin No. 159 of the Commonwealth of Australia Council for Scientific and Industrial Research "Poisonous and Harmful Fishes" says: "This poison is extremely virulent, the Stonefish being the most venomous fish known, and immediately causes fearful pain so that a person may become almost demented . . . he may die."

Fortunately, there is an effective antivenin for the stab of the stonefish. There are, too, chemical agents which reduce or destroy the lethal effects of the venom. Anyone collecting specimens of this fish (they are relatively rare in, and therefore highly prized by, American and European aquaria), or working in waters where they are found, should be advised to (1) know the animal well and (2) to go prepared to combat the extremely serious effects of an encounter, should one take place.

If the stonefish is one of the ugliest fish in the sea, the related and dangerously venomous Zebrafish or Lionfish (*Pterois* sp.) is one of the most beautiful and bizarre. Once considered rare and highly treasured by aquaria for the spectacular display piece that it is, the zebrafish is now a familiar sight. They have become so common that any good aquarium supply store can obtain one on order. Admittedly, the asking price for this beautiful creature limits its practical appeal to the more advanced home aquarist. The enthusiast who does bring one to the tank in his living room will do well to treat his pet with respect. The zebrafish is a decidedly dangerous animal.

Whether referred to as the Lionfish, Dragonfish, Firefish, Devilfish, Zebrafish, Turkeyfish, Featherfish, Butterfly Cod, or Sausaulele, the family *Scorpaenidae*, or Scorpion Fishes, are spectacular animals. Hid-

Scorpion fishes. A, B, C, D are forms of the genus *Pterois*. E is *Pteropterus radiata;*
F is *Pteropterus antennata.*

Courtesy of Prof. J. L. B. Smith.

den in flashy displays of maroon or gray stripes on a creamy silver background and among the peacock-like dorsal, anal, and ventral fins are eighteen venomous spines. Thirteen are in the elegant dorsal fin, three in the anal and one in each ventral. The largest and showiest of its fins, the pectorals, are harmless. Each of the venomous spines has its own venom-producing tissue which is exposed by pressure when the apparatus is brought into play. This tissue is often injected into the wound along with the spine. The amount of venom injected, however, is considerably less than that of the stonefish.

Found over pretty much the same range as the stonefish, the zebrafishes have no authenticated human deaths to their credit, but a lot of agonizing injuries. The pain is reportedly severe in the extreme and can last for a day or more. The deaths reportedly caused by these animals have never been substantiated. It is not possible, of course, to say that none have occurred. It is actually much more likely that some have.

Saunders and Lifton reported a case history in the *U.S. Armed Forces Medical Journal* for February, 1960. A thirty-eight-year-old man "in good physical condition" received two spines in the fingers of his right hand while skin-diving off the Marshall Islands. Extreme pain, involving his whole arm, increased in intensity until the patient "was stuporous and in a state of severe shock." The two affected fingers were twice normal size and his entire arm was markedly swollen. His blood pressure dropped dangerously, and only swift medical care enabled him to survive cardio-vascular collapse. It is safe to say that had the patient not been attended by physicians, given epinephrine to maintain blood pressure, and treated for shock, he would have succumbed. Such cases apparently indicate that an injury from one of these animals can be fatal. That, however, remains for the moment an indication and not a proven fact.

Like the stonefish, the zebrafishes do not retreat, but hold their ground when threatened. However, unlike the stonefish, they do not wait to be stepped on passively, but constantly maneuver their venomous spines into position, turning rapidly. If the intruder comes too close, an effort is sometimes made to jab at him. While they can hardly be accused of swimming around looking for people to injure (such has never been demonstrated to be the case), they are much more aggressive than the more virulent stonefish. But, aggressive though they may be, they are relatively easy to avoid. The appearance is spectacular and can hardly be confused with other forms. They are not fast swimmers and nature gave them this other defense: Stand pat and dare anything to touch you! Carelessness may result in an occasional agonizing injury, but thoughtful behavior on the part of a man in the sea makes swimming or diving in the shallow waters where the zebrafish abound reasonably safe. (A possible danger factor may result in very brightly colored shallow reefs where an overabundance of spectacular growths could serve to mask the fish.)

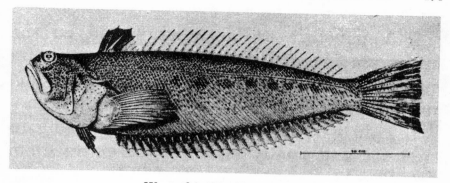

Weeverfish (*Trachinus draco*).    Official U.S. Navy Photo.

The piscine family *Trachinidae* is represented by four dangerously venomous species ranging variously through the North Sea, the Mediterranean, and the Eastern Atlantic south along the west coast of Africa. *Trachinus araneus, T. draco, T. radiatus,* and *T. vipera* are all commonly known as Weevers, although dozens of local names are used. The Romans knew them as *Tragine;* in England today they are called Sea Dragons; in Germany, *Ragno;* in France, *Claquedit;* in Greece, *Drakaina;* and so on, throughout their extensive range. They are small fishes, seldom more than eighteen inches long, and are found in shallow bays and coastal waters. Known to be aggressive when approached in their natural habitat, they are also quite dangerous to handle when netted. Even dead specimens can cause extreme pain if improperly handled, and they are almost certainly the most venomous fishes in temperate and northern seas.

The extremely painful venom can be administered by any of the five to seven dorsal spines, or by either of the two opercular spines located on either side of the head. Each spine has its own venom-producing tissue, consisting of large pink cells filled with a finely granular substance. Once again, excruciating agony is reported as a primary symptom and even psychological disorders reportedly can result. It has been recorded that in at least one case, a fisherman amputated his own finger to gain relief. Other victims have reportedly plunged an affected hand into fire! The central nervous system may become involved, and deaths reportedly have occurred, although none are known to the author at the time of this writing.

Weevers are esteemed as food and many tons are marketed each year. Some countries have enacted legislation requiring the removal of venomous spines before marketing, but the practice is probably not universal.

In addition to the stingrays, weevers, stonefish and zebrafish, there are several other venomous forms reported from most of the tropical, subtropical, and temperate seas of the world. It would be impossible to discuss all of these forms in this book since much of the information is sketchy, often contradictory, and generally unsubstantiated. The table on pages 253 to 255 combines reports from most areas, including the forms already discussed.

Reports from all over the world beg for further study. From Teheran comes a report of a diminutive black fish found in the Shatt al Arab River. It reputedly has killed twenty-eight people with a venomous *bite*. Death is said to be swift. No other information is presently available.

A fresh-water armored catfish of the genus *Cataphractus* is said to cause a number of deaths in South America each year. It has a sharp conical spine in its "armpit" behind the base of each of its recurved, blade-like pectoral fins. Although a small creature, it reportedly delivers an extraordinary amount of particularly virulent venom. However, no real research has apparently been done on it.

There are, at the very least, 25,000 species of fishes, and that is a conservative estimate. The total number of species venomous enough to be of any possible danger to man is probably less than one hundred. There are undoubtedly many more than that capable of causing some discomfort. These figures are given only to underscore the simple observation that the seas and oceans of the world are not teeming with virulent forms. In a chapter such as this, filled with stonefish, weevers, and the like, it it easy to give, and get, the opposite impression. The majority of fishes in the world are not horrific forms, or dangerous to man. They are shy, retiring, generally very beautiful creatures without either the brains, brawn, or specialized equipment to be dangerous. However, there are those few forms that can be exceedingly dangerous, even deadly, by virtue of highly specialized apparatus and an extremely agonizing neurotoxin. Few, if any, venomous land forms can give so painful an injury. As it is with the snakes, most aren't dangerous; some few are. Beware the few.

A poisonous South American Catfish (*Acanthodoras spinossimus*).

From *Illustrated Dictionary of Tropical Fishes.*

## KNOWN VENOMOUS FISH OF THE WORLD

| Common Names | Scientific Name | Range | Remarks |
|---|---|---|---|
| Weever, Sea-Cat, Sand-Eel-Bill, Sting-bull, Adderpike, Black-fin, *Abo*, *Abobor*, plus many more. | *Trachinus araneus* | Portugal, Mediterranean, south along Atlantic coast of Africa. | Family Trachinidae—most dangerous temperate forms. |
| As above, plus *Foersing, Fjärsing, Petermännchen, Drachenfische, Ragno, Meerlam*, Great Weever, plus many more. | *T. draco* | Norway, British Isles, south to Mediterranean and coasts of Africa. | As above. |
| As above, plus many more. | *T. radiatus* | Mediterranean, south along west coast of Africa. | As above. |
| As above, plus Lesser Weever, plus many more. | *T. vipera* | North Sea, Europe, Atlantic coast, Mediterranean. | As above. |
| Spiny Dogfish | *Squalus acanthias* and spp. | North Atlantic and North Pacific. | Not very dangerous as reported. |
| Stingray, Whipray, Butterfly Ray, Bat Ray, Spotted Eagle Ray, and many more specific to species and area. | Seven families: *Dasyatidae Potamotrygonidae Gymnuridae Myliobatidae Rhinopteridae Mobulidae Urolophidae* | World-wide—all tropical, subtropical and coastal regions—specific to species, and in some tropical freshwater. | Indeterminate number of species; very large and important group. Some may cause fatal injuries. |
| *Chimaeras*, Elephant-fish, Ray Fish, King-of-the-Herrings. | *Chimaera* spp. *Hydrolagus* spp. | All temperate, tropical and subtropical Atlantic margins. West coast of U.S. | Painfully venomous. Probably not lethal. |

## KNOWN VENOMOUS FISH OF THE WORLD (*Continued*)

| Common Names | Scientific Name | Range | Remarks |
|---|---|---|---|
| Moray Eel | Gymnothorax spp. | All tropical and subtropical seas. | *Highly questionable* report of venomous bite. |
| Catfish, etc. | Many and various. | World-wide, fresh water and marine. | Over 1,000 species of many genera. Most only mildly venomous. Sting of some tropical forms *may* be deadly.* |
| Scorpion Fishes Family: *Scorpaenidae.* | Genera include: *Choridactylus, Emmydrichthys, Erosa, Hypodytes, Inimicus, Leptosynanceja, Minous, Pelor, synanceja, Scorpaena, Scorpaenopsis, Sebasticus, Sebastodes, Snyderina, Synanceja,* and others. See below. | Tropical and subtropical seas. Particularly Indo-Pacific complex. Into eastern Pacific. | Large group of most dangerous venomous fish. Include Stonefish as below. Some forms are lethal. |
| Stonefish | Synanceja verrucosa, S. horrida, S. trachynis. | Tropical Indo-Pacific—east coast of Africa, Red Sea, Indian Ocean, Australia, Philippines, etc. | One of the *Scorpaenidae.* MOST DANGEROUS FORM KNOWN. *DEADLY.* |
| Zebrafish, Lionfish, Butterfly Fish, Featherfish, Feather Fins, Dragonfish, Firefish, Stingfish, Butterfly Cod, plus many more. | Pterois volitans and others. | Tropical Indo-Pacific complex. | One of the *Scorpaenidae.* VERY DANGEROUS. *Possibly deadly.* |

* *Cataphractus* spp., a fresh-water, South American armored catfish is reputedly violently venomous, having conical spines under blade-like pectoral fins. Reputedly lethal.

| Common Names | Scientific Name | Range | Remarks |
|---|---|---|---|
| Rabbitfish | Family: *Siganidae* | East Africa to Central Pacific islands. | Painful, but not lethal. |
| Toadfish, *Munda*, Oysterfish, *Sapo*, and others—specific to species and area. | Family: *Batrachoididae*. Many genera. | Virtually global in tropical, subtropical and temperate coastal waters. Few fresh water and estuarine forms known. | Not lethal as reported. |
| Surgeonfish plus many more. | Family: *Acanthuridae* | Tropical. | Not known if venomous. Can inflict painful cuts with retractable lateral spine. |
| Star-Gazer plus many more. | Family: *Uranoscopidae* | Indo-Pacific and Atlantic complex. | Degree of venomousness not known. |
| Fortescue Waspfish | *Centropogon australis* and spp. | Australian coast. | Painful but not believed lethal. |
| Bullrout Sulky | *Notesthes robusta* and spp. | As above. | As above. |
| Red Rock Cod | *Ruboralga jacksoniensis* | As above. | As above. |
| Cobbler | *Gymnopistes marmoratus* and spp. | As above. | As above. |
| Spinefeet | *Amphacantus* spp. | As above. | As above. |
| Frogfish | *Halophryne* spp. | As above. | As above. |
| Bastard Stonefish | *Pseudobatrachus* spp. | As above. | As above. |

Note: Plus the following families: *Plotosidae*, *Tachysuridae*, *Siluridae* and others of which little is known. The preceding table is by no means complete, but does offer a cross-section of venomous fish distribution.

# CHAPTER 21

# *Some Other Fish*

THE WATERS of the world, fresh and salt, play host to a number of animals not yet discussed in this book which are potentially dangerous to man, at least on occasion. In this chapter, we will discuss the more significant of these.

Late in 1941, two native "keepers" in the Brazilian state of Amazonas were walking on a plank stretched across a large cement pool. Nobody seems to know precisely how it happened, but one end of the plank slipped from its mooring and the two men fell into the water. They were killed instantly. The pool contained a number of Electric Eels (*Electrophorus electricus*). These fishes had been collected at the request of Dr. Christopher W. Coates, Curator of the New York Aquarium, and Dr. David Nachmansohn, on assignment for the United States Army Chemical Corps. The greater part of the research in which they were engaged is still secret, but much of it had to do with finding an antidote for the devastating nerve gas "G" developed in Germany in the 1930's. The gas became available to Russia after the war and is still a matter for grave concern. The whole episode with the electric eels, and their subsequent transport to the United States, appears in retrospect to have been in the best tradition of a spy melodrama. Before it was over, at least one other man (an anti-Nazi German working on the project) was killed by the fishes.

The electric eel is not an eel at all. It was, until very recently, included in the family *Gymmotidae*, but, at the time of this writing, it is being put into a family of its own. It grows to a length of ten feet (eight feet is average for a large specimen), and can weigh as much as ninety pounds. It is decidedly eel-like in appearance, and is a fairly common shallow-fresh-water fish found in Brazil, Colombia, and Peru, at least and very possibly in surrounding areas. It has rudimentary gills that cannot sustain it under water and it will quickly drown if held under; it is strictly an air-breather, and is found only in fresh water. The electric eel releases a massive electrical discharge to compensate for the low conductivity of relatively salt-free waters. Blind at maturity, it undoubtedly uses these discharges for locating prey, as well as for stunning it, and also for protection. All truly electric fishes are believed to use their powers for one or more of four purposes; navigation, locating prey, obtaining prey, and self-defense.

256

Electric Eel (*Electrophorus electricus*), with the actual *body* delineated by fingers.
Fritz Goro.

There is no doubt that the Electric Eel (*Electrophorus*) is the most powerful and dangerous electric fish known. This South American river dweller can discharge 550 volts at one ampere. Average discharges run around 400 volts, although Dr. Coates told me he has personally measured as much as 650. These discharges come with a frequency as high as 400 per second, and, uniquely, the fish can keep it up for days, although the frequency of discharge drops as time passes. The fish is capable of killing a man on contact, and horses have been knocked out at a distance of twenty feet. It is probably the only electric fish capable of killing a full-grown man in good health.

The power of the electric eel comes from the fact that it has more special cells for the propagation of electricity than any other fish. More than one half of its body is given over to this one function. Since, as we have noted, the fish can reach 90 pounds, we have the potential of 45 pounds of electricity-generating apparatus! All vital organs of the fish are contained in the front 20 per cent of its body, and that part is strictly non-electric. The remaining 80 per cent of the fish is between 60 and 65 per cent electric and nothing else. Each cell in the special tissues produces $\frac{1}{10}$ of a volt, no matter what its size. This produces a paradox, whereby a specimen 6 inches long, producing 300 volts or more, is at its maximum electrical-production-per-unit-of-length stage. As the fish grows, the cells increase in size, but *not* in number or output. It is at this stage, approximately 6 inches, that the fish leaves the protection of the parents and goes on its own. At 6 inches, it is still able to see, but it loses this ability soon after. At no stage is the fish able to control its own voltage; but it can control the bursts of "trains" of its emissions, with ten or eleven discharges constituting a "train." In laboratory tests, these discharges continue 8 to 9 hours after death. When a specimen is electrically active, the discharge starts a point 20 per cent tailwards from the front end, and passes along the length of the animal running off at the tail tip. As one discharge sequence reaches the end of the tail, another is starting behind the head. This goes on as long as the animal is stimulated. A metal conductor attached to the two ends of the fish's electric tissue mass will cause a short circuit, making the discharges constant and uncontrollable and eventually killing the specimen.

When the electric eel is not stimulated it gives off a regular pulse of mild discharges used for navigation. When stimulated, the pulse shoots up to a peak and then, by controlling the rate of the discharge, the fish is able to cope with the situation, be it self-defense or food-getting. Strangely, the electric eel does not kill its prey (amphibians and other fishes, mainly) but stuns them. If they are dead, the eel will not touch them!

Fossil fishes have been found with what appears to have been tissue identical to the electricity-producing tissue of contemporary forms. Probably a very ancient refinement, the ability to generate electricity on demand is one of the most remarkable and bizarre developments in the animal kingdom. Since it is found, as we shall see, in a wide variety of different groups of fishes, and since it serves at least four separate functions, it is strange that, today, it is limited to probably no more than forty species. In fact, all animals, from the primitive worms to man, produce some electricity but, in all but the few electric fishes, this is an internal phenomenon—the nervous system. We feel, hear, smell, taste, see, move, and think electrically. Only fishes, because they live in a medium that is a natural conductor (and only a few fishes at that) are capable of transmitting this chemically-produced energy to the external world.

There are three separate organs involved; the *large electric organ*, the *bundles of Sachs,* and the *organs of Hunter.* There is no reversal of polarity; the head end is positive, the tail end negative. In marine forms polarity is ventral to dorsal (down to up), dorsal being positive. In the electric eel, the *large electric organ* is the main battery, the *bundles of Sachs* are for small single releases, probably for navigation. The chemical production of electricity within the cells and tissues of the fish has been intensively studied.[1]

---

[1] The interested reader will find some of the many technical papers that have been done on the subject listed in the Bibliography.

Electric Catfish (*Malapterurus electricus*).
From *Fishes and Their Ways of Life*.

Africa also has an Electric Catfish (*Malopterurus electricus*) that is found in both the Nile and Congo River complexes. The animal grows to a length of four feet and can weigh twenty pounds. The electric output probably doesn't exceed 90 volts, at a tenth of an ampère. It has a relatively small electric organ. The device is apparently defensive, the fish tires easily, and it cannot keep up a sequence of discharges long enough to seriously injure a man. Nevertheless, the form was known for its peculiar talent even to the ancients. Egyptian hieroglyphics dating to 4000 B.C. call it by the name, "He Who Releases Many," the implication being that fishermen hauling in nets in which a specimen was caught would get enough of a jolt to make them drop the nets and lose their catch. The fish is definitely not in the same class as the electric eel and I know of no human deaths. Contact must, however, be a somewhat startling experience.

The most powerful electric marine fish are undoubtedly the widely distributed Torpedo Rays (*Narcine* and *Torpedo* sp.). They are found all over the world in warm and temperate seas. The torpedo rays grow to a weight of 200 pounds and can give a discharge of 80 volts at high amperage. The relatively low voltage (when compared with the electric eel) is explained by the high-conductivity of salt water. The device is apparently protective and is strong enough to be dangerous. The danger factor is somewhat mitigated by the fact that the torpedo ray tires very quickly; ten to twenty discharges generally exhaust the animal. I know of no serious accidents with these animals, although 80 volts at high amperage offer good reason to avoid direct contact. For a person of advanced years, there are incipient dangers present here.

In dealing with the electric fish in general, there is no question of "disposition" or "chances of attack." These fishes do not "attack," they respond to stimulation in a perfectly predictable pattern and there is probably no group of animals in the world more predictable! An expert can draw a graph showing exactly how the fish's response will look on an oscilloscope when a man enters the water near it! To get near

Electric Ray (*Torpedo nobiliana*).
Courtesy of the Harvard Museum of Comparative Zoology.

one, in the water, or to touch one, is to be shocked. The intensity of that shock depends on species more than on size.

Of the world's thirty-five to forty electric fish, only the electric eel and the torpedo rays appear capable of injuring or killing a healthy man, and 95 per cent are entirely harmless. Deaths are known, but no possible means exist for estimating the number that may have actually occurred. Thus, there can be said to be a menace of the mildest proportions, only.

It was a President of the United States who first made the general public aware of a fish which may be the direct cause of more human deaths than any other. It was Theodore Roosevelt, quite naturally, and he told stories of "the most ferocious fish in the world" after a South American hunting-exploring trip. The fish was *Serrasalmus nattereri*, one of the piranhas. There are twenty or more closely-related species of fishes all known as *Piranha*, *Piranyas*, *Piris*, or *Pirai*, but only four appear to be particularly dangerous. *S. nattereri* grows to a length of nearly eleven inches, and travels in immense schools. It is the most widespread species and reportedly is responsible for more human deaths than any other. It is known to range through most of eastern and northern South America, as far south at least as Central Argentina. In the words of Dr. James Atz: ". . . it is prevalent enough to make swimming or wading an extremely risky pastime over about half an entire continent." Dr. Atz says further, "To all intents and purposes, it is *the* Piranha."

The Black Piranha (*S. niger*) is reportedly less savage (a permissible anthropomorphism since it refers not to the fish's attitude but to the effect on the human being), as is the fifteen-inch *Pirambeba* (*S. rhombeus*). The São Francisco River in eastern Brazil reportedly has a two-foot piranha or *pirai* of great ferocity. *S. spilopleura* is often accused of being a confirmed man-eater, but its range, like that of most piranhas, is crossed by that of *S. nattereri* and it is difficult indeed to get definitive estimates of danger by species.

When President Roosevelt's book, *Through the Brazilian Jungle*, first appeared, the piranha blossomed as the darling of the jungle writers; and little wonder, with this kind of send-off (in Roosevelt's words):

They belonged to one of the most formidable genera of fish in the world, the Piranha or Cannibal Fish, the fish that eats men when it can get the chance. . . . They are the most ferocious fish in the world. They will snap a finger off a hand incautiously trailed in the water; they mutilate swimmers—in every town

Brazilian Black Piranha (*Serrasalmus* sp.).
From *Living Fishes of the World.*

in Paraguay there are men who have been thus mutilated; they will rend and devour alive any wounded man or beast; for blood in the water excites them to madness.

The account continues in this vein and, with a few changes in punctuation, has appeared adjective-for-adjective in untold numbers of tales of jungle travel over the past decades.

The late William T. Innes, godfather of the home aquarists, described a movie taken of an attack. A young pig was dipped into a Brazilian stream several times. "Each time it was lifted out of the water, it was reduced in size." After two minutes, only the skeleton was left. I have seen two such films, one involving a bullock and the other supposedly a living human being. [In the latter case, a human skeleton did appear in the snapping frenzy caught by the motion-picture camera. I rather suspect a dead human body was used for the episode, although I do not know. Having had some motion-picture production experience, I am perhaps a little too suspicious. I rather believe that if a person were in such distressful circumstances, picture taking would be the last concern of his companions. I should like to think so, at least.]

Professor George S. Myers of Stanford described the piranha this way:

A fish only a foot long with teeth so sharp and jaws so strong that it can chop out a piece of flesh from a man or an alligator as neatly as a razor, or clip off a finger or toe, bone and all, with the dispatch of a meat cleaver. A fish afraid of nothing, which attacks any animal, whatever its size, like lightning! A fish which never attacks singly but always in schools of a hundred or a thousand. A fish which is actually attracted by splashing and commotion in the water! And a fish which, when it smells blood, turns into a raging demon! This is the piranha, feared as no other animal is feared throughout the whole length of South America.

Until quite recently, piranhas were imported alive into the United States and, although expensive, were sold to advanced home aquarists. The high price was a result of the fishes' cannibalistic nature. A can that would normally be used to ship a hundred smaller fishes had to be used for a single piranha. One to a can was the rule, because that was the count at the end of the trip, if not at the beginning. Now, I am told, there are Federal injunctions against the importation for sale of these creatures. It appears that some were known to have been liberated in our inland waterways and there was a mounting fear that they might become established. Bizarre behavior is known among man, to be sure, but the dumping of piranhas in a local lake certainly would appear to be extreme. It is a kind of fish we can do without, although several species are good eating, if somewhat bony. When it is a toss-up as to whether the angler eats the fish or the fish the angler, few sportsmen would protest being denied their fun. Nevertheless, the various species of piranha are common enough in home aquariums, for a rather large literature has grown up on their care. All such literature advises caution in their handling. More than one aquarist has been bitten, it is reported.

The piranha, or rather the several piranhas, have been so popular with popular writers since the days of Theodore Roosevelt that it is impossible to tell where fiction leaves off and fact begins. Everything seems to point toward acceptance of any and all claims. Indeed, while I know of no reason for not accepting them, except that I do not, of course, know them to be true, I do not know the name of a single victim nor a date, a place or a reliable witness to a piranha-caused human death. While there would appear to be no definite reason for discounting the claims so often heard, I bear in mind that when I began these researches there was no reason for discounting the equally horrific tales about the killer whale.

Of course, the piranha has been demonstrated to be a voracious carnivore. So has also the Killer Whale. The piranha is feared throughout its range. So is the Killer Whale. What, then, is our point? Simply this: the piranha is assumed to be exceedingly dangerous to man. A certain sameness is evident in all the claims made against this fish, so that all look as if they stemmed from a few early accounts by men like Theodore Roosevelt and have simply been repeated again and again. The danger is undoubtedly very great, and, in fact, the piranha may be the most dangerous fish in the world from the point of view of both potential and actual numbers of people injured and killed; but, it would be nice to see some valid eye-witness reports, without the tired old adjectives (five-to-the-line was an actual count in one article). In the meantime, anyone visiting an area where the various species of *Serrasalmus* abound might do well to exercise a great deal of caution.

The general name Barracuda is used for over twenty species of swift, carnivorous fish of the family *Sphyraenidae*. Many of the species are of little concern to the average swimmer, but one or two at least appear to have been implicated in authenticated attacks. The Great Barracuda (*Sphyraena barracuda*) grows to a length of eight feet and is reportedly very aggressive—on occasion. The mouth is huge and filled with particularly sharp teeth. The range of the species is world-wide, from Brazil to Florida, and from the Red Sea to the Hawaiian Islands, and encompasses a number of resort areas.

As for attacks on man, the International Oceanographic Foundation at the University of Miami has records that "show some thirty-one attacks which were either definitely proven to be by barracuda or were thought to be due to barracuda." Dr. Donald P. de Sylva, at The Marine Labora-

Barracuda (*Sphyraena barracuda*).     Fritz Goro.

tory at the University of Miami, did his doctoral dissertation at Cornell University on this subject and this paper included "a survey of the literature in which there were authenticated records of barracuda attacking human beings." I have not had an opportunity to study that paper, but Dr. de Sylva wrote to me in June, 1962, and said, "I have located about 33 of these which can be for the most part attributed to barracuda." He wrote further, "In general, the likelihood of being attacked by a barracuda is much smaller than that of being attacked by a shark. . . . However, there is always a small possibility that a barracuda will attack a human being. . . ." Since the paper was completed in 1958, Dr. de Sylva has learned of several new cases. One was recently reported from Pompano Beach, Florida.

As is noted in Appendix III, barracuda can be dangerous to eat and severe poisoning is not uncommon. Our concern in his chapter, however, is not barracuda-eating men, but just the opposite. It appears as if this sometimes does occur.

The barracuda is a particularly swift fish and strikes with great force. Its long, narrow jaws leave a wound quite distinct from the jagged u-shaped excavation accomplished by the sharks. A large barracuda, and certainly a five- to eight-foot specimen, could easily do enough damage in one bite to kill a man. Gross damage is generally the case in barracuda attacks, and shock is severe. Reports generally have a question mark attached, and a shark is frequently thought to be the offending animal by many, even when the barracuda is specified.

In 1922, Dorothy McClachie died from shock and loss of blood when she was attacked near the Municipal Pier at St. Petersburg, Florida. A barracuda was blamed for the attack, but the shape of the wound suggested a shark was involved. In July, 1953, twenty-six-year-old Mrs. D. F. Gunn was attacked at Juno Beach, Florida, and her left leg was almost severed between the ankle and the knee. She was standing in water only knee-deep at the time and a barracuda was blamed. An attack on Eleanor Nelson at Miami Beach in 1957 was blamed on the barracuda. Again, the victim was wading in shallow water.[2] In a paper in the *Journal of the American Medical Association* in 1928, Gudger and Breder said, "There is little doubt that the barracuda, of all marine fish, is the one most dangerous to man." Total amputations are characteristic of attack by large specimens, according to several researchers.

Bruce Wright made a study of "releasers of attack behavior pattern" in shark and barracuda and reviewed over ten thousand man hours in the water by divers in close proximity to these animals. His conclusions included the following statements:

1. Blood without movement did not release a feeding pattern in shark or barracuda in the Bahamas.
2. Fish blood and jerky, rapid movements released the attack pattern in both shark and barracuda.
3. Jerky, rapid movement alone released the attack pattern in both shark and barracuda.

He also observed: "A man in the water, alone or in a group, acting quietly and smoothly did not release the attack pattern."

It appears that barracuda respond to stimuli in very much the same way sharks do. There would appear to be steps that can be taken to reduce the likelihood of an attack:

1. Avoid murky water. You are not as apt to spot the fish, and the fish is not as apt to get a clear idea of what you are. It appears that barracuda do not have particularly keen eyesight and a movement in murky water might invite an attack that would not occur in clear water where the fish could get a good estimate of your size.
2. Do not wear flashy metallic swim suits or gear. A flashing object that can catch and reflect light in an irregular pattern might appear to the fish to be the silver belly of a food fish. Think in terms of the silver lure you would use if fishing. Don't be a lure yourself.
3. Never tow speared fish along with you. The blood they trail, and their convulsive movements, will attract predators. Even if the fish are dead, their smell and your movements can combine to spell disaster.
4. Don't molest any fish that can obviously be dangerous if aroused. Spearing 'cuda is a popular sport in some areas, but it is patently a dangerous one and should never be engaged in without a full awareness of the very real hazards involved.
5. There are hundreds of reports of swimmers and divers working and playing around barracuda without suffering harm. Don't be misled. Attacks have

[2] Pablo Bush Romero, doyen of Mexican skin-divers, reports a man had the flesh stripped off one leg while standing in water only a foot deep near the town of Tancah on the Quintana Roo coast of Mexico, in November, 1962. A Barracuda was seen to be the offending animal. It was the second incident in that area.

evidently occurred and will surely occur again. If you elect to go into the water where barracuda are known to be around, be prepared for trouble. It can occur, and, as is the case with sharks, it is not possible to predict the outcome with accuracy enough to eliminate risk. The best swimmer or diver in the world is clumsy and inept when compared with a barracuda. When and if the attack does occur, it will not only be at the fish's election, but at its advantage. A man and a barracuda in the water are not equal adversaries.

6. Beware of large solitary specimens. School barracuda (the schools are sometimes vast and dense), are seldom if ever implicated in attacks on man.

The big barracuda, although apparently less prone to attack man than some species of sharks, are dangerous enough when they do attack, and so unfathomable in their response patterns as to justify extreme caution in all dealings with them. Someday, a great deal more will be known about them than is known now and at that time, perhaps, some definitive guide lines will be drawn up. In the meantime, anyone exposed to the pike-like barracuda, particularly the large solitary animals (*S. barracuda* and *S. jello*) as opposed to the smaller school fish, should recognize that among the possible eventualities is sudden death.

Like the barracuda, the Moray Eels are responsible for many cases of severe poisoning when they are used for human consumption. Here the similarity stops since unprovoked attacks on man are all but unknown. Members of the family *Muraenidae*, Morays are confined to tropical and subtropical seas, for the most part. There are several species found in temperate waters, but they are seldom involved in incidents with human beings.

Blackedge Moray (*Gymnothorax nigromarginatus*). Ernest Libby.

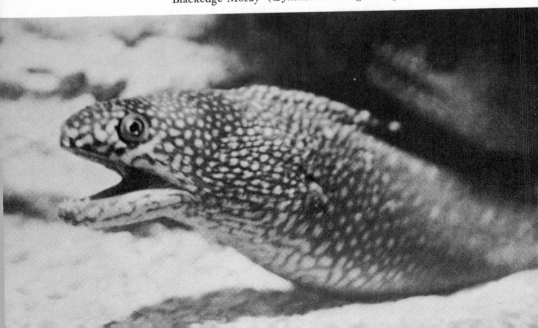

Morays can achieve a length of ten feet in some species. There are about forty species world-wide, those in the genera *Muraena* and *Gymnothorax* reaching the greatest size and offering the most profound threat. They are all bottom dwellers and are seldom found far from cover. Coral reefs, old wrecks, and similar bottom rubble offer the caves and crevices ideal to their way of life. They remain hidden from view most of the time, waiting for prey to come close enough to be grabbed. Occasionally, one will be spotted undulating along the bottom, snakelike in sinuous movement. They are extremely muscular and slippery and grasping one with bare hands is all but impossible. Their jaws are immensely powerful and their teeth sharp, numerous, incurved, and designed for grasping and tearing. They are very numerous in some reef areas where they establish territories that they defend vigorously. The threat they offer to man is involved with these territorial claims. Quite simply, anyone intruding on the territory of a moray eel with hand or foot is apt to be severely bitten. Reaching into a crevice or stepping close to a coral cave inhabited by a large moray can result in hospitalization. The bite is deep, crushing, and tenacious.

Contrary to a thousand-and-one reports, the moray's bite has never been demonstrated to be venomous. It is extremely unlikely that any species of moray eel is equipped with venom glands, although the bite is frequently filthy and can result in gross infection.

Moray eels are not known to hunt man. They strike out, much as venomous snakes do, in defense of their privacy. Accidents with these animals can be dangerously damaging but are undoubtedly always the result of carelessness. I know of no human deaths caused by these animals.

A number of reporters have suggested that the Giant Groupers or Sea Bass (family *Serranidae*) have caused human injuries or worse. They are bold fishes with monumental appetites, are generally quite curious, and they can weigh a quarter of a ton or more. Presumably, someone might get bitten, but I know of very few cases of consequence. The Australian Council for Scientific and Industrial Research uses the word "vicious" to describe huge tropical groupers of the genus *Promicrops*. Some care would seem to be indicated on the part of skin-divers.[3]

Fish and Cobb quote Whitley as saying of the Australian Black Rock

[3] The *Sydney Morning Herald* (November 30, 1943) reports salvage divers repeatedly attacked by Groupers attracted by the shiny helmets. One fish engulfed an entire helmet and made off with the diver. The man's rescue came just in time. The magazine *Australian Outdoors* (July 1955) carries accounts of attacks. The Brisbane Department of Harbours and Marine says, "It is thought that the mysterious loss of some native divers of the Torres Strait pearling fleets was due to groupers," in their "Know Your Fishes." There are, perhaps, another half dozen such references.

A Grouper (*Cephalopholis* sp.).

Ed Fisher, The Marine Laboratory, University of Miami.

Cod or Giant Sea Bass (*Epinephelus forsythi*), ". . . a savage species and several of us were rushed by them as we waded on Middleton Reef and we had to beat them off." Apparently, some large fish, although generally inoffensive, will on occasion see a man as food. Danger would seem to be slight with most species when compared to those other forms known by repeated demonstration to be man-eaters.

In 1930, Dr. R. Biddle, in the *Journal of the Royal Navy Medical Service,* reported that two species of East Indian Puffers (*Tetraodon fluviatilis* and *Spheroides oblongus*) are not only poisonous to eat but have a particularly disconcerting habit as concerns waders and swimmers; they attack and bite the genital organs. Similar reports about one or the other of these species come from the Philippines, Malaya, China, and several other areas. In light of certain known facts about other fishes, this strange accusation may be valid.

Certain minute parasitic catfish of the family *Trichomycteridae* (called Pygidiids until recently) have a strange affinity for human (and other animal) urine and thus the urogenital openings of both men and women. This truly bizarre behavior constitutes a very real hazard in many South American rivers and streams. The species *Vandellia cirrhosa*, known as the *Candiru,* is chiefly involved, but others may also be.

These small (2½ inches), scaleless fish, not much thicker than a pencil lead, are quipped with erectile, rear-pointing spines and these they use once they enter the urethra of a bather. The pain, as one might suspect, is agonizing and, unless surgery is immediately available, the results can prove fatal. Bathers in streams where the infamous *Candiru* abound generally wear tight protective clothing over the genitalia.

The Candiru (*Vandellia cirrhosa*).

After Cuvier and Valenciennes.

I am yet to encounter a satisfactory explanation of why certain Asiatic puffers might attack the genitalia, or why these South American catfish attempt to take up residence in the urethra or bladder. Indeed, the two phenomena may have nothing whatsoever to do with each other, or may be related only on grounds of affinity for urine or the odor thereof. The hazard in the latter case is apparently very real, although I do not know of a specific victim. Perhaps, as is our practice in this book, we should say it is reportedly real, but the records of hospitals in the Guianas and Amazonas are rich in case histories which substantiate the very real danger of an unguarded encounter with one of these strange little parasites.

John E. Randall of The Marine Laboratory of the University of Miami did considerable research on the bizarre behavior of the various Houndfish or Needlefish (*Strongylura*). He refers to them as "living javelins." These fish are surface feeders, more active at night, and can achieve a length of nearly five feet and a weight of ten to twelve pounds. When excited, confused, or otherwise overstimulated, they swim at great speeds and leap clear of the water. In 1959, Clyde Mitchell of Homestead, Florida, received a deep neck wound apparently when struck by a needlefish, although the newspapers reported an attack by a barracuda. In 1936, a wader had a needlefish ram its beak clear through his neck. In 1953, twenty-year-old Lorelei Sullivan was rammed on the side of her nose near the corner of her eye. A piece of the fish's beak was removed surgically at Miami's Mount Sinai Hospital. Captain William B. Gray of the Miami Seaquarium was pinned to his boat when a needlefish ran him through the leg. *Pacific Islands Monthly* of June, 1958, carried a report of a Papuan killed when his jugular vein was punctured. *Collier's* of January, 1948, reported two more deaths near Acapulco, Mexico. Randall learned of another death in Tahiti. All of these cases are reported by Dr. Randall in his article "The Living Javelin," in *Sea Frontiers* magazine for November, 1960.

The needlefish may be confused by or attracted to light, as most "attacks" occur at night and on men fishing with lanterns. The incidents do not really constitute attacks as much as they do collisions. The danger,

Needlefish (*Potomorrhaphis guianensis*).
From *Living Fishes of the World*.

however, appears to be real enough and fishing at night, with lights, in an area where needlefish are common would appear to be safer with a protective shield between the fisherman and his lantern.

On November 16, 1962, the Associated Press office in Tokyo, reported that two ships were speeding to the rescue of the fifteen-man crew of the 39-ton *Genyo Maru*. It seems that a swordfish rammed the vessel midships and she was sinking!

The *U.S.N.S. Mission Capistrano* was conducting acoustical research not far south of Bermuda in 1962 when her instrumental lines were viciously attacked by a 300-pound Swordfish (*Xiphias*). The animal rammed its spear about a foot into tightly braided line. When the line was pulled aboard, not even the fish's 300 pounds pulled it loose as it hung suspended above the water. The whole performance suggests great force and commendable accuracy on the part of the fish.

There are many more such reports of various billed or beaked fish[4] becoming involved with human beings, or their enterprises. Dories get run through in dozens of reports. Whether or not 39-ton vessels are really sunk by these animals is somewhat difficult to determine, but they certainly are powerful creatures with a formidable weapon. It is a fact

[4] Black Marlin, Blue Marlin, Pacific Blue Marlin, Silver Marlin, Striped Marlin, White Marlin, Atlantic Sailfish, Pacific Sailfish, and Swordfish.

that crew members on big game fish charter boats are careful when handling hooked specimens. More than one man has been badly injured when he misjudged the direction of an infuriated captive's lunge.

The big fish with beaks are in far more danger from man than man is from them. Care is suggested, however, when live specimens are handled or otherwise encountered. They are huge and powerful animals.[5]

The seas and oceans cover nearly three-fourths of our planet. When the ponds, streams, lakes, rivers, and swamps are added, a vast area is found to be under water. Much of this water teems with life in seemingly endless variety. Some of these forms grow to be very large, many are equipped for self-defense with very real weapons, and some are prone to attack. From time to time, from place to place, there is bound to be a measure of hazard. It is wrong, though, to think of the world of water as a totally hostile environment. It makes good sense to be careful and to know the ways of the forms encountered in the pursuit of individual enterprises. While common sense won't keep a needlefish from jumping out and impaling you, it will go a long, long way towards reducing whatever hazards do exist.

[5] The Black Marlin (*Makaira*) is known to exceed 1,500 pounds and 14 feet. The Pacific Sailfish (*Istiophorus greyi*) can exceed 10 feet and 225 pounds. The International Game Fish Association's record Swordfish (*Xiphias gladius*) is 1,182 pounds, 14 feet, 11¼ inches.

# PART VI

## The Invertebrates

# CHAPTER 22

## *Insects*

THE INSECTS of the world outnumber the mammals both in variety and numbers by a margin that is absolutely astounding. There are more species of insects than all other animal and plant species combined. Insects outnumber us in numbers to a degree that is quite impossible to comprehend; they even *outweigh* man. There are probably more insects in ten square miles of Arctic tundra than there are mammals in all of North America. There are probably places where one square mile would satisfy this claim.

The insect is the dominant life form on our planet. We need them to pollinate plants on which we depend, but they need us for nothing, although they use us mercilessly. We kill them by the billions but can't make a dent in their strength, while they make human habitation impossible, or at least extremely difficult, in vast areas of badly needed land surface. In relation to over-all world population, they kill more of us than we do of them each year. While it is true the majority of human deaths resulting from insects are due to diseases they transmit in the form of microorganisms, many insects are capable of causing sickness and death directly—in the first person.

The earliest known insects appear more than 305,000,000 years ago; how much more we cannot say because these frail creatures do not fossilize well. Maintaining certain basic characteristics (antennae, six legs, fourteen post-cephalic segments, etc.) they diversified and specialized until today there are somewhere between a half and three quarters of a million known species. It is only possible to guess at the numbers left to be described but there are, at the very least, tens of thousands. The range of this subphylum is universal; some insects are marine and live entirely in the sea, no desert is known to be without them, and a wingless, degenerate mosquito is the largest land animal on the six-million-square-mile Antarctic continent. Man knows no natural environment not known better and longer by insects. They utilize every imaginable form of food, reproduce at a rate almost impossible to believe, and are terribly destructive. Indeed, they have inherited the earth!

There is a great temptation to refer to the social structures of many insect forms (they exceed in complexity even the societies of man) but we have to be realistic and refrain. In plain fact, just about all we can

A Deer-fly (*Tabanus* sp.).
U.S. Department of Agriculture.

do is to pick examples of the particularly dangerous or harmful types of insects and examine their potential threat. We must do this in rather random fashion and the reader must not look on this chapter as in any way a comprehensive study of insects. It is indicative only of known troublesome groups, and those which *directly* cause injury or death.

The order *Diptera*, the fourth-largest of the insect orders, contains more than 60,000 species. Best known are the various gnats, flies, and mosquitoes. We need not enlarge on the fact that some hundreds of the

A Mosquito (*Culex* sp.).
Walther Rohdich (via Frank Lane).

Screw Worm fly (*Callitroga americana*).

U.S. Department of Agriculture.

species in this order carry disease, often lethally so. *Simulium columbaczense*, a gnat of Central Europe, reportedly causes death by attacking persistently in swarms and entering body orifices. Death, however, probably follows a generally weaked condition from blood loss. The *Potu* of the Himalayas (*S. pecuarum*) is about as bad, and the species of the Canadian tundra have kept the Indian inhabitants there in a state of virtual shock for generations. The constant irritation and blood loss have depressed these races of man until they are often like automatons. Reports from officials who visit these regions read like accounts of visits to other planets.

In some areas, swarms of mosquitoes are so thick that people are blinded by them and perish. Fliers downed in mangrove swamps are believed to have suffered such a fate. Many people are allergic to the "sting" of the mosquito and suffer terribly.

The True Flies of the world (*Diptera*) are carriers of disease as well as suckers of blood. They are found everywhere man is found and constitute an ever-present menace. Vast areas in Africa are considered uninhabitable because of flies of the genus *Glossina*—the Tsetse Fly, carriers of the dreaded sleeping sickness. With its permanent damage to the nervous system, the disease is one of the greatest deterrents to progress in vast areas in Africa.

There are many species of parasitic and obnoxious biting flies that make areas in South America virtually uninhabitable. Blood poisoning is not an uncommon result of the continued bites of many species.

Many species of flies are extremely damaging to eyesight and blindness is directly attributable to them in many parts of the world. As for the obnoxious qualities of certain flies, ask any New Englander about the black fly that frequents beach areas. Their bites can all but drive you wild and infections are common. The *No-see-ums* of American Indian fame are another group out of hundreds that harass man on every continent except Antarctica. In plain fact, if I were to choose the group of animals, out of all the animals in the world, that was most consistently dangerous to man, I would choose flies. They bite, they are parasites, and they spread many diseases—at least forty seriously damaging to man!

The Screwworm Fly (*Callitroga americana*) invades the nasal passages of humans, bores into the tissues, and there deposits its eggs. "The developing larvae inflict serious injury which often results in death in a matter of days."[1] The eyes, ears, and mouth are also attacked. Mortality is reportedly as high as 13 per cent. One case will serve to illustrate the nature of this unfortunate affliction: An itinerant laborer was hospitalized in Texas with a temperature of 103 degrees. Examination revealed that the patient's nose and throat were infested with mature larvae. Nearly two hundred were removed. This particularly distasteful problem is not as rare as might be thought. In the southwestern United States it is a real health menace, and undoubtedly much more so in tropical parts of the world with the other species involved.

[1] Quoted from Dr. D. W. Micks and Dr. Victor C. Calma, "Nasal Myiasis of Man Due to the Screwworm Fly."

Kissing Bugs (*Reduviidae*).

From *Handbook of Pest Control.*

Puss Moth Caterpillar
(*Erura scitiscripta*).
From *Living Insects of the World*.

Conenose Bugs (*Triatoma sp.*, also the Kissing Bug, Bellow's Bug, Walpai Tiger, Cross Bug, and others) are suckers of blood and will feed on human beings. About 5 per cent of the people bitten develop severe allergic reactions that include symptoms up to and including shock and coma. Other species of the Kissing Bug group (family *Reduviidae*) from tropical areas are reported to be much more offensive, and appear to be disease carriers as well. These forms seldom attack people while they are awake but move in to feed after dark. Like scorpions, they often hide in bedding during the day.

Strangely enough, there are a number of moths that are quite troublesome to man in the caterpillar stage, if not the adult. In July, 1961, the National Safety Council warned, "*Caterpillar is Health Menace.*" The article reported that there were 2,130 reported stings in southeastern Texas alone in the summer of 1958. In 54 Texas victims in 16 cities, Dr. Micks found 80 per cent to have been involved with *Megalopyge opercularis*, the caterpillar of the Puss Moth or Tree Asp. Reactions to contact ranged from a slight rash to shock. Fainting, nausea, and vomiting were common. Severe shooting pains were noted in a number of cases. Far from Texas—in Europe, Africa, and Asia—other species of moth and caterpillar cause distress to thousands annually. *Automeris io, Euproctis sp., Suana concolor*, and *Dendrolimus sp.* are a few of the species known to have been involved.

Although I have never heard of a human death from contact with a caterpillar, and although most species are perfectly harmless, some few can variously annoy or disable even healthy adults. Individual sensitivity is the determining factor, whether you get a slight rash or end up in an oxygen tent in a hospital. The venom of the caterpillar is administered by sharp little hairlike structures concealed in its "wool." Each hair has its own venom supply, often only a single cell, and contact is enough

Caterpillar of a South American Emperor Moth (*Automeris* sp.).

From *Living Insects of the World.*

to cause envenomation. The symptoms, as suggested above, run the gamut, as do degrees of sensitivity, which is apparently increased by exposure in any one victim.

Writing of the Bushmen of Africa's Kalahari Desert, in the June, 1963, *National Geographic,* Elizabeth Marshall Thomas captioned a photograph of an arrow:

Crushing a beetle pupa, a hunter rubs its juice behind the arrowhead. One drop kills a man if it enters the bloodstream.

The beetle involved was *Diamphidia simplex* and the pupae are found encased in earth beneath infested Marula trees. So powerful a toxin would suggest further research into the order *Coleoptera,* or the beetles. This is the largest order of insects and some specialists place the number of species at a quarter of a million. Much remains to be learned about this group generally and, if the story of the *Diamphidia* pupa is correct, the investigation may prove to be both exciting and medically worthwhile.

Our discussion of insects dangerous to man in the first person has been limited thus far to the minor kinds, but now we must look to the true villains—the order *Hymenoptera*—the social insects such as the ants, the wasps, hornets, bees, and their allies.

The ants of the world (superfamily *Formicoidea*) are among the most amazing creatures known to our planet. Their social organizations are as complex as any on earth, their varieties seemingly endless, and their numbers astronomical. The destructive capabilities of ants can be positively cyclonic in effect, and their economic significance is thus immense. The army ants of the New World and the Driver Ants (subfamily *Dorylinae*) of Africa are much feared, and gruesome and improbable stories of their forays are endless.

The African forms particularly are reputed to be lethal; literally consuming everything in their path as they emigrate from one breeding ground to another. It is easy to see how humans *could* be consumed if overrun and borne down by hundreds of thousands of these biting insects but I have been unable to obtain any documented evidence of this having occurred. In South America, the appearance of a column of Army Ants (*Eciton burchelli*) is reputedly welcomed by the natives, who evacuate the area temporarily and then return to homes free of vermin.

The marching-wandering of these ant columns of various species is apparently cyclic, with static periods intervening between nomadic exoduses. The timing is believed to be a matter of ovaries and not of appetite. The ripening of the queen triggers a wave of stimuli that cause the wandering to stop long enough for a cycle of egg-laying and hatching. Once the column is on the move again, everything before it must flee or be consumed. It seems likely that a wounded hunter, an abandoned child, a feeble old-timer (or an enemy staked out for the purpose!) must, from time to time, have fallen victim somewhere along the line. The study of these foraging hordes is fascinating, and not the least interesting aspect of it is the idea that, in special conditions, they are possibly dangerous to man.

Many reports indicate that some South American species split their columns into what amounts to a pincer movement. Caught in the middle of such a maneuver any animal not covered with extremely dense fur would be in serious difficulties. The African Driver Ants, on the other hand, move on fronts up to two miles wide, according to a number of reports, and the line may be several miles long. These millions upon millions of *Bashukoy*, as they are called in some areas, constitute a formidable problem for humans in their path. Since these movements are usually nocturnal, serious problems to human inhabitants almost certainly arise. Reports from the Cameroons are particularly common.

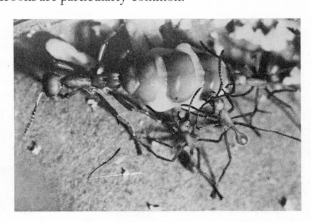

Army Ant (*Eciton hamatum*)—"Queen" with "Nurses."

From *Living Insects of the World*.

Fire Ant (*Solenopsis saevissima*).
U.S. Department of Agriculture.

A number of ants (notably of the genus *Solenopsis* in the United States) give a very painful bite. They can be a real handicap to agricultural field workers. Tropical Fire Ants,[2] the Australian Bulldog Ant, and dozens more can give a vicious bite and also sting brutally.

Dr. D. W. Micks has been conducting a study in Texas of insects and other arthropods of medical importance. A report covering a five-year period (1954–59) appeared in a 1960 issue of *Texas Reports on Biology and Medicine*. On ants, Dr. Micks reported:

Twenty-five physicians in twenty-one communities treated a total of seventy-five cases of ant sting. Twenty-seven of these patients were stung by a large red ant, two by Fire Ants and the identity of the remainder is unknown. . . . Twelve (16 per cent) of the . . . cases were characterized by systemic responses to the sting. Anaphylactic shock was the most prominent feature in five . . . and was accompanied in three instances by asthmatic rales, edema of the face, lips and glottis, and a massive generalized urticarial reaction. Fainting and/or vomiting, abdominal cramping . . . were present in the remaining cases. . . .

For *some* people, at least, the sting of ants may be a dangerous matter.

In his *A Textbook of Pathology*, Robert A. Moore commented:

In an occasional person bitten by a bee or a wasp, death results within 30 minutes, frequently within 5 minutes. At autopsy there are edema of the lungs and petechiae in the adrenal and in the serous membranes.

Writing of his adventures in the forests of India, Kenneth Anderson noted in 1961:

Twice more we cross the stream that snakes alongside the track. At the eighth milestone we pass the hamlet of Kundukottai, overshadowed by a rocky

---

[2] Stinging Argentine Fire Ants are now endemic in a dozen states in the South, where they cause great damage and are impossible to eradicate.

A. Male
B. Female

A                               B

Yellow Jacket (*Vespa communis*).

General Biological Supply House, Inc.

hill noted for two things—panthers and the large rock-bee. And remember that of these the bees are far more dangerous when really roused.

The story can be told in plain statistics: during the years 1950–54, 71 people in the United States were killed by venomous snakes while 86 were killed by hymenopterous insects—1 by ants, and 85 by bees, wasps, and hornets. Bees alone accounted for 52. Only 3 of the 71 snakebite victims died in the first hour while 66 of the 86 *Hymenoptera* victims did. The American Medical Association reports that bees and wasps claim a minimum of 17 lives a year in the United States alone. One researcher (Dr. Henry M. Parrish) believes many deaths from poisonous stings are erroneously attributed to heart attacks, heat stroke, and other causes. It has been suggested a number of times that otherwise unac-countable automobile accidents, unfortunate cases where cars traveling normally suddenly go out of control and crash into bridge abutments, etc., are actually caused by drivers going into shock after being stung by a wasp or bee.

No matter how you approach the subject, medically, statistically, or otherwise, bees, wasps, and hornets can be dangerous to man. Spiders, scorpions, and reptiles combined fail to take as many lives in most years in the United States as these diminutive creatures. Many times as many people suffer agonizing pain as actually succumb.

The very large, yellow and black *Geting* of Sweden, a wasp, is reputed to give an extremely painful sting. The giant red bee, found over much of South America, is said to kill even the mighty jaguar. Similar reports come from all over the world, especially tropical regions.

Most people suffer a bee sting sooner or later, and it may be difficult for a person not particularly sensitive to the venom to understand all the fuss over such a seemingly simple occurrence. First of all, it is not a simple matter. A small wasp or bee, weighing less than $\frac{1}{100}$ of an ounce, injects a relatively large dose of dangerous matter. An acid gland supplies inflammatory and stupefying substances, and alkaline glands produce a convulsant factor and various enzymes, and then there is the poison sac itself. This mixture of glandular substances is injected through two hollow shafts. Formic acid is also present. The venom alone is powerful enough to account for the severe local and general reactions. There is considerable variation between the venoms of different species of *Hymenoptera* so that some people are sensitive to certain species but not to others. The pharmacological action of some of these hymenopteral venoms is similar to that of cobra venom.

An example of a reaction will illustrate the severity that can be encountered: In 1960, an adult male was stung by two wasps in Baltimore, Maryland, once on the face and once on the neck. Eight hours later he had a temperature of 105 degrees and had become mentally disoriented. His limbs were twitching by the time he was brought to the hospital. Despite all emergency and follow-up treatment available, it was seven

Honey Bee (*Apis mellifera*).

U.S. Department of Agriculture.

days before his fever could be cracked and before his mentality started to improve. He was one of the *lucky* sensitives—he might have died.

Even for persons not particularly sensitive, the danger can be very real. Note the following medical report extracted from an article by M. F. Koszalka in the *Bulletin of the U.S. Army Medical Department:*

A patient, a 25-year-old officer, had received innumerable bee stings after he jumped off a ledge during a scout patrol and landed in the midst of a swarm of bees. He tried to scramble away as thousands of bees began to sting him and crawl over his body, into his ears, nose and mouth, but he fell to the ground from exhaustion and lost consciousness. When he came to, he was violently ill, with vomiting and urinary and fecal incontinence. Bees were still swarming over him and he was too weak to move. He was found several hours later . . . on admission his temperature was 101.8 . . . all exposed surfaces of his body were inflamed . . . and covered with bee stingers . . . unable to open his eyes, could barely speak, and complained of constricting pain in his throat. His urine was red brown . . . over 300 stingers were extracted from the patient's eyelids, ears, tongue, lips, face, neck and the backs of the hands and wrists; another 300 from the diffusely swollen scalp.

The patient described above obviously was not very sensitive or he could never have survived his fearful experience.

In many parts of the world (Malaya, India, and Africa) there are bees and hornets which are extremely aggressive. It is all but impossible to work in their vicinity without being attacked, and that first, burning stab can be the least important aspect of the sting, as we have seen. In other parts of the world, stings are rare and of little concern to all but the most hypersensitive. It is true that bees, hornets, and wasps, when aroused, will chase and attack a man, singly or in swarms. Pursuit can be relentless and the danger great.

The bees of the world are of enormous importance. Some experts believe that their underground activity in many areas does more to loosen, mix, and aerate soil than the labors of earthworms! Many of the plants most important to man are dependent on bees for pollination. Parasitic wasps are one of the best natural controls of many plant-eating pests. The production of honey and wax and their subsequent uses by man are well known. Life on this planet would be unthinkable without bees and wasps, so here at least is one dangerous animal group we must learn to live with.

We shall always have bees, wasps, and hornets around us. They are important and, for the most part, not particularly harmful. Anyone can be careful in his dealings with wasp nests or beehives. People who suspect themselves of sensitivity should see a doctor, determine the degree of that sensitivity, learn the problem it poses, and inquire about the possibility of desensitization.

The millions of billions of insects on this planet (harmless, destructive, and dangerous alike) pose one of the greatest enigmas facing man in his unending effort to control his environment. He may one day (indeed, unfortunately he probably will!) kill every bear, wolf, and big cat left in the wild, but at the very, very best, man can only strive for a livable balance with the insects.

# CHAPTER 23

# *Spiders and Scorpions*

ARTHROPODA, a phylum of the animal kingdom of the utmost importance to man, is a vast network of life, including as it does the Insects, Arachnids, Crustaceans, Centipedes, and several other related forms.

The arachnids encompass a wide variety of forms, including the scorpions, the spiders, mites, ticks, harvestmen, and a number of less common types. The mites and ticks are important to man because they are often vectors of infectious disease. Relapsing fever, typhus, scrub typhus, and Rocky Mountain spotted fever are among the known disabilities that are carried by these animals. The animals themselves, however, are harmless to man. Only the microorganisms they play host to can kill our kind; and so, by the frame of reference we have established for this book, we must pass them by. The spiders and scorpions, on the other hand, can be dangerous in the first person by reason of the venoms with which they are equipped.

*Arachnidism* is most properly defined as poisoning or envenomation caused by the bite or sting of a venomous arachnid. Only spiders and scorpions, among the arachnids, and only relatively few of them, have been properly demonstrated to be dangerously venomous to man under normal circumstances. The bites of certain other arachnids may be extremely dangerous to some few persons, but the reactions, however drastic, are best described as allergic.

Arachnids lack the insects' paired wings, and are without the antenna system so characteristic of the class *Insecta*. All are air-breathing, and their distribution falls barely short of universal. The spiders alone range from high airborne altitudes, where they have been caught, windblown, in the scoops attached to the wings of aircraft, to the littoral zones of the sea, into the shallow depths of which they descend, taking captive air down with them in bubbles. They are an ancient, adaptable, rapidly reproducing, and altogether successful animal group.

The true spiders belong to the order *Araneae*, although the Daddy Longlegs, or Harvestmen (order *Phalangida*), and the so-called Sun Spiders (order *Solpugida*) are popularly thought of as spiders as well; just as spiders in general are popularly and erroneously thought of as insects, or "bugs." The distinction is quite real, however, and no spider, true or otherwise, is an insect in any sense of the word.

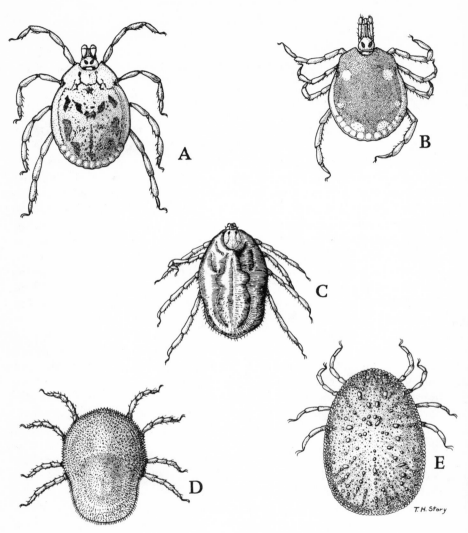

Ticks.

General Biological Supply House, Inc.

A. Dermacentor venustus (andersoni)
   (Rocky Mountain Spotted Fever
   Tick)
B. Amblyomma americanus (Lone Star
   Tick)

C. Boophilus annulatus (Cattle Tick)
D. Ornithodoros megnini (Spinose Ear
   Tick)
E. Argas persicus (Fowl Tick)

*All spiders are venomous*—that is how they paralyze and kill their prey, which is often very much larger than themselves. Very few spiders, however, have fangs long enough, or venom toxic enough, to endanger the health of man. Very few can administer a bite anywhere near as dangerous or painful as the sting of a wasp or bee. Some few, as we shall see, can be exceedingly dangerous.

Spiders have the power to give people the creeps second only, perhaps to snakes. They are feared and hated far beyond their power to do harm. As a matter of plain fact, they are exceedingly useful animals, doing infinitely more good than harm. They are predators and live almost exclusively on insects. With the well-publicized exceptions of the few dangerously venomous forms, they do no harm. They destroy nothing, and in no way compete with man for food. They constitute an extremely useful natural control of insects. However, those few that are capable of injuring man are well worth avoiding. The agonizing pain and rigid muscle cramps that follow their bites contribute to one of the most agonizing experiences man can undergo.

In the United States, the genus *Latrodectus* is the group which contains the species potentially most lethal to man. First and foremost is the Black Widow (*L. mactans*). The female of the species is the deadly one, and the bite, while seldom fatal, is excruciatingly painful, from all reports. It is rather like getting a Charley horse all through the extremities, and the abdomen. The species is well distributed throughout the United States, being more common in the rural South than elsewhere, and extends down through Mexico and Central America into South America. It is known in every state in the Union and is more than common on vacant lots in all big cities, like New York. Many of the islands of the West Indies have them, as do the Hawaiian Islands. Close relatives give rise to problems of human injury, but rarely death, in areas around the world: *L. tredecimguttatus* in the Mediterranean periphery, *L. hasselti* in Australia, New Zealand, New Caledonia and other South Pacific Islands, and *L. indistinctus* in South Africa are examples of troublesome species.

In their excellent study, *The Black Widow: America's Most Poisonous Spider*, Thorp and Woodson list all of the known cases of injuries and deaths caused by the black widow in the United States between 1726 and 1943. In that 218-year period there were recorded 1,291 bites, 55 of which were known to have proved fatal. The list is almost certainly incomplete. Two subspecies were involved in the cases recorded.

There appear to be three subspecies of the Black Widow in the United States (*L. m. mactans, m. texanus* and *m. hesperus*) and there may be a difference in toxicity, but the general effect and the mechanism of the bite are the same. The venom is produced in glands in the cephalo-thorax, and passes by exceedingly slender ducts running through the upper segments of the chelicerae into the two fangs. The venom is introduced by a stab, not a sting or a bite, as no jaw mechanism is involved—the spiders' mouthparts are devised for sucking.

The Black Widow is essentially (but *not* exclusively) a rural animal and there are bound to be more bites in underdeveloped areas where plumbing is more primitive. The little house with the half-moon cut into the door is a favorite haunt of the Shoe-Button, as the Black Widow is often called. It is a small, shiny black creature with a bright red mark, often in the shape of a perfect hourglass, on the underside of the larger segment of the body.

The Black Widow is not a deliberate foe of man. In fact, it is shy and retiring like most spiders and will seldom seek issue. If trapped in

Black Widow Spider (*Latrodectus mactans*).
From *The Lower Animals*.

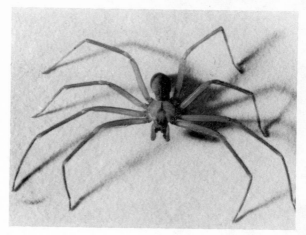

The Brown Recluse Spider (*Loxosceles reclusa*).
Courtesy of Dr. Don W. Micks, University of Texas.

your shoe by your foot it will, of course, attempt to defend itself. The relatively large number of cases reported from outdoor privies have occurred because of the creature's poor eyesight. Like all web-spinners, it responds automatically to vibrations set up by prey in collision with its carefully spun strands. It attacks at the place where the disturbance occurs. Privies generally boast a large insect population, and it is quite natural that there the Black Widow builds its nest. Humans are painfully vulnerable in this domain, and as unfortunate as the results may be, they are quite understandable.

Other species found in the United States which have serious effects on man number five. All are second to the Black Widow, although two are closely related:

*L. geometricus*—the Brown Widow or Gray Widow, found in southern Florida and *perhaps* in southern California. Resembles the Black Widow in size and markings, although the characteristic hourglass is orange rather than red. Other abdominal markings are bold and colorful. It ranges into Central and South America, the West Indies, Pacific Islands, Africa, Australia, and India. It is apparently much less likely to bite than its cousin, and the effects of its venom, while marked, are not known to be fatal to man.

*L. bishopi*—believed to be limited to the southern half of Florida. It resembles the Brown Widow and was once thought to be a variety or subspecies of the Black Widow. Bites are rare and milder than those of the Black Widow, although generally similar.

*Loxosceles reclusa*—a long-legged, medium-sized, brownish creature with six instead of the usual eight eyes found in spiders. Common in Missouri, and *perhaps* ranges into surrounding states. It is a "House Spider." The bite feels rather like the sting of a bee, but the effects are much more pronounced. While fever and chills testify to a systemic effect, the main cause of concern

A Large Hairy Spider or Avicularian (species unknown).

Roy Pinney.

is the local damage. Necrotic tissue forms despite medication and infections are common. It is a nasty affair, at best, but not known to be fatal to man.

*Chiracanthium inclusum*—a very small spider (about ⅓ inch long) with a locally neurotoxic bite. The male is venomous as well as the female, although neither is apt to bite except under most unusual circumstances. Reports of incidents are very, very rare. This greenish white spider occurs over much of the United States.

*C. diversum*—common in Hawaii, is apparently more prone to bite than its near relative *inclusum*. The bite of this diminutive creature is painful but not known to be deadly. The case reported widely in 1956 of a woman who died after being bitten was an unfortunate coincidence. An autopsy revealed another cause of death not associated with the bite.

As a boy working in a grocery store, I heard many tales about the fearful, hairy tarantula. Every banana delivery occasioned stories of stowaway spiders leaping out of the great stalks of yellow-and-green fruit to administer an immediately lethal bite. Such stories persist today and appear to be generally accepted. In plain and simple fact, the Tarantulas (family *Aviculariidae*—the "bird-eating spiders") are calm, docile, very mildly venomous animals of no appreciable menace to man. A bee sting is at least as painful and frequently far more dangerous than the rare bite of one of these interesting creatures.

The family *Aviculariidae* is comprised of approximately 600 species, about 300 of which are now customarily (though quite erroneously) called tarantulas. About 10 per cent of these 300 live in the southwestern part of the United States. The other 270 species find homes in Central and South America, many Caribbean islands, several large areas of Africa, Australia, India, and on Madagascar, New Guinea, and Ceylon.

The Tarantula in popular concept. This poster for a Universal International movie reflects the general attitude of the public toward this harmless creature.

The real Tarantulas (family *Tarantulidae*) are not even spiders but constitute a separate order of arachnids known as the *Amblypygi* or (one of the) Whip-Scorpions. They are short-bodied, excessively flat, and have exceedingly long limbs, the first pair of which are carried like those of a praying mantis, but horizontally, and are grasping devices, while the second pair form long whip-shaped feelers. They are of world-wide distribution in the tropics, subtropics, and some warmer temperate areas. They are in no way a menace to man. Their close relatives, the *Uropygi*—the other Whip-Scorpions—may possibly be, as we shall see in a moment.

However, this is not all there is to this confusion of terms, for there is also a true spider popularly known as the *Tarantula* to a considerable segment of humanity since long before animals were first named and classified in the modern scientific manner. This is a southern European spider named *Lycosa narbonensis*, whose bite has been known since Roman times to be of a toxicity not to be ignored. However, these effects were greatly exaggerated in the Middle Ages, resulting in the most extraordinary outbreaks of mass hysteria that swept through Europe.

A Tailed Whip-Scorpion or *Uropygid*.
General Biological Supply House, Inc.

The REAL Tarantula
(formerly *Tarantula in-
quilina,* now *Lycosa narbonensis*).

From *The Love Life of
Animals.*

This took the form of wild and furious dancing, ultimately to specially composed music, which was called the *Tarantella.* The name derived from the south Italian city of Taranto where, in ancient times, continuous dancing was advocated as the only cure for the bite of a tarantula spider and which, if not kept up till its symptoms had subsided, would result in death. This dancing however became infectious, resulting in the strange hysteria called *tarantism.*

The famous French entomologist Fabre conducted studies on this spider and found that its bite was instantaneously fatal to insects but that a young sparrow took three days to die, while a large mole succumbed in thirty-six hours. His conclusion was that a human being bitten by this species would be seriously affected and should take all measures possible, be they traditional or scientific, to counteract them. The *Lycosa* are the long-legged spiders usually called Wolf Spiders or House Spiders. How the name first became transferred to the much less dangerous hairy and trap-door spiders (*Aviculariidae*) is not known; however, it is now firmly established in both the American and all British dialects of the English language.

The Avicularid tarantula Spiders are long-lived—up to twenty years has been proven—and are cannibalistic. They may live close to each other in some areas, but not in colonies. Each reigns over a separate domain that may range from a nest in a tall tree, for some species, to a hole in the ground up to two feet deep for others. These animals are apparently virtually blind and can have trouble distinguishing one of their own kind even at a distance of two inches.

When attacked, a tarantula rises on its four hind legs and offers its fangs to the intruder. The venom is very, very mild. The hair of the tarantula is, however, somewhat irritating and affects humans variously, depending on individual sensitivity, and can cause an uncomfortable urticarial rash. Professor William J. Baerg, who spent more than thirty years studying these animals, tested the venom of twenty-six species, twelve of the tests on himself. He states in his book, *The Tarantula*, that, "All the species in the United States, as far as I have been able to determine, are harmless to man." Some from the tropics can cause painful local reactions, but none are known to be deadly to man except, perhaps, in cases of massive anaphylactic shock.[1]

Very large tropical species are said to feed on small birds. Allegedly they wait in trees for birds to come close, and pounce on them. Perhaps this is so, but the normal diet of the tarantula consists of insects. They cannot chew or otherwise deal with any solid matter. They liquefy their prey by the repeated insertion of their fangs during the long feeding process and the use of certain digestive juices. The image of a huge, hairy spider munching on a song bird is about as exaggerated as the stories of its deadly qualities. Most people do not find spiders, particularly the American tarantulas, very attractive. For this reason the legend of the immediately lethal bite will probably persist. It is, however, without any foundation.

Australia has three spiders known to be at least harmful to man: the relative of the black widow, the Red Back (*L. hasselti*), and the Funnel-Web Spiders (*Atrax robustus* and *A. formidabilis*). The Red Back has been known to cause death, particularly in small children. It is the most dangerous spider in New Zealand. It is, however, a shy animal, most frequently involved in human injuries in outdoor privies. Worth avoiding, it is seldom a menace. There have been enough bites, though, to justify the development and production of an antivenene by the Commonwealth Serum Laboratories.

South Africa reports injuries, and a few deaths, from *Latrodectus indistinctus* and *L. geometricus*. A species of the genus *Harpactirella* (probably *lightfotti*) is also reportedly troublesome. It is difficult to tell which species caused the few reported deaths, although the natives fear greatly the so-called *Knoppiespinnekop*, or Button Spider. It is the common name for the female of *L. indistinctus*.

It is not necessary or even possible to catalog the spiders of the world, but the same general rules seem to apply nearly everywhere that venomous forms are to be found. Spiders are useful destroyers of insects,

---

[1] Anaphylactic shock is an exceedingly dangerous reaction to a foreign substance due to individual sensitivity.

seldom aggressive toward man unless interfered with (and not even always then), are rarely dangerous and seldom deadly. Very few species indeed can possibly kill a human. Unfortunately, fatal cases generally involve small children. If you are to be in an area where venomous spiders exist, learn to know them and then to avoid them. Be careful about using primitive toilet facilities and other areas with a thick concentration of insect life. You stand very little chance of becoming the victim of a spider if you observe these rules. If it ever happens, the chances are you should be thankful it wasn't a wasp or bee!

The Scorpions, order *Scorpionida,* are of great antiquity and were almost surely the first terrestrial arachnids. They are venomous, nocturnal, solitary creatures found in all the warm regions of the world. They are particularly abundant in deserts, but are sparsely represented in the temperate zones. They are extremely adaptable and can stand fierce-burning heat. There are about 650 species of some six families. Some are very dangerous to man.

The venom apparatus of the scorpions is situated at the tip of their five-segmented tails. There is a single sharp stinger at the end with an exceedingly small orifice. Two relatively large venom glands feed this single opening. In animals like the seven-inch African scorpion *Pandinus imperator,* the sting is huge and the venom plentiful. The Lobster-Scorpion of Sumatra is even larger but, being a shy denizen of the deep forest, has never, to my knowledge, been indicted for stinging a human.

Six-inch-long scorpion (species unknown) from Liberia.
Chris and Barbara Hansen.

298  ·  The Invertebrates

The pinchers, or *pedipalps*, are harmless. The principal danger represented by these animals is their practice of entering temporary and permanent human habitations. The scorpion-in-the-boot-in-the-morning is an old tale for most adventure story readers. It is very often quite true.

The United States has about 40 of the nearly 650 known species. These 40 range from harmless, to pain-producing, to deadly. Only two North American species fall into the last category: *Centruroides sculpturatus* and *C. gertschi*, both found in the extreme southwest. Dr. Herbert L. Stahnke, Director of the Poisonous Animals Research Laboratory of Arizona State University, reports that Arizona alone suffered 64 human deaths from these two animals between 1929 and 1948. The peak month was July, throughout this period.

Scorpions, like spiders, are found around the world, but most commonly in the tropics. More species of scorpions than spiders, however, are dangerous to man and the problem is very much more real. While the stab of a dangerous spider is rare, the sting of a deadly scorpion is all too common. In North America, principally in the United States and Mexico, many more people are killed by scorpions than by snakes.

Belo Horizonte is the capital of Minas Gerais State in Brazil. At an altitude of over 3,000 feet, it has a population of about 200,000. In 1954 alone, more than 171 people received emergency medical treatment after being stung by scorpions. Algerians suffer more from scorpions than snakes, and the Sudanese species *Leiurus cinquestriatus* is worse than many dangerous reptiles. Several Indian species are decidedly dangerous, as are a number of other African forms. New Zealand and Oceania are uniquely free of this problem.

Frequently, the scorpion population is very dense around human habitations. One catch, which was later described by Dr. P. J. Deoras of the Haffkine Institute in Bombay as "casual," turned up 14,903 specimens, in an area with only 13,000 human inhabitants. A thorough search would have undoubtedly turned up many times that number.

The scorpion, from the human point of view, is far more insidious than the spider. The scorpion regularly establishes itself in beds, closets, bureaus, shoes, under carpets, in furniture—in short, just about everywhere in and around human dwellings. In the open, they are found under bark, leaves, and rocks. They crawl in the open at night, and turn up with startling and dangerous regularity in houses and even vehicles. Living in an area where they are common can be hazardous for the careless and unobservant. Insecticides are generally effective against all species and are often used with excellent results in limited enclosed areas. It is a useful practice to keep children's beds and cribs away from walls, with the legs of the furniture standing in tin cans of kerosene. Children, of course, are much more vulnerable.

It may be of value to review a case history of a scorpion sting. Dr. Deoras reported the following medical history in *Probe*, in 1961. The incident occurred in Ichalkaranji, India, two years earlier. The offending animal was *Palamneus sp.* The report below is condensed to some degree:

A girl aged 15 years was admitted . . . about 1½ hours after a scorpion bite. She was . . . in a collapsed condition, pulseless, perspiring profusely, skin cold and clammy, and having chills. She had vomited 4–5 times soon after the bite, and was complaining of burning sensation in the abdomen. Immediately an injection of coramine, glucose 25% 100cc, and calcium gluconate 10% 10cc was given. She felt a little better and the pulse was felt at the wrist. Soon after, she began to shiver again and her pulse became imperceptible. . . . Then, adrenaline 0.5cc was given . . . in addition . . . an antihistaminic, but the perspiration and shivering continued . . . sweating so profuse that clothes had to be changed every ½ hour. When her shivering became less, hypertonic saline was started. Since admission, oxygen was given . . . and it was observed that the patient was mentally quite clear and answered all the questions. Perspiration continued and she began to get difficulty in breathing . . . went into respiratory distress, was restless and finally succumbed (15 hours after bite) with profuse frothy fluid coming out of the mouth and nostrils.

Certain Centipedes (which are *not* arachnids but of the class *Chilopoda*) grow to large size, and some are dangerous to man. The southwestern deserts of the United States have *Scolopendra heros* which achieves six to eight inches and which gives a painful venomous bite (not sting). It is not known to have caused fatalities. Its forty-two legs may prick, scratch, or otherwise break the skin and introduce infections, but they are harmless. Venom produced in glands at the base of the jaw is introduced by a bite only.

Tropical Asiatic species grow to be nearly a foot in length and the bite is reportedly very severe. Cases in India and Burma have kept victims bed-ridden for as much as three months. A Malayan species (identity not known to the author) is said to be particularly dangerous, with symptoms more spectacular than those from the bite of indigenous vipers.

Relatively little is known about many of the tropical centipedes, and caution is advised in dealing with them. Many are apparently quite harmless, some few administer a damaging bite, and some few may be far more dangerous yet. Some species of this class (*Chilopoda*) from Ceylon may similarly be particularly dangerous. Reports are confusing, often contradictory, but care is advisable in all cases where the species is not specifically known to be harmless. Since more than 1,500 different kinds have been identified, all centipedes are best left alone by anyone not expert in their identification.

The 6,500 known Millipedes of the world (class *Diplopoda*) differ from centipedes in several obvious ways. They are essentially vegetarians

Giant Centipede (*Scolopendra heros*).

Eliot Porter.

(centipedes are believed all to be carnivorous), and they have two pairs of legs on each body segment—200 legs in all. They are not known to have a venomous bite and are generally safe to handle. They can secrete hydrocyanic acid, and this can cause a rash. Small animals are reportedly blinded by this acid. A species of the genus *Spirostreptus* found in the Sunda Islands, and a species of *Julus*, on Amboina Island, have been reported as venomous. One or two species are much feared in Malaya. Here again, reports are contradictory and information is lacking. It does appear, however, that most if not all of the world's many millipedes are quite harmless to man.

The so-called Whip Scorpions (not scorpions at all) are believed by many to be dangerous. However, they are not venomous and not demonstrably dangerous to man. One of the *Uropygi*, the *Ecrebiche Bois* (Crayfish of the Woods) found in Haiti, is feared because of its reputed habit of squirting acid. Also known as *vinegaroons*, these whip scorpions smell acidic and do secrete a noxious substance. Any real danger is only to the eyes and is likely to occur only to woodcutters. Logwood used once to be Haiti's principal export and it was then that these animals obtained their reputation.

Certain "false spiders" (order *Solpugida*) *may* be troublesome, according to some reports. One large desert dweller from North Africa is reported quite painful to encounter, and is commonly seen rearing its front parts off the sand in a fighting posture. Once again, unfortunately, specific information is lacking.

It has not been possible in this chapter to review all of the forms of the arachnids. The group is vast, world-wide, and not yet by any means completely known. Most are harmless, some are capable of a painful, or even a harmful bite, and a very few are really dangerous. Certain of the scorpions, as we have seen, kill more people than snakes in several parts of the world. Anyone visiting areas where venomous forms are found, and who anticipates field work, is urged to obtain as much information as possible. In many places, the sting or stab of an arachnid is the one dangerous animal eventuality worth considering.

# CHAPTER 24

# *Venomous Mollusks*

IN ALL THE SHAPES in which you would expect to find an animal deadly to man, a delicately designed and beautifully colored sea shell would seem to be the least likely. Nevertheless, there is such a danger. It is a lesson a few people, at least, have had to die to learn.

The phylum *Mollusca,* a major division of the animal kingdom containing all of the so-called "shellfish," is divided into six great classes: the *Gastropoda* (the whelks, snails, etc.—single-shelled animals); the *Pelecypoda* (clams, oysters, etc.—bivalves, or two-shelled animals); the *Cephalopoda* (nautilus, squid, cuttlefish, octopus—shell-less, or nearly so, for the most part); the *Amphineura* (the chitons or hinged-shells); the *Scaphopoda* (tusk shells); and the *Monoplacophora,* only discovered in 1956. Most, or all, of these classes contain animals that are dangerous for man—*to eat.* But that is not our concern here. We are here interested in one class, containing animals that actually sting with a venom strong enough to kill a man.

The class *Gastropoda* (the snails and allies) contains thousands of species, many of the most interesting being in the order *Prosobranchiata,* and the family *Conidae.* There are some four hundred species of Cone Shells (genus *Conus*), and all of them probably have a highly-developed venom apparatus. These sea shells are among the most beautiful and most sought after in the world. Collectors have paid highly for them at auction and one—called the "Glory-of-the-Seas"—is worth up to $600 for a single good specimen. The cones are found in most of the world's tropical and subtropical waters, and are commonly found under coral and rocks, or crawling about on sandy bottoms. The animals that construct and live in these delicately beautiful shells are shy and generally retire into their inner sanctum when disturbed. Handling of live specimens can, however, cause a violent and shocking reaction.

The device used by the cone shell to administer its poison is unique. A fleshy snout, or proboscis, of surprising length is extended from the head and pushed, suddenly, against the skin of the assailant. This snout contains a number of rigid, hollow, harpoon-like devices that are actually modified *radula* teeth—normally used by the snail for rasping its food. A tooth, or several teeth, is thrust into the skin of the victim, and a venom flows forward from a poison gland situated behind the animal's head. The

302

venom runs through the hollow teeth into the wound. The effects range from bee-sting-size pain, to death within four or five hours. The entire stinging process is rapid and usually takes place before the victim knows what has happened.

A person is unlikely to suffer the sting of a cone shell unless he actually picks one up and handles it without regard for the animal's soft parts, the shell itself, of course, being harmless. One can suppose that it would be possible to step on one and get stung, but in almost all of the cases reported the victim was a shell collector handling a live specimen.

The *United States Navy Diving Manual* gives these animals a danger rating of 2 plus, putting them on a par with the octopus, groupers, and tiger, porbeagle, sand, Lake Nicaragua, and lemon sharks. Kohn, Saunders, and Wiener open their paper, "Preliminary Studies on the Venom of the Marine Snail *Conus*," with the statement, "One of the most virulent, but least studied of animal venoms is that produced by marine snails belonging to the genus *Conus*." Dr. Bruce Halstead treats of these cone shells at some length in his *Dangerous Marine Animals*. Most contemporary literature in this field refers to the animal's deadly qualities, and there can be little doubt as to the danger inherent in handling living specimens. The venom is apparently a neurotoxin.

Dr. Alan J. Kohn reports ("Recent Cases of Human Injury Due to Venomous Marine Snails of the Genus *Conus*") that "twenty-five humans are known to have been stung as a result of handling cone-shells—and five have died!" A 20 per cent mortality rate exceeds that of the common cobra and the rattlesnake! Indeed, very few venomous animals cause such a high rate of death.

Hirataka Yasiro gave a detailed report of a fatal cone shell bite that was translated by Dr. Joe Niiya of the United States Army's 406th Medical General Hospital:

Deadly Cone Shells (*Conus textile* and *Conus geographus*).

Lee Ball.

Mr. Kamekichi Fujisato age 32, eldest son of Kamato Fujisato, residing at 1126 Hechichiya, Katsuren-mura, Nakagami-gun was collecting sea shells on the beach on 29 June, 1935 when he was bitten. He was attended by a doctor, but died the same day. Mr. Kiyokage Asato was asked to obtain data from the local police box, town office, and physician concerning the accident. The shell was obtained from the town office, and forwarded to the author by Mr. Asato. This shell was damaged badly, but was clearly identifiable as *Conus geographus*. The length of the shell was 13.5 cm, rather large for the species in that district. On the day of the accident, Mr. Fujisato went to the beach to swim and collect sea shells. He was collecting shells on the southeast beach, which faces Nakagusuku Bay, when the accident occurred at about 10 o'clock in the morning. Mr. Fujisato had picked up the shell, not realizing it was venomous. His friend, who did recognize the shell, shouted a warning, but Mr. Fujisato was stung on the thumb before he could drop the shell. He did not feel any pain at first, but when pain commenced, he began to walk towards the road which bordered the shore. This was about 15 chos distant (1 cho is about 119 yards). Mr. Fujisato finally reached the road, but was not able to walk any further, and rolled into the potato field near the road. When the physician arrived the patient was still conscious, but was having difficulty in breathing. The pulse was slow, and the temperature was low, 36.7 degrees C. Soon after the arrival of the physician, the patient lost consciousness, and his extremities became purple-violet in color. He expired between 1400 and 1500 hours, about three or four hours after he had been stung. There was no swelling around the puncture mark on the thumb. The site of the sting appeared to have been scraped.

Dr. Kohn reports cases from the Moluccas, Melanesia, New Hebrides, New Caledonia, Tuamotu Islands, New Britain, Fiji, Japan, Australia, Seychelles, New Guinea, the Hawaiian Islands, Marshall Islands, and Guam in the Marianas. Although the Hawaiian Islands are in the Central Pacific, and the Seychelles are far to the west in the Indian Ocean, most of the trouble has occurred in the Western Pacific from Japan to Australia.

Dr. Halstead gives the symptoms of a cone's bite as: localized numbness, lack of blood supply, and bluish coloration of the skin. A sharp stinging or burning sensation may be experienced. Numbness and tingling, starting at the site of the wound, may spread rapidly and affect the entire body. It is particularly severe about the lips and mouth. Paralysis may set in with coma and eventual death, probably due to cardiac failure. The symptoms can, of course, be very much less severe and pass in a matter of minutes or hours.

Which of the four hundred cones are most dangerous to man? There is not too much latitude in the opinions of the experts:

| Common Name | Species | Range | Halstead | (1) Listed by: Kohn | Hiyama | Hermitte | Fish & Cobb |
|---|---|---|---|---|---|---|---|
| Court Cone | *Conus aulicus* | Polynesia to Indian Ocean | * | * | | * | * |
| Geographer Cone | *C. geographus* | Indo-Pacific: Polynesia to East Africa | * | *(2) | * | * | * |
| Marbled Cone | *C. marmoreus* | Polynesia to Indian Ocean | * | * | | * | * |
| Striated Cone | *C. striatus* | Indo-Pacific: Australia to East Africa | * | | *(3) | | * |
| Textile Cone | *C. textile* | Polynesia to Red Sea | * | *(2) | * | * | * |
| Tulip Cone | *C. tulipa* | Polynesia to Red Sea | * | * | * | * | * |
| | *C. obscurus* | Hawaiian Isl. plus | | * | | | |
| | *C. lividus* | Marianas plus | | * | | | |
| | *C. imperialis* | Seychelles plus | | * | | | |
| | *C. omaria* | New Guinea plus | | * | | | |
| Cat Cone | *C. catus* | Indo-Pacific | | * | | | |
| Oak Cone | *C. quercinus* | Indo-Pacific | | * | | | |
| Flea Cone | *C. sponsolis* | Indo-Pacific | | * | | | |
| | *C. pulicarius* | Indo-Pacific | | * | | | |
| Lettered Cone | *C. litteratus* | Indo-Pacific | | * | | | |

(1) This list is probably complete: 14, and perhaps 15, appear to be most harmful to man.
(2) Kohn states that all known fatalities were caused by either *C. geographus* or *C. textile*.
(3) No reported cases; listed by Hiyama, however, so included here.

Kohn, in the summary of the paper cited above, notes, "All species of *Conus* are potentially dangerous to man, but certain species are particularly venomous." There can be no serious doubt that these beautiful animals are dangerous and, in some instances, deadly. However, snakes kill more people in a three-hour period than all the known *Conus* deaths in history combined. How, then, are these animals important enough for discussion here as dangerous?

It is almost a certainty that at least ten people have been killed by these mollusks. The range of these deaths covers some of the most remote human outposts on our planet—Pacific and Indian Ocean islands. Most of these smaller islands are seldom visted by outsiders, and, since the cone shells prefer shallow water, they are found in isolated bays and inlets on some of the larger islands. Thus, there is no way of knowing how many victims there have been in these remote areas.

Another factor is that the collecting of sea shells is not only a science but a world-wide hobby with many thousands of enthusiastic adherents. With the advent of readily available skin-diving or SCUBA (Self-Contained Underwater Breathing Apparatus) equipment, tens of thousands of adventurous souls have been following Jacques-Yves Cousteau to his "silent world" in the littoral zones of the sea. More people, too, have taken to traveling to distant lands in recent years. With some cone shells bringing high prices from collectors, live animals of the genus *Conus* will be picked up and handled as never before. With office workers, doctors, lawyers, truck drivers and enthusiastic teen-agers entering the sea with a kind of freedom never before available, shell collecting will move from the beach where it has usually stayed, and become a matter of hunting rather than finding. A lot of people are going to be hurt, and some will die, unless it becomes common knowledge that some pretty sea shells also can be pretty dangerous.

# CHAPTER 25

# *The Giant Clam*

EVERYTHING about the pearl is romantic and mysterious. The innermost secrets of the sea glimmer tauntingly in its rich lustre, and the fantastic design of the misshapen baroque pearls seems to picture gods or demons. The very fact of the pearl's origin, the birth of a treasure in the bowels of a lowly oyster, is in itself magical. Men have died for pearls, killed for pearls, and kings' ransoms have been spent for them.

A complex of legends has grown up around these coveted prizes of the warm seas and the mass of this fiction could fill many volumes. The dangers experienced by the natives who dive in tropic seas in search of these treasures are often quite real. Reality, however, hasn't been enough. Fabled hazards have been compiled with real ones to fill out the vision of these romantic figures. The fictionalizers of fact have had a field day with the realm of the pearl and the arena of the pearl diver.

No legend of the pearl diver has been more often repeated, more apparently based on fact, nor more readily accepted by one and all, than the story of the giant *man-eating* clam. In 1962, the year in which men circled the earth in space ships, a gentleman from Minneapolis, Minnesota, wrote to the editors of *Sea Secrets* magazine, a question-and-answer publication of The International Oceanographic Foundation, and asked: "What is the giant man-eating clam? Is there such a thing?" Those are perfectly legitimate questions in the light of what has been put into print on the subject. We shall examine them in this chapter.

*Tridacna gigas, T. derasa,* and perhaps a few other forms are all variously known as the Tridacna Clam, Giant Clam, Killer-Clam, or Man-Eating Clam. In fact, these clams *are* giants, the soft parts of the largest (*T. gigas*) weighing as much as twenty pounds, and the shells as much as a quarter of a ton. The shells are known to exceed four feet in length. They are common animals in much of the Indo-Pacific region, and abound off Australia and many South Pacific island groups. They are well known off the east coast of Africa. These animals are the largest known shelled mollusks in the world. Without its shell the Tridacna clam is small when compared to the great cephalopods—mollusks with which we deal in another chapter.

That is the answer to one question; the giant clam does exist. It is a well-known living animal whose shell is often used in interior decorating.

The Giant Clam (*Tridacna gigas*). Fritz Goro.

Polynesian restaurants in New York, Philadelphia, and San Francisco use them as light fixtures. The giant is not at all rare over much of its range, and, strangely enough, it is as big as they say. The question then remains: Is it dangerous to man?

C. M. Yonge, in his report of *A Year on the Great Barrier Reef*, reports that men have been killed by the Tridacna clam. C. J. Fish and M. C. Cobb repeat the claim, crediting it to Yonge, in their *Noxious Marine Animals of the Central and Western Pacific Ocean*. Dr. Halstead makes the claim in his worth-while *Dangerous Marine Animals*, and gives instructions for releasing yourself by severing the great adductor muscles with which the animal controls its massive valves, or shells. The *U.S. Navy Diving Manual* gives it a 2 plus (out of a possible 4 plus maximum) danger rating, with the comment, "Traps legs and arms between shells." It is not possible to estimate how many other times the claim has been repeated, although generally on less authority than the sources cited above.

If you examine one of these great shells, it is difficult to see how they could fail to be a trap for man. Muscles that can control such weights must be immensely powerful. The serrated edges of the shell fit together like giant teeth, and the fit is a tight one. Are the stories then true?

The first examination of this problem attempted by the author offered one peculiar problem. Nowhere were there recorded names, dates, and places. It has apparently been assumed by most people (specialists and nonspecialists alike) that men have been killed by these animals. There have been no witnesses; or at least none who have cared to go on record. What descriptions do exist are all too obviously fiction and cannot be relied upon. As in the case of the killer whale, in the absence of recorded facts, a survey of the specialists was the only solution. The following are some very authoritative opinions:

Bruce S. Wright, Director, Northeastern Wildlife Station, Fredericton, N.B., June 18, 1962:

. . . I have never heard or seen reference to a human death from this clam, but I do not doubt its capability to hold a man as long as it wants. I have on several occasions worked in an area where these clams are around. They are like bear-traps set on the reef, and I always made a point of closing them up by dropping stones in them before I began work nearby.

Donald P. de Sylva, The Marine Laboratory, University of Miami, June 22, 1962:

. . . There are many tales attributing people being drowned or killed by these. Dr. Gilbert Voss, Chairman of our Biology Division, believes that it is unlikely that a person would accidentally step in one of these because of the large, brightly colored mantle in these which would tend to make them very conspicuous. There are rumors that occasionally divers do make a false step and are held down by these until they drown, but these clam shells close so slowly that it is unlikely that one would snap shut quickly enough to grab a man's foot.

S. Wiener, South Caulfield, Victoria, Australia, August 10, 1962:

The evidence which incriminates the giant clam in causing injury to man is circumstantial and largely hearsay. However, it must be remembered that whenever such injury may have occurred, the chances of having it recorded by a competent observer would be remote. I do not know of any authentic record of injury or death. . . .

George Mack, Director, Queensland Museum, Brisbane, Australia, July 11, 1962:

I have no record of the clam . . . causing any harm to a human being. In my opinion, the fanciful tales . . . are the creations of novelists and newspapermen. . . .

Harold A. Rehder, Curator, Division of Mollusks, Smithsonian Institution, Washington, D.C., May 24, 1962:

We here feel . . . that such an occurrence could happen only by accident, through a person not looking where he was putting his foot, because the mantle of these clams are of such a vivid color that they act as conspicuous danger signals.

Donald F. McMichael, The Australian Museum, Sydney, June 18, 1962:

. . . I was unable to find any evidence that anyone had ever been caught by one of these animals. That they could be dangerous seems without doubt . . . it seems likely that if a really big clam did grasp onto a limb, it would certainly be able to hold on long enough to cause a drowning.

R. S. Irwin, Glen Innes, New South Wales, Australia, June 17, 1962:

The late Hugo Flecker of Cairns was, I think, the best authority in Australia on Marine Zoology in the tropics and he told me personally that this giant clam was, in fact, practically harmless, and that reports of its clamping the leg of a victim only occurred in fiction and in the movies. He said that the jaws approximated so slowly that there was plenty of time for a possible victim to get his leg out of danger and that he had heard of no authentic case where any harm had been done.

John E. Randall, Professor of Zoology, University of Puerto Rico, Mayaguez, May 14, 1962:

I know of no injuries or deaths resulting from man's contact with . . . Tridacna. One biologist told me that the giant clam does not close its valves rapidly and even if it did, he doubted that it could hold a man's leg.

W. D. L. Ride, Director, Western Australian Museum, Perth, July 25, 1962:

I have asked Dr. R. W. George, our Curator of Invertebrates and a marine biologist, whether he has any information on case histories of . . . damage done to man by Tridacna. . . . He informs me that we have no authentic reports at all here.

Gilbert Voss, Chairman, Biological Sciences Division, The Marine Laboratory, University of Miami, July 25, 1962:

As far as the giant clam is concerned . . . I have been unable to unearth a single case history of an attack. Mr. Roughly in his book on the Great Barrier Reef states that several cases occur each year in that area. However, he too fails to cite a single case. I am afraid . . . are myths.

J. L. B. Smith, Professor of Ichthyology, Rhodes University, Grahamstown, South Africa, May 8, 1962:

. . . we worked over a great area of tropical East Africa where it occurs, and while we did not ourselves encounter any case of fatality, native divers were extremely wary of this creature and told us that divers had been caught and drowned. However, our experience of the natives of East Africa . . . will invariably tell you what they think you would like to hear. What I do know is that we ourselves treated them with great respect and on one occasion when a net handle was pushed into a moderate clam that was open, it closed on this with great force.

Alan J. Kohn, Department of Zoology, University of Washington, Seattle, May 23, 1962:

. . . I know of no published records of human fatality due to this animal, and furthermore, I very much doubt that there are any. I believe it would be rather difficult for a diver to be trapped, but it is not impossible. You can certainly line me up on the negative side; I have seen no evidence to the contrary.

R. V. Southcott, Honorary Zoologist, South Australian Museum, Hyde Park, South Australia, July 6, 1962:

. . . as far as I know there is no authentic story on record; I have made as exhaustive a search as possible for this, without success. Halstead (1959) gives the traditional view, which is stated in Whitley and Boardman (1929), also by Younge (1936, on the advice of Iredale). MacGillivary (in Cleland 1942) disputed these earlier statements, which have never been authenticated by case histories. Roughly (1940) also was dubious, and Flecker (1957) also declared that there was no authentic case of a diver being trapped. In view of these challenges, which have never been met, it must be concluded there has been no real evidence of human injuries.

*Sea Secrets* answered the gentleman from Minneapolis to the effect that there were no known records. Paul A. Zahl did an impressive article for *The National Geographic Magazine* (January, 1957) entitled "On Australia's Coral Ramparts." On page twenty is a picture of Dr. Zahl holding a large specimen out of the water. He had introduced a stout pole between the valves and had been able to haul the animal out by its grip on the piece of wood. No conclusion is drawn, but the caption on the photograph does point out that "firsthand evidence is scarce," and "The subject is a favorite with fiction writers." The photograph is impressive nonetheless. G. H. Gunter in *Adventures of a Trepang Fisher* reports on seeing an octopus held fast by a Tridacna off the coast of North Australia. And so it goes. References occur in great numbers. What are the facts? What conclusions can be drawn?

Despite its immense size, the Tridacna clam feeds much the same way as do other bivalves. It opens its valves, spreads its mantle and filters food.[1] It does not clamp down on large animals in order to eat. The mantle, as so often recorded, is vividly colored and boldly marked. It is not something one is apt to miss although it should be pointed out that it dwells in areas where brilliant colors abound in profusion. Most of the stories of this

[1] From algae raised within its own shell, at least as an adult.

312  ·  *The Invertebrates*

animal clamping down on men are fairly logical on all but one point. When these reports refer to the "bear-trap" snapping shut, they may get off into pure fiction and give themselves away. When a Tridacna clam closes, it must not only move two ponderous dead weights towards each other, it must also displace a great quantity of water. No matter how powerful the adductor muscles, the shell could not be snapped shut, no bear-trap effect could probably be approximated.

Here, then, is what we have. A diver is not *likely* to miss a giant clam if it is wide open, the only time it could be dangerous. If a diver did put his foot in between the valves, the valves would close slowly, but close they most certainly would. There is no known authentic record of anyone ever being caught. Does, then, the Tridacna clam trap men? This author does not know, and doubts very much that anyone else does. Frankly, I doubt that the animal ever has, but that is not evidence. In seeking a definite answer, this author's doubts and other people's beliefs are not admissible evidence. What is evidence in the context of this book is this: Until an animal has been demonstrated to be dangerous, we ought to vote it not guilty. No one seems equipped to demonstrate that the "Giant Man-Eating Clam" has caused human death or injury. In conclusion, it should be pointed out that the serious claims which do exist do not accuse the Tridacna of seeking man to eat. The trapping of man is described as a defensive reflex action. Even this, however, remains, for the moment, in the realm of fiction, or at least, of speculation.

# CHAPTER 26

# *Octopus and Squid*

IF ANYONE is really intent on creating an animal horror story to end all animal horror stories, and wishes to launch his tale from a supposedly familiar point, he can do no better than choose the octopus and squid, mollusks without external shells. Indeed, many writers (it is impossible to estimate how many) have done just that. Wonderfully morbid tales have been drifting around for centuries. Because these incredible stories have often been offered as personal narratives, legends have grown to absolutely monstrous proportions. This ancient race of animals (400 million years for some fossil remains) has inspired an almost impenetrable fog of ignorance and misinformation which rivals even that concerning poisonous snakes. It is really astounding to review what has been said about these creatures!

Considering the amount of attention the cephalopods have received in fiction, it is rather confounding to discover how little *accurate* information is common knowledge. In conversations with even well-educated people it is surprising to note that the fact that these animals are invertebrates is not always appreciated. If the facts of their physical structure are not universally realized, how much more confusion must there be about their behavior? Since these animals are remote from the lives of most people, this ignorance is perhaps understandable. However, since many cephalopods—from the Greek, meaning "head-footed"—are accused of appalling crimes against mankind, the purpose of this book will be well served by a general clearing of the air.

The cephalopods are broken down into an impressive family tree of three subclasses, a number of orders and suborders, and seemingly endless families. It is a large and diverse group, but we will concern ourselves here with only two groups: the Octopuses (order *Octopoda*), and the Squids (suborder *Teuthoidea* of the *Decapoda*). This for two reasons: the other cephalopods (cuttlefish, the nautilus, etc.) are rarely accused, and quite probably never involved in human injuries and deaths, and the state of cephalopodan systematics looms up like a giant *New York Times* Sunday crossword puzzle, in a combination of Braille and Sanskrit! (Even teuthologists—specialists in this class of animals—are frequently confused.)

313

Octopuses (yes! that is a correct plural form), the best known of the cephalopods, are recognized in somewhere around 150 living species today. A number of these species are exceedingly rare insofar as collected specimens go, no more than a single example being known in some cases. Since many species are believed to live at extreme depths, there is no telling to what extent the list may be expanded as abyssal oceanography develops in the coming decades. Everything we have to say about the group in this chapter will apply to the shallow-water species that are well known. We don't know much about the nature of the truly deep-sea beasts.

Perhaps no single aspect of the octopus' appearance and nature gives rise to more conversation than the matter of size. For some reason, people always ask, when the subject of the animal is raised, "How big *do* they grow?" The size range runs from approximately 2 inches (*Octopus arborescens*) to 35 feet (*Octopus hong-kongensis*).[1] The latter form, the presently-known giant of the group, seems to reach maximum size in Alaskan and State of Washington waters. It must be pointed out that even a 35-foot specimen, and that is being generous, is about $16/17$ arms, the head and body accounting for less than 2 feet of that length.

[By the way, those are *arms, not tentacles*. Octopuses do not have tentacles; these are found in the decapods, which include the squid. The fictionalizers of fact will probably be writing about the octopus' tentacles one hundred years from now, but it doesn't have them!]

Octopus, like squids, are active hunting animals. Specimens establish territories, and either chase away or eat intruders. They can move with startling speed by jetting water from an adjustable siphon, cloud the water around them with their ink, change color to a degree and with a speed that puts the legendary chameleon to shame, and hold on with a tenacity that is nothing short of astounding, once they obtain purchase with their suckers—adjustable discs that line the inner surface of their arms. These devices consist of a muscular membrane with a thick rim. The center acts somewhat after the fashion of a piston and is controlled by the animal with delicate precision.

Octopuses can squeeze themselves through any hole or crevice large enough to admit their hard, parrot-like beak, walk on their arms, hang suspended in mid-water, jet around with fine control, or lie patiently for hours waiting for their prey.[2] They are stubborn, tenacious, efficiently predatory animals of considerable economic importance to man. In many

[1] That is, the diameter of its eight arms stretched equally in all directions to form a circle like the spokes of a wheel.

[2] Octopuses apparently do occasionally come out of the water, according to many reporters. Their ability to run, jump, *and even climb trees* is less than perfectly understood, to say the least, although frequently referred to.

The Common Octopus (*Octopus vulgaris*).

Franz Thorbecke.

parts of the world they are fished for as food along with other "cephs." Squids are more significant as a food source, however. The range of the various octopus species is virtually global. The author has seen them in coral formations astride the equator, and once sat watching a newly-caught specimen acclimate itself to an aquarium in a biology laboratory 840 miles from the South Pole. It had been taken only a few hours before in a net through a hole in sea ice several feet thick, a few hundred yards off frigid Ross Island. They range into Arctic waters as well.

Is any octopus dangerous to man? Only under very special circumstances. A man in a boat is almost assuredly safe from them as long as he leaves the octopus in the water. Attacks on boats by cephalopods appear to have been made by squid, not octopus, even though the latter animal, being better known, has been accused. A man in the water, if attacked, could be placed at considerable disadvantage, particularly if the attack occurred near a solid anchor point. In mid-water, the octopus might have a great deal of trouble overcoming a well set up, well organized man. Skin divers from Washington regularly catch the largest known octopuses with their bare hands, as a kind of sport! Frank W. Lane, whose recent *Kingdom of the Octopus* is a masterpiece of nature writing, gives these figures: a man weighing 200 pounds can be held below the surface by a pull of about ten pounds, if he doesn't struggle. A medium-sized octopus can exceed that pull several times over. If a man were grabbed firmly by an octopus that was anchored equally firmly to a solid foundation, he might be held down long enough to drown. Certainly, if the man was inexperienced in the water and panicked, the octopus might very well have considerable advantage. It is a reasonable assumption—but only that—that this has happened on rare occasions. It is certainly not a common occurrence, however, and must be looked upon as a freak accident involving a very large, and particularly determined animal, and a very weak and inept person. A diver inadvertently intruding into a cave lair might trigger an attack, particularly with a sexually excited animal that could mistake an arm or leg for a potential mate's member.

Once engaged, an octopus frequently, but not always, tends to hang on, and trouble can ensue. As capable a predator as the octopus is, however, its energy is expended on practical prey like fish and mollusks. The octopus has many enemies in the sea—even the larger octopuses are regularly attacked by moray eels, sharks, and members of the whales—and are wary of large animals approaching them. Faced with anything as formidable as a man, the octopus is generally shy and retiring. To characterize it as an inveterate enemy of man (at least any of the species presently known) is absurd. Man is certainly an enemy of the octopus (he collects millions every year for food), but the converse is rarely true.

Frank Lane researched a number of cases of attack and came to the conclusion that there is occasional danger to man. In 1940, in Poverty Bay, New Zealand, a Maori lad was grabbed by a 36-inch specimen, and was unable to free himself. Friends saved him in time. During the First World War, a parson was taking a group of boys on an outing along the Victoria coast of Australia. An octopus *left the water* and attacked the parson, rapidly encircling him with its arms. It was apparently a good-sized animal and it took the combined efforts of several teen-age boys to rescue the man. Since octopuses are occasionally reported leaving the water to attack shore-dwelling rats, this may not be as strange as it sounds. Just how far from the water they will go, or how long they will stay out is not clear. There are other accounts, as well, of attacks on men, that would appear to be reliable, but they are few in number, and the circumstances under which they allegedly took place are generally open to question.

Under no circumstances does any octopus strangle or crush anything to death with its arms. Its arms are for holding things. When hunting, it holds victims while it eats, or first administers a venomous bite. Some octopuses, at least, are venomous. Their posterior salivary gland produces a glycoprotein of immense complexity. This substance paralyzes their prey and enables their chitinous beaks to dismember and devour their meal without struggle. The venom apparently inhibits respiration. Tests on laboratory animals reveal it to be quite potent. It is known that it can affect man.

The bite of the octopus usually consists of two small puncture wounds. The beak is not particularly dangerous, although a good-sized animal is capable of giving a pretty good bite. Suggestions that arms or legs of men can be severed with the beak seem, however, to overstate the case altogether too much! When venom is involved, a local burning sensation will be the first symptom. There may be an anti-coagulant constituent in the venom, since profuse bleeding has been reported a number of times. Octopus bites are relatively rare, and reactions to the venom beyond that of purely local discomfort, rarer still. But there is one case, reported over and over again, that does give cause for thought.

On September 18, 1954, twenty-one-year-old Kirke Dyson-Holland, an Australian skin-diver, was reportedly killed by the bite of a *six-inch octopus*. He and his diving companion, John Baylis, were coming ashore near Port Darwin when Baylis saw the little blue creature. He caught it, played with it, allowing it to crawl over his arms and torso, and tossed it to Dyson-Holland, a perfectly natural thing for a skin-diver to do. Octopuses, it seems, are rarely left in peace by energetic young SCUBA enthusiasts out for a day of play in coastal waters. The animal evidently hung on to Dyson-Holland's arm or shoulder for a moment, then crawled across to the middle of his back before dropping off into the water. The men came ashore without further regard for the diminutive creature which made off in typical fashion the moment it hit the water.

No sooner had the two men come up on the beach when Dyson-Holland complained of a dry sensation in his mouth, and difficulty in swallowing. Baylis said he noticed a small puncture wound and trickle of blood on his companion's back where the octopus had lodged briefly. The afflicted man rapidly became violently ill. He vomited, began to lose muscular coordination, and finally collapsed. He was carried to a car and rushed four miles to a Darwin hospital muttering, "It was the little octopus." He lost consciousness during the brief but frantic run for medical help. By the time they got to town he had turned blue (cyanosis), and his breathing could no longer be detected. Adrenalin and an iron lung failed to help. Without rallying, he died fifteen minutes after being placed in the respirator. Less than two hours after handling a six-inch octopus, Kirke Dyson-Holland was dead. The exact species is not known, although the questionable name *Octopus rugosus* has been suggested. It is questionable because the precise animal it describes is not clear, any number of species being misidentified and given that name. This kind of confusion is not uncommon when dealing with the octopuses.

How was Kirke Dyson-Holland killed? Several explanations are possible, although few are likely. One remote possibility, in the author's opinion, although admittedly formulated with no firsthand knowledge, is that the youth was not killed by an octopus at all. He was spear-fishing just prior to the encounter, presumably near the bottom, and he could have encountered another venomous marine form, of which there is no shortage in Australian waters. He might not have noticed another bite, sting or stab. This is decidedly possible since injuries received under water can go unnoticed. Even quite massive injuries inflicted by sharks are not fully appreciated, in many instances, until the victim is out of the water. People bitten by sea snakes, as discussed elsewhere in this book, are sometimes unaware that they have been victimized until they feel a tug or see the serpent. The wound noted by Baylis was not found in the autopsy. That wound, or another unnoticed by either man, could have been caused by another animal.

That is all highly speculative, however. Young Dyson-Holland has been listed as the victim of an octopus, and we should go along with that report rather than write another script. How, then, was he killed? The medical history of the boy showed a mild form of asthma which could indicate an allergic configuration, although the autopsy did not reveal a typical allergic death. However, the possibility was not ruled out by the pathologist. It is possible, perhaps even likely, that he was violently allergic to the proteins involved and suffered massive anaphylactic shock. A simple bee sting, uncomfortable but harmless to most people, can kill susceptible people, and does so every year in not inconsiderable numbers.

Finally, it is possible that some species of octopus, at least, are lethally venomous. Perhaps they are deadly only at certain periods during their lives. All of this is distinctly possible, but has not so far been adequately demonstrated. Kirke Dyson-Holland is the only recorded human death attributed to the bite of an octopus. Others may be claimed, but none have been supported with sufficient evidence. The only real facts known are that an otherwise healthy young sportsman handled an unidentified octopus of very small size, promptly became violently ill after being reportedly bitten by the creature, and quickly died. Further investigation, certainly, is indicated.

Although the octopus is the cephalopod with the reputation for mayhem, it is the squid which might answer to some of the seemingly fantastic tales that are told. If there are sea monsters, certain squids are the most likely suspects. They are the most varied and colorful of the class, the most numerous, and among them are numbered the largest of the cephalopods. Lane says they are the most ferocious of all invertebrates. Aside from the giant *Cyanea* jellyfish with their endless stream of tentacles, these giant squid are the largest invertebrates known to exist. They might even exceed the *cyanea's* length of 120-odd feet!

A 30-foot *kraken* strand-ed at Ranheim, Norway, in October, 1954. This is about half the pres-ently accepted maximum length.

Erling Sivertsen.

There are over 350 species of living squid recognized today. The smallest known is probably *Sandalops pathopsis*, measuring under one inch at maturity. The giant is *Architeuthis* sp., whose maximum length is a matter of great debate with 60 feet at one end of the spectrum, and 300 at the other! Squids are widely distributed in the seas and oceans, both vertically and horizontally. In addition to eight arms, squids have two tentacles which they shoot out with amazing speed to capture prey and draw it toward their powerful beaks.

Since before the birth of Christ, writers had been recording tales of monster cephalopods. The conservatives in the sciences tended to pooh-pooh the whole thing right up to the end of the last century, when it finally became eminently clear that they *did* exist. *Architeuthis* came into being officially, and is the genus now used to define the animals popularly known by the old Norse name of *kraken*. Giant squid, true giants, do exist, and are to the everyday squid what the 110-foot blue whale is to the common dolphin. Thirty- to sixty-foot specimens have been taken, and the maximum size they may reach is not known. They are evidently nocturnal creatures of the deep coastal shelves. The fact that they have been occasionally troublesome when encountered during the day may indicate that only sick and disoriented specimens come up to the surface when the sun is high. Nothing like a definitive answer exists.

Mr. Carl C. Cutler of West Mystic, Connecticut, a gentleman long interested in and connected with marine matters, kindly supplied a quote from the *Mystic Press*, dated July 31, 1874:

### SCHOONER SUNK BY A SQUID

Schooner PEARL, 150 tons, James Floyd, master, with a crew of six, was reported sunk by a giant squid in Lat. 8.50 N., Long. 84.05 E. on May 10th, 1874. The sinking was witnessed and reported by passenger steamer STRATHOWEN bound from Columbo to Madras. Passengers first noted a large brownish mass lying on the surface between the steamer and the schooner, which was becalmed two or three miles away. Someone on the schooner fired a rifle at the object and it began to move toward the schooner and squeezed on board between the fore and mainmast, pulling the vessel over and sinking it. Its body was as thick as the schooner and about half as long, with a train that appeared to be 100 feet long. The steamer put out boats and picked up five of the crew swimming in the water. The other member of the crew was crushed between the mast and one of the creature's tentacles, which were as thick as a barrel.

The remarkable thing about this eighty-nine-year-old account is its matter-of-factness. "Of course there are squids big enough to sink a schooner," it seems to say. One can't help but wonder how a contemporary tabloid would treat a similar report from Latitude 8.50 N! How many adjectives would be used?

This story of the disaster of the *Pearl* has been quoted innumerable times. It has been a favorite of the sea-monster set. Plainly and simply, any attempt to really evaluate it at this stage of the game is virtually hopeless. Witnesses swore it was true, and we are stuck with what they had to say. Either we accept the notion that squids exceed 100 feet in length, or we don't. Since the burden of the *Pearl* is known to have been 150 tons, there are calculations of a sort that might be made to determine what pull would have been necessary to roll her over. However, unknown factors like the weight and distribution of cargo, skill of the skipper, direction of sail in relation to the prevailing wind, velocity of that wind, amount of ballast being carried, and amount of water in the bilges would tend to make these calculations about as speculative as your own good guess! Peter Ianuzzi, a specialist in oceanographic engineering, pointed out the highly problematical nature of such calculations when asked to pass judgment on the *Pearl* story. What it boils down to is this—it may have happened—we just don't know.

The *Pearl* wasn't the only vessel reputed or reported to have encountered these giants of the cephalopod tribe. Captain Haley, a harpooner on the last of the old wooden whalers, the *Charles W. Morgan*, wrote in his *Whale Hunt* of seeing a squid 300 feet long! He judged its length by comparing it to the vessel on which he was sailing. Mr. Cutler, the gentleman who kindly supplied the report on the *Pearl*, is a relative of Captain Haley's and refers to him as a sober and trustworthy man. Captain Haley reported that the monster was accompanied by two smaller squids, each about 150 feet long. Mr. Cutler, as a boy in the nineties, knew a good many old whalemen. He reports there was a general acceptance among them of the existence of these giants. The French steam despatch boat *Alecton* met and unsuccessfully attempted to capture one in 1861. This latter reported incident, however, involved a specimen very much smaller than 150 feet.

In the 1870's, for reasons not known, kraken considerably larger than the ones known as good bait to European fishermen, began to appear off

A large squid being oiled down preparatory to a museum cast being made.
David D. Duncan.

Angling for the Humboldt Current squid.

David D. Duncan.

Newfoundland. A large specimen, inadvertently prodded with a boat-hook, attacked a fishing dory off Portugal Cove, Newfoundland, on October 26, 1873. Quick action with a hatchet by the twelve-year-old son of one of the two fishermen aboard saved the three occupants from drowning. The severed tentacle of the beast was presented to an amateur biologist, Rev. Moses Harvey, of St. John's. It was Rev. Harvey who subsequently purchased the carcass of a 32-foot specimen taken in the same general waters in November, 1873.

It is known that the Sperm Whale (*Physeter catodon*) feeds on giant squids. Captured sperms almost always are heavily scarred by sucker marks. The suckers of the giant squid are tooth-rimmed, and, once affixed to a whale's hide, cannot be ripped free without the squid's co-operation except by colossal effort, and not without leaving scars. Sucker marks have been found on sperm whales' heads measuring three inches across. Whalers reported harpooned sperm whales vomiting up hunks of squid arms as thick as barrels, while in their death throes. The battle between a sperm whale and a giant squid must be a sight to behold!

There is a Humboldt Current squid (*Ommastrephes gigas*) taken regularly by fishermen off the west coast of South America. These animals are very aggressive and may weigh 300 pounds and stretch twelve feet in length. It is said that their beaks can do more damage to a steel

Humboldt Current squid (*Ommastrephes gigas*) taken on gaff when it went for a smaller hooked specimen.

Courtesy of Michael Lerner.

boathook than the bite of a big shark. Native fishermen allegedly fear these animals more than any other in the sea.

Are squids dangerous to man? Aside from a sailor who was reputedly pulled under as he clung to a raft following the sinking of the troopship *Britannia* in the mid-Atlantic, on March 25, 1941, there are few if any authentic reports of men in the water being injured or killed by these creatures. Certainly, anyone in the water when a 30- to 60-foot *Architeuthis* is around had better get out. Similarly, a swim in the Humboldt Current at night when masses of feeding squids are on the prowl would be unwise. These animals are certainly dangerous under the right set of circumstances. Large squids are almost always nocturnal animals and lie off in deeper water during the day, making an encounter with one by a man in the water an exceptional case. Serious injuries could result from carelessness with freshly caught specimens, however.

As for the giants who attack vessels: it is pretty much a case of what you want to believe. All manner of logic can be applied, but logic isn't the answer when the number of unknowns surpasses the number of established facts. The answers are reliable eyewitnesses, photography, and calm evaluation. The eyewitnesses of these recounted tragedies of course aren't around any longer, no pictures are known to exist, and calm evaluation of an event that occurred scores of years ago isn't too profitable. Time will no doubt yield further information.

# CHAPTER 27

# *Jellyfish*

THE OPENING COMMENT of an article in the *United States Naval Medical Bulletin* for March, 1943, reads: "Contrary to popular belief, the sting of a jellyfish can be extremely dangerous, *even fatal*." That statement, with the author's italics added, is, unfortunately, quite true.

New York papers, on Tuesday, August 7, 1962, carried an AP release datelined Newport, Rhode Island. It read, in part, "Second Beach here was closed to bathers yesterday when ten persons—nine of them children—were stung by Portuguese Men-of-War."

The *Cairns Post,* a Queensland, Australia, newspaper carried this account in the issue for January 21, 1937 (only the first paragraph is quoted):

> Within eight minutes of being stung by the deadly Portuguese man-o'-war while bathing at Bramston Beach (40 miles south of Cairns), 12 miles from Mirriwinni, this morning, D.W.T. (19) collapsed and died. Young T., who had been holidaying with his aunt at Mirriwinni, was in the water with a friend. They waded out waist deep and almost instantly the man-o'-war tentacles became wrapped around the victim's abdomen. His companion helped to free him and assisted him to the shore. T. staggered about 50 yards and collapsed. He was dead within eight minutes. . . .

What is the nature of the animal involved, and to what extent is it a danger to man? The answers to these questions are not as well known as they should be. We will discuss what has, in fact, been established.

The jellyfish belong to the Phylum *Coelenterata*, or group of animals known as Coelenterates, which is a general term embracing several related types of animals such as the hydroids, corals, and sea anemones. They are found, in one form or another, in all of the world's seas and oceans. They are simple animals composed of many highly specialized cells. Many of them are venomous to man, on contact, and what we have to say about the true jellyfish will apply to these related forms as well. A major difference between the jellyfish *per se* and these other forms is that the former are free to drift or float for much of their life, while the others are generally fixed and stationary during that part of their lives when they are dangerous to man. Of course, to the man who rubs against "fire coral" and thus suffers the agony of coelenterate envenomation, the jellyfish are not the most dangerous forms. In actual fact, however, they are. The free-floating characteristic of the jellyfish greatly increases the likelihood of an encounter between them and man. Also, it now appears that the most virulent coelenterate venom is produced in this group. Anyone who dives in waters where any venomous coelenterates—such as hydroids, anemones, and corals—abound would do well to learn to recognize the dangerous forms.

A major exception to our division of coelenterates into sessile and mobile are the Siphonophores, which include the much-feared Portuguese Man-of-War (*Physalia physalis*). This is not a true jellyfish, but a free-swimming colonial hydroid: a collection of specialized hydroid animals living together in a kind of grand cooperative, each with a special job to do, and each benefitting from the actions of the whole colony. It must be pointed out that, once again, common names let us down. The Portuguese Man-of-War, or Bluebottle, is properly any animal in the

Portuguese Man-of-War (*Physalia* sp.).

Charles E. Lane, Marine Laboratory, University of Miami.

genus *Physalia*, but the names are used in various places for animals of at least half a dozen other genera. Here, we refer only to *Physalia*. But we must deal with the true jellyfish or *Scyphozoa* first.

These range in size from the almost microscopic to the giant *Cyanea capillata*, which ranges northward to Arctic waters, and may reach a body diameter of over seven feet, with 100-foot tentacles. Deep-water biological work now in progress may reveal even larger forms. All known coelenterates employ a similar stinging mechanism, and all are to a degree venomous. Some are harmless to man, some can cause mild discomfort, some inflict agonizing pain, and a very few can cause death. The difference apparently lies in the venom and not in size of the animal or the method of stinging. Dr. R. V. Southcott, a scholar who has written extensively on the subject, states in the *A. M. S. S. Review* for May, 1962: "At present, about two dozen species of jellyfish are known to have some medical effect. This number is growing rapidly."

Jellyfish characteristically have tentacles hanging from their globe, the jelly-like umbrella by which they are usually recognized. The outer layers of these tentacles contain highly specialized, microscopic stinging mechanisms (specialized intracellular structures or organelles) known as nematocysts, which are in turn contained in cells called cnidoblasts. A hair-like trigger, the cnidocil, projects out of these and it is when the victim touches or is touched by this trigger that the mechanism is released. A lid on the nematocyst springs open (it is called the operculum), and a pointed and barbed, thread-like tube flies out of the nematocyst like a coiled spring, carrying venom with it. This whole device is exceedingly small, and the man who encounters one of these animals does not trigger one cnidocil, but many thousands, in some cases hundreds of thousands. So powerful are these devices they have been able to penetrate laboratory gloves in experimental encounters. In effect, the victim is shot with thousands of tiny, sinuous and venomous darts. Most jellyfish stings cause nothing more than a slight burning or itching sensation—if that. Unfortunately, this is not always the case. The most feared of all "jellyfish" (as was pointed out, not a true jellyfish at all) is the Portuguese Man-of-War. The tentacles of this animal can run to many feet in length, and a man who unknowingly dives into their midst is in for a very bad time.

On July 14, 1942, a twenty-year-old soldier encountered a Portuguese Man-of-War while swimming off Puerto Rico. He was stung across the back and left shoulder, and "his appearance was as though he were recovering from an epileptic convulsion." (Stuart and Slagle) The report in the *U.S. Naval Medical Bulletin* goes on to say:

. . . the skin of the whole body was flushed . . . expression of marked anxiety . . . he breathed with great difficulty . . . coughing expirations . . .

Greatly simplified drawings of undischarged (*top*) and discharged (*bottom*) coelenterate nematocysts. Pointed tube carries the venom. (After Kreuzinger.)

Chris Bottomley.

complained of severe oppression of the chest . . . pain in the abdomen and lumbar regions . . . board-like rigidity of the lumbar and abdominal muscles . . . muscle cramps in the extremities . . . skin was raised in an urticarial rash. . . .

A twenty-seven-year-old sailor was involved in the same kind of accident on the same day and, as reported, "Four weeks later the marks of the tentacles were still plainly visible." A report in the *U.S. Armed Forces Medical Journal* (Klein and Bradshaw) tells of a case off North Miami

Beach in April, 1950. The last of the lesions disappeared twenty-four days after the encounter, but white hair-like scars remained, perhaps permanently. There have been untold thousands of such cases, both reported and unrecorded, but seldom, if ever, are they fatal where the Portuguese Man-of-War—that is, an animal of the genus *Physalia*—is involved.

Although the author cannot pin down the actual point at which it started, some time back some fiction writer apparently made the statement that the Portuguese Man-of-War was the only deadly jellyfish. I clearly recall being raised on this bromide and never really thought to question it until research for this book was begun, and I read the medical reports. Doubtless this belief still has world-wide currency and so strongly is it believed that cases of death and injury by coelenterates are credited to the man-of-war—without the truly offending species ever being seen. H. Flecker of Queensland, a specialist in marine biology, among others, doubted the validity of these assignments and attributed many recorded accidents to "*Irukandji* sting," i.e., unidentified animal stings. In actual fact, although the Portuguese Man-of-War is a dangerous creature to encounter physically, it is probably only deadly, if ever, in rare cases. The author knows of no case where a death was finally attributed to this animal after proper identification by a qualified person, although the report from the *Cairns Post* cited earlier does blame the death of a nineteen-year-old boy on this animal.[1] The report may be accepted, but only with reservations.

In 1941, a seven-and-a-half-year-old boy died rapidly after being stung in shallow water. His mother identified the attacking animal as a Portuguese Man-of-War from strands of tentacles she saw sticking to the boy's legs when he ran ashore in agony. This identification cannot be accepted when we take into account the evidence used, and the mental condition of a woman as she bent over her dying son.

And so it goes: a ten-year-old boy at North Mission Beach in 1949, a fourteen-year-old girl at Kissing Point Baths, Australia, and a number of other incidents from the Philippine Islands. Time after time, someone yelled, "Portuguese Man-of-War," and the legend was intensified. More than likely, all of these cases, or certainly the vast majority, were victims of the various "Sea Wasps" or "Box Jellies." The genera involved (small, roughly cuboid jellyfish) could have been *Chiropsalmus*, *Chironex*, or *Carybdea*. The first named is common in Philippine waters; the second around Australia; the third, although having a wider range, is probably the least virulent of the group.

---

[1] Since the above was written, a 73-year-old man died in Miami after being stung by a Portuguese Man-of-War. An autopsy revealed that he died of heart failure.

The relatively small sea wasps are decidedly dangerous to man as witness this 1938 report:

> . . . A half-caste boy aged 12 years, was bathing in the local swimming baths (Darwin, Australia). He dived into the water and when he came to the surface was distressed and just able to reach the beach. He said that he had been stung by a jellyfish. He died shortly afterwards . . . witnesses stated that the jellyfish was still sticking to the boy when he staggered to the beach. This specimen was submitted to the Australian Museum and identified as *Chiropsalmus quadrigatus* Haeckel, commonly known as the "Sea Wasp."

That account was given to Dr. H. Flecker by Professor E. Ford, Director of the School of Public Health and Tropical Medicine, Sydney.

Although the sea wasps have relatives as far away from Australia as the Atlantic coast of South America, most, if not all, deaths have been reported from the southwest Pacific and the Indian Ocean. So swift is the onslaught of violently painful symptoms that anyone in deep water would probably simply sink and drown without a trace. There are some forty cases, however, reported in scientific literature, and a far greater hazard evidently exists here than has been generally realized.

Simplified drawing of a Sea-Wasp, or Box-Jelly (*Carybdea* sp.), most dangerous of the jellyfish.
Chris Bottomley.

At certain times of the year, single jellyfish will be encountered floating free. At other times, the water will be cluttered with them. Entering the water at such a time is a hazardous practice. These swarms that occur offshore, and in harbors and bays result from the animals being released from budding forms that have been fixed to the bottom. When the release into a free-floating form occurs, and before the tides and currents can disperse them, these hordes are extremely dangerous when and if virulent genera are involved. There is no known way of controlling these invasions of the surface waters. Man has no choice but to avoid contact. In the case of the Portuguese Man-of-War, such assemblages are generally produced at interfaces or boundaries between water masses offshore, or by the continued action of onshore winds. Very little is known about the reproductive life of *Physalia* or its relatives.

The venom of the coelenterates appears to be essentially neurotoxic. It causes violent local symptoms up to and including permanent scarification, and it can result in dangerous systemic reactions. Since jellyfish frequently infest certain areas by the hundreds of thousands during specific seasons, and since man hasn't yet devised a means of ridding himself of this dangerous pest, he had best use his powers of observation and common sense. Jellyfish don't swim around attacking men, they pulse and float along their own stupid, blind way waiting patiently to bump into something they can eat. They sting anything they encounter. They are never in a hurry and have been floating around this way for untold years. It is obviously a successful way of life since billions of them are still around. While they can't very well make a meal of a man, they don't know it. They just bump and sting, bump and sting. To avoid the sting, man has only to avoid the bump. While he may be able to depend on the fear, quiet good nature, or the escape "reflexes" of other potentially dangerous animals, he cannot do this with jellyfish. He must learn to keep out of the way.

# PART VII

*Epilogue*

# CHAPTER 28

# *Other Potential Dangers*

In the preceding twenty-seven chapters we have reviewed some facts about a varied number of "unpleasant" creatures. If it has appeared that I have been trying to construct a collection of horror stories, I have failed to make a basic point. What I have, in fact, been attempting to do is simply shed some light on a very cloudy subject—the story of animals potentially hazardous to man. Biology is not an exact science. We do not yet fully understand life; we cannot simulate it; and we still know comparatively little about animal behavior—human as well as other animal. To draw what I think is a reasonable parallel we need only look at the record of human crime.

A shocking number of crimes of violence are committed by men and women who have been paroled from prison or released from mental institutions. If human beings under restraint and under searching psychiatric care do not provide valid clues to their future behavior, how then do we dare say what a lion, a shark, or a bear will do? These "lower" creatures, some will say, have less complex minds and therefore are more fathomable. Less complex perhaps, but therefore automatically less known or understood. In fact, categoric statements as to what any animal will, or will not, do are worthless.

It is quite possible for an experienced game ranger to approach a pride of lions in full view in relative safety. He knows his cats and the risk is minimal for the expert. However, we must never forget that it is the exceptions, the miscalculations that provide the statistics with which we have been dealing in this book.

By a very wide margin, most people injured or killed by wild animals are victims of circumstances rather than of intent on the part of the creatures themselves. While some elephants may indeed suffer a kind of insanity, and some cats may take to man-eating and actually hunt man as prey, most accidents are caused by a misunderstanding on the part of an animal as to man's intentions, and even more so a misunderstanding on the part of the man as to the animal's reactions. Snakes and spiders strike in defense, big carnivores, if wounded or in defense of young, and animals in general in reaction to territorial incursion.

In this book I have tried to determine what, if any, facts exist to substantiate the most oft-heard claims. In many cases, this has not been

333

Robber Crabs (*Birgus latro*). Arrows point to crabs, which, in both photo and in real life, are difficult to see.

From *Shelled Invertebrates*, Smithsonian Institution Series.

possible, and the best we could do was attempt a logical examination of what the facts probably are. There are many more marginal cases left that cry out for study. Some examples follow.

Some time ago, a slick men's magazine told of foot-long crabs called Robber, Birgus, or Coconut Crabs (probably referring to a species known as *Birgus latro*) found on the shores and islands of the South Pacific, the Indian Ocean, and adjacent seas. The statement that they grow to be a foot long is not an exaggeration. It is also true that these huge creatures climb trees, cut down coconuts with their pincers, and tear the extremely tough covering apart to get at the meat. But what of the article's contention that twenty-six people were killed by these crabs, when they attacked thirty marooned Moslem pilgrims on an island in the Red Sea, and punctured the skulls of those too weak to escape or defend themselves? This reputedly happened in 1951. The "facts" were revealed in a court case in Massowa, Eritrea. Since island people regularly hunt the giant *Birgus latro* for food, and not vice versa, the case, if true, is rather exceptional, to say the least.

Many stories exist about a Platyhelminthine (flatworm)—a Planarian of biology-class fame in this case—in Central America that "slimes" about in and on rotten logs exuding a perfectly dreadful poison. The results of contact with it are variously described as raising everything from a rash to a gravestone. (Why anyone would go around touching such a thing defies understanding!) The story is not surprising if geography be taken into consideration, for just about everything in Central America has been accused of being venomous by some "explorer" or another, a surprisingly large number of whom have operated exclusively from the area lying between 39th and 67th Streets on Manhattan Island! Nevertheless, as long ago as 1860, some of the brightly-colored land planarians were reported to be "disagreeable to the taste of man and some birds." (Why anyone would go around tasting such things *completely* defies understanding.)

Many of the corals and anemones are venomous and sting with a device very similar to that of the jellyfish. None are known to cause death, although the discomfort may be acute. Accidents with these forms occur by the thousands and perhaps tens of thousands annually. In some areas, the phenomenon of dermatitis resulting from simple contact with them can be a health problem.

A number of leeches (class *Hirundinea*) feed on man and, although they do not transmit disease, they can be debilitating. Large, tropical, aquatic leeches are said to be capable of taking from a man as much as ten cubic centimeters of blood in as many minutes. Troops working their way through tropical swamps are said to have picked up as many as a hundred leeches a day per man. Stories abound about men being killed by swarms of leeches at night, although I know of no documents that bear this out. Widely distributed throughout southeast Asia is *Dinobdella ferox*, a naso-pharyngeal leech that works its way into the throat and nasal passages of mammals (including man) who drink from streams. Although not deadly, leeches are a horrible nuisance and terribly disturbing to even the slightly sensitive.

Many sea urchins (*Echinodermata*) can cause serious injuries when trodden upon by unwary swimmers and waders. Some are actually venomous, and some have spines up to a foot in length which are acutely pointed and very brittle. Reputedly, too many of these broken off in a man's body can cause death. Certainly, being impaled on one or more spines ten to twelve inches long (that are bound to break off in the wound) is a serious matter.

Some segmented, notably the marine bristle worms (Annelids), can bite and cause painful rashes. Deaths are not known to have occurred, but injuries are very common in a number of areas.

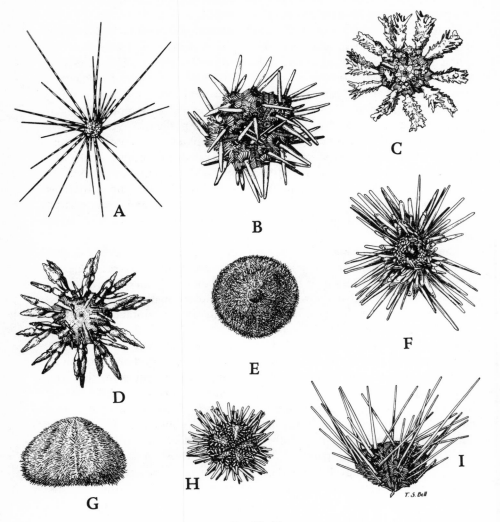

Sea Urchins.

General Biological Supply House, Inc.

A. Salenia cincta
B. Phyllacanthus irregularis
C. Goniocidaris tubaria (aboral view)
D. Chondrocidaris brevispina (oral view)
E. Asthenosoma varium (oral view)

F. Heterocentrotus trigonarius (oral view)
G. Salmacis virgulata (side view)
H. Arbacia spatuligera
I. Histocidaris elegans (side view)

The list of animal forms that can and do cause injuries to man is, at this stage of our knowledge, endless, and an examination of the new claims made each year would fill many volumes. Professional medical and scientific literature of Australia, India, many parts of South America, and Africa contain numberless case histories, reports, and suggestions, and even postmortem findings. For instance, in March, 1963, a supplement was issued to the *Bulletin of the Post-Graduate Committee in Medicine,* University of Sydney. This, the *Proceedings of the First International Convention on Life Saving Techniques, Part III, Scientific Section,* is 131 pages long and contains twenty-seven separate articles with attendant discussion—all dealing with dangerous marine organisms. Many case histories are cited in detail. Medical units of military organizations have issued similar material. The literature is quite overwhelming. Taken on the surface, this mass of material would make it seem that life anywhere except in your own living room is hazardous in the extreme. Such is not the case.

If you had the time and the energy, you could walk completely around the world in any latitude you might select (at least across the land surfaces in any given latitude) and never fall victim to more than an occasional insect bite. In point of fact, it would be extremely rare for you to suffer any ill at all from contact with wildlife. When you take into account the numbers of people in daily contact with or at least in proximity to wild animals, attacks upon and injuries to man are really very, very rare.

There are, however, some forms of animal life that are really dangerous to man, and some that are deadly. Although contact even with these is extremely rare, from a statistical point of view, these forms are well worth knowing when travel or residence in the places where they live is anticipated.

*Appendices*

# APPENDIX A

# *Treatment of Injuries Caused by Wild Animals*

As HAS BEEN STATED a number of times in this book, an injury resulting from a traumatic encounter with a wild animal frequently constitutes a medical emergency. The size of the injury may vary from a slight pin prick, to gross amputations and extensive mutilations. While some injuries will more obviously demand immediate professional care than others, even the smallest injury may require the help of medical specialists. A nip from a small bat that barely draws blood can mean that the (fatal) rabies virus has been transmitted. A sting from a scorpion's tail is hardly represented by gross tissue damage, yet a lethal substance may have been injected.

For our purposes, there are three considerations in the evaluation, care, and treatment of an animal-caused injury:

1. Introduction of microorganisms: bacteria, viruses, protozoans, etc.
2. Tissue damage: bleeding, shock, and other gross local or systemic effects.
3. Venoms: the introduction of noxious substances, and resultant complications.

Each of these considerations indicates a separate health problem and a separate course of treatment.

## I. THE INTRODUCTION OF MICROORGANISMS

Animal bites, gorings and clawings are inevitably dirty wounds. The puncturing effect of a bite, the raking lacerations of claws, and goring by horns and antlers will almost always introduce inimical microorganisms into the victim's tissues and blood stream. It would be a rare injury of any of these types that would heal uneventfully if left untreated. Even in cases where normal body defenses are able to engulf and destroy invading hosts, dangerous chemicals are liberated and the body will suffer. In two very special cases, the natural, unaided body defenses are totally incapable of any effective defense.

In the case of rabies, as we shall see, the human body is defenseless. The viruses involved will destroy the nerve and brain tissue of the new host and bring inevitable death. The human body has been unable to "learn" how to meet this threat; an antibody must be stimulated or the victim will die. The utter helplessness of man's natural defenses in the face of newly incubated rabies virus can not be overestimated.

Tetanus, or "Lockjaw," is caused by an anaerobic bacterium, *Clostridium tetani*. Anaerobic bacteria are microorganisms that can grow and reproduce

341

only where atmospheric oxygen is totally lacking, or severely reduced. Once deposited deep in human tissue, as in an animal bite, and particularly in wounds that scab over and start to heal, they grow rapidly and begin to secrete poisonous substances that bring on the characteristic disease. *Clostridium tetani* is inevitably introduced in animal injuries. This microorganism is present in stools, on the body, and in the saliva of most animals—including man. It is a natural inhabitant there. Specific medical treatment can prevent the uncontrolled growth of these organisms and can head off the deadly disease. Introduction of the tetanus organism into a wound is almost impossible to avoid. If the wound closes quickly, or is at all deep, it will then permit these bacteria to begin to reproduce. *Virtually all animal injuries indicate tetanus prophylactic measures.*

A catalog of the other microorganisms that can be introduced by animal injuries would be far too extensive to present here, both by virtue of the number of organisms involved and the qualifying statements required for each. Suffice it to repeat the statement above, *animal bites, gorings, and clawings are inevitably dirty wounds.* The wounds themselves require careful cleansing, and the body needs help in preventing the uncontrolled growth of dangerous microorganisms. Help, such as rabies vaccine, tetanus shots, or a broad-spectrum antibiotic course are invariably indicated. But the decision as to which are so indicated is for the doctor to make. The speed with which the victim is put under a doctor's care will, in many cases, be a major factor in determining the speed with which he will recover. Of course, some microorganisms allow a more flexible time factor than others.

Recapitulating briefly, non-venomous animal wounds, from the point of view of microorganisms, require:

1. the same first aid indicated by any filthy injury, and
2. professional medical consultation and care.

## II. Tissue Damage

Of immediate concern—even more immediate than the problem of microorganisms—can be the matter of tissue damage and the loss of body fluids. In the majority of animal injuries, such as bites and stings by small venomous and non-venomous reptiles, fishes, insects, and arachnids, tissue damage is not primarily a first-aid problem. The concern for the safety of the victim will center around, in order of urgency, (1) venoms and (2) microorganisms. Only in the minority of cases, will tissue damage be the primary concern.

On the other hand, shark attacks, injuries inflicted by big cats, bears, and other carnivores, and gorings by hoofed animals can result in appalling damage. Rule number one in such gross injuries is *Stop the bleeding.* Nothing you or a doctor can do for a patient will have much value if he bleeds to death. In the really massive traumas, such as those characteristically inflicted by sharks, the prevention of run-away hemorrhage is just about all a bystander can do—except treat for shock and try to obtain professional help. Any first-aid manual will outline the three ways to control bleeding: pressure point, tourniquet, and pressure bandage. Anyone exposed to wildlife should know basic first aid, and basic first aid includes the control of blood loss at the top of the list. The "*environments,*" the surroundings in which you will find wildlife are more apt to do you injury than the wildlife itself, but first aid is still the first and most essential knowledge for everyone in the field. A knowledge of artificial respiration, mouth-to-mouth resuscitation, basic bandaging techniques, and the immobilization of injured limbs are also essential information for everyone to have. The interested reader is referred to any good first-aid manual, and is urged to take a comprehensive first-aid course.

Shock is always attendant upon gross injury. It can have a wide range of effects and manifestations, from a slight giddy feeling, or weakness in the knees, to nausea, cold sweat, coma, and death. *Anyone injured by a wild animal will suffer from shock. Shock can, and does kill.*

More often than not, shock is more severe than the victim realizes. The number of injured people who have said, "I'm O.K. now," or "I'm all right," seconds before passing out are legion. In an injury of any size, or where much pain or particularly disturbing circumstances have been involved, *treat for shock.* Try to make the patient remain calm, sitting, or lying down. Keep him or her warm, avoid artificial stimulants, discourage the examination of the wound by the victim, and, as much as possible, avoid fuss and confusion. The patient's mind and body will be struggling valiantly to offset and overcome the trauma that has been forced upon him. Help him in that struggle with calm, firm control, warmth, pain relief (other than depressant drugs), immobilization, comfort, bandaging, quiet, and reassurance.

In most injuries, particularly gross traumas, the conscious patient will be in a dangerous state of mind. The horror of what has happened can help increase the disposition to shock; stark terror can impede first-aid measures; and an inability to accept a true evaluation of the situation can reduce the victim's ability to cope with his problem. Calm, quiet, isolation from crowds of the morbidly curious, and assertive reassurance are all part of effective first aid. There will always be loads of "experts" around. Above all, keep them from getting at the victim with their shouted advice, ghoulish admiration of the extent of the injuries, and generally appalling lack of appreciation of how the victim feels. Categorically, anyone who knows he cannot help but runs to look, is an enemy of the patient. Keep them away even if you make enemies; but don't let the victim see or hear you rushing them off. That will only add to the horror of the moment.

Animal injuries inevitably come as a shock. Seldom does the victim even see the creature, except perhaps at the very last moment. It is a rare individual who is emotionally prepared for an assault on his person by a wild animal. A skier shouldn't be too surprised if he breaks an arm or a leg and anyone working with sharp instruments is at least subconsciously aware of the hazards to which he is exposed. A hiker, on the other hand, is literally stunned when an unseen venomous snake lashes out from a pile of dead leaves; a swimmer is utterly horror-stricken when suddenly grabbed from below; and a Black Widow Spider under a toilet seat can transfix almost anyone. Take this into consideration when dealing with the victim of an animal injury. The state of mind resulting from this kind of accident is highly conducive to shock.

### III. Venomous Bites and Stings

While there are rare but nonetheless notable exceptions (the bite of a sea snake, for one), an injury caused by a venomous animal is generally accompanied by excruciating pain. The pain may be immediate (venomous fishes), quick in coming (many venomous snakes), or relatively slow in developing a peak (spiders), but pain is invariably a major factor in an encounter of this kind. The agony of a stonefish sting (immediate), or the over-all Charley horse reputedly resulting from the bite of certain spiders can make a victim difficult to help. Restraint may sometimes be necessary.

The author was called upon to perform first aid on a young man bitten by a Cottonmouth snake in a Louisiana swamp and required the assistance of three strong men to hold the victim down. The pain, coupled with the horror of the moment, not only makes first aid at times difficult but contributes to shock. Pain, agonizing pain, is usually a major problem in venomous bites and stings.

The best method for dealing with these injuries is not clear cut. Advice from different experts is not always in agreement, and medical literature today contains open controversy between declaiming parties. It is difficult for a layman to take a position relative to these arguments, and a general description of the two virtually opposing schools of thought is all that can, within reason, be attempted.

The best-known method for the treatment of venomous stings and bites is the so-called T-C-S technique, the initials standing for Tourniquet-Cut-Suction. This method has been the standard first-aid system for years, and relatively few laymen realize that it is held in disfavor by many doctors today. This technique simply involves the placing of a tourniquet, when possible, between the wound and the body, making small cross cuts over the punctures, and applying suction. Regular "snake-bite kits" containing a tourniquet, a sterile scalpel encased in wax, a suction pump, iodine, and a capsule of ammonia are sold in drug stores, by mail-order houses, and issued by the armed forces to units in the field. The American Red Cross First Aid Book, and most others on the subject, seem almost automatically to set forth this method with each new printing. But, is it the best method to use?

Dr. Herbert L. Stahnke, Director of the Poisonous Animals Research Laboratory at Arizona State University, has set forward the four principal problems in cases of envenomation as:

1. Rapid entrance of the venomous substance into the blood stream,
2. The dangerous effect this noxious material has, once it is in the body,
3. The potential destructive chemical action of the poison at the site of its introduction,
4. The dangerous conditions that can arise as a result of microorganisms inevitably introduced with the venom.

Dr. Stahnke claims that the T-C-S method "inadequately takes care of the first problem and does nothing for the other three; in fact, it actually increases the danger in the last two problems."

Dr. Stahnke has long advocated the L-C technique of treatment, the initials in this case standing for *ligature* and *cryotherapy*. In this system, a ligature, or tight tie-off is placed between the bite or sting and the body, as close to the wound as possible, and without regard for pressure points sought in applying a regular tourniquet. As quickly as possible, the injured member is packed in ice, or iced water. In the case of bites by pit vipers, cobras and other really dangerous large species of snake, the ice therapy should be kept up for at least 24 hours. Ice bags are not adequate, and the whole member is kept at as low a temperature (above the freezing point of body tissues) as is possible, while the rest of the body is kept warm. Simple *hypothermia* (or reduction of temperature) of the injured member is only used as a stop-gap measure when ice is not immediately available. Bottled gases, not applied directly to the skin but used to make frigid pads, can be used, as can $CO_2$ fire extinguishers and a number of other commercial devices. Care must be taken to avoid $CO_2$ burns. When the skin turns white, treatment must be stopped until color returns. In cases of injury by a scorpion, *hypothermia* may be enough until antivenin can be administered.

It is Dr. Stahnke's contention that antivenin (which *must* be administered no matter what first-aid technique is used) will take care of the venom in the body. The L-C technique is reported to retard the activity and the spread of the venom (unless an artery or vein is hit during the strike) and deter the extensive tissue damage at the site of the wound that can result from the digestive action of the venom. Amputations, necessitated by gangrene resulting from this tissue damage, are not uncommon in cases of bites by large pit vipers. The L-C technique is reported also to retard the growth and reproduction of microorganisms until the necessary prophylactic shots can be administered. For further explanation of the L-C method of treatment, the reader is referred to Dr. Stahnke's *The Treatment of Venomous Bites and Stings,* available from his laboratory in Temple, Arizona, for fifty cents. For details on the T-C-S method, any first-aid book will do.

The basic difference between the T-C-S and the L-C methods appears to center around the matter of cutting at the wound site (T-C-S for and L-C dead-set against), cryotherapy (L-C insistent upon and T-C-S not providing for), and tourniquet (T-C-S) vs. ligature (L-C). A tourniquet, properly applied, is placed at a pressure point, while a ligature is a tight tying-off very close to the wound. If the wound is on the head or torso, neither a tourniquet nor a ligature can be used. Both methods require professional help as soon as possible and the professional administration of an antivenin.

It occurs to this author that, as a whole, medical science should take a position on this argument that can be considered definitive. Obviously, one system is right and the other, while not necessarily wrong, is less effective. There must be a *best* way to deal with venomous bites and stings at the first-aid level, but it is not easy for a layman to decide which it is. This author suspects that L-C will come into favor. Of course, there will be times when cryotherapy will not be possible, such as in a desert. If the L-C method does emerge as the proper treatment, what does one do when caught hours away from ice or medical facilities? Perhaps a fire extinguisher should be carried.

Antivenin (not *anti-venom*) kits can be purchased in a drugstore by any layman and, with due attention to the instructions enclosed, can be used in an emergency. It is always better to have the administration of such materials done by a professional but that is not always possible.

*A note of caution:* Antivenin can kill. It is made from horse serum, in many instances, and some people are violently allergic to this serum and can die from its use, whereas they might not succumb to the venom itself. Antivenin kits include materials and instructions for testing for horse sensitivity. *Do not panic* and start plunging needles into people. Read those instructions and test for sensitivity. The victim of a venomous bite or sting has enough trouble without your putting him into fatal anaphylactic shock, or even into a severe hyper-allergic state.

Antivenins are happily now available for a wide variety of venomous bites and stings. Hospitals, and frequently doctors, in areas where venomous species are found, generally stock fresh supplies. All of the common venomous animals in North America are now covered by available antivenins, many of them broad spectrum polyvalents. However, exotic species may pose an altogether different problem, and field work in new areas where venomous forms may offer a problem should be preceded by a check on antivenin availability, as a matter of course. Anyone importing, working with, or otherwise exposed to foreign forms should certainly bring in supplies to hold in readiness. There is no excuse for a fatal accident with venomous forms for which antivenin is readily available. *The antivenin should be imported before the venom!*

There are many bites and stings for which no antivenins are available. This is particularly true of marine forms, and the reader is referred to Dr. Bruce W. Halstead's *Dangerous Marine Animals* for specific details of treatment for these many forms. [The Bibliography will further guide the interested reader to researchers in the various specialized fields.]

Most of the people in this world will never be called upon to aid someone who has been attacked by a wild animal. Despite the astounding statistics we hear, these injuries are rare. However, a camper who is mauled by a bear, bitten by a venomous snake, or stung by a scorpion is in serious trouble. Knowledgeable first aid and prompt, professional medical attention will keep the death rate low. It has not been high since the advent of sophisticated medicine and surgery, but could be lower yet. Except in the extremely rare cases of massive trauma (big cats and sharks being the principal offenders), many of those who do succumb could be saved with the proper attention. Don't go into the field without first-aid equipment, and don't take equipment you haven't really learned to use. You will probably never use it on an animal-attack victim, but the saving of a human life is a motive grand enough to warrant all of the preparation and investment each of us can afford. What is more, it could be *your* life.

# APPENDIX B

# *Rabies*

THIS BOOK is about reputedly dangerous animals that can be seen with the naked eye. In it we avoid discussion of bacteria and viruses. Not only does there have to be a limit to the size of any book, the matter of "disease" resulting from microorganisms constitutes quite a separate subject, and would require a whole new frame of reference. Two exceptions are, however, required; the subject of the disease commonly called *rabies;* and, as discussed in Appendix G, poisoning caused by eating certain fishes.

Rabies, hydrophobia, or lyssa, is an acute, infectious disease of mammals, and particularly carnivores, that is *always fatal* to man once it takes hold; viz., passes the incubation period. A person exposed to the saliva of an infected animal by reason of a bite and who receives the causative neurotropic virus in his tissues (or who drinks the milk of an infected animal) is doomed to a particularly horrible death unless immediate and extensive counteractive measures are carried out. Anywhere from ten days to two years after the bite (fifty to sixty days is average) the symptoms will start.[1] Restlessness and depression will be followed by gradually increasing anxiety. Fear will grow into terror, periods of violent, uncontrollable rage will alternate with sudden listless calm, as the brain tissues are first irritated and eventually injured beyond control or repair. A ringing telephone, a draft from a small electric fan, or the light from a cigarette lighter will induce convulsions. Spastic contractions of the pharynx and larynx will cause agonizing pain when an attempt is made to swallow. Extreme thirst, coupled with a dread of strangling, will turn the victim into a raging maniac on the sight, or even mention of water. Mercifully, death from cardiac or respiratory failure will usually come within three to five days after the onset of symptoms. There is a second form of rabies generally referred to as the "dumb form"[2] where the violent, convulsive symptoms are lacking, and paralysis precedes death.

In 1884, Pasteur developed the counteractive vaccine used today. A person who has been bitten by a suspected carrier *must* receive repeated doses of this vaccine (prepared from the brain tissue of an infected animal) *before* the symptoms appear. Since fourteen days are required for the human body to produce rabies antibodies, this serum is used to cover this dangerous gap. Pure carbolic acid on the wound may prolong the incubation period, but it cannot be relied upon to kill all the viruses and its use has fallen into general disfavor among

[1] Among those working on bat-transmitted rabies, 48 hours is held to be the limit before professional medical countermeasures are instituted.
[2] That is, *"paralytic"* as opposed to *"furious."*

most doctors. *No first-aid measure can defer the absolute necessity of a vaccine course.*

The incidence of rabies in nature is peculiar and complex. It infects the central nervous system and finally concentrates in the brain in an area called Ammon's Horn where it forms minute black clots called Negri or Inclusion bodies. These are readily identifiable on autopsy.

Rabies seems to be a universally distributed malady, and used to be, before the discovery of its cause, a constant menace. Even the ancients recognized that it followed animal bites, and long before Pasteur's work, pariah and other feral dogs were slaughtered whenever it broke out in epidemic form. It must be stressed that it still probably remains all over the world in endemic form; that is to say, there are "reservoirs" of it, in a latent form, in some species of animals in almost all countries. It appears to become increasingly common as one approaches the equatorial regions, and (perhaps) less so as one goes toward the poles.

The disease occurs in the two distinct forms already referred to (these are *not* different strains or "kinds," they differ only in symptoms) and may alternate, in that carnivorous animals usually display the furious, while their vegetarian victims display the paralytic. However, there is usually a comatose period in the former and often a furious phase in the latter. All animals—including man—infected with this disease will, or may, bite uncontrollably, but the worst are perhaps (naturally) the meat-eaters. Some animals, like man, may go into coma before they reach this stage. Herbivores may simply become paralyzed; and this paralysis may involve the jaw muscles at an early stage, thus preventing them from biting. However, the most dangerous of all animals as transmitters of rabies are the bats, because they can fly at you or at other animals; and, among the bats, there are two genera, *Desmodus* and *Diphylla*, that far exceed all other bats (and all other animals) as a menace in this respect because they are, by nature, blood-lappers, and cannot eat anything else.

These, so-called, true Vampire Bats (several other kinds of bats are called vampire bats in various areas but are either fruit or insect eaters) are inhabitants of South and Central America and, it seems, have in the recently-passed decades been slowly extending their range northward into North America. They live in caves and other retreats along with other kinds of bats and are just about the only animals that can infect these other bats. *Desmodus* is probably the great natural reservoir of rabies today, and it is only since it has reached our southern border that other (insect-eating) bats have turned up in a rabid condition in this country. Many of our common bats migrate in winter to the far south and become infected there, then fly north again to infect other bats that then start biting other animals they would normally avoid.

A further and added menace of *Desmodus* is that it apparently can carry rabies for very long periods, if not indefinitely, without displaying symptoms of the disease. In fact, much of the *Desmodus* population may even be immune to it, though still housing Negri bodies.

Today, rabies is not a major health problem, although it is an ever-present menace. In 1959, seven people in the United States died of the disease, five in 1958, and five in 1957. At times, however, it can assume alarming proportions, and particular care must be exercised in special situations.

Strangely enough, it wasn't until 1953 that clinical data substantiated the long-suspected fact that bats were transmitting rabies in the United States, for *Desmodus* is not found much north of the Mexican border. On the morning of June 23 in that year, the seven-year-old son of a Florida ranch employee ran into some bushes after a ball. A bat flew at him and bit him on the chest, maintaining a firm hold. It was knocked to the ground and killed. The ranch owner, recalling that vampire bats were known to be infected with rabies in Mexico, sent the bat to a laboratory in Tampa, where Negri bodies were found in the brain. Further tests were conducted at Jacksonville and Montgomery. The boy was put into an immunization course and recovery was uneventful. Had the rancher not remembered a piece he had read about Mexican bats, the boy would have died.

Of the world's estimated two thousand species and subspecies of bats, sixty-five are regularly found in the United States. How many of these are reservoirs of rabies is not known, but presumably all can be, since all mammals, it is believed, can be infected.

After the 1953 Florida attack, a careful study was made of bat bites. It turned out that a woman was bitten by a bat in Texas in 1951, and died in less than a month. An autopsy revealed Negri bodies in her brain. An insectivorous bat bit a Pennsylvania woman in 1953, and was found to be rabid. A man was bitten in Harrisburg, Pennsylvania, in April, 1957, by a bat that proved to have been infected.

Although it is now clear that any bat that bites a human must be immediately suspect, these small, flying mammals are not the only wild creatures involved in the spread of this disease. At the end of the Civil War, it is reported, skunks were infected throughout the western states. Campers were attacked in their tents at night, and, reportedly, many died. Skunks were dreaded by everyone and killed on sight. Foxes, and more particularly coyotes, are known to be carriers, and probably help to spread the disease among domestic dogs.

Rabies is not only of concern to man because he can contract it and be killed by it but because it is also deadly to domestic stock and causes "mad" (or dumb) and unpredictable behavior among wild animals. There can be little doubt that some attacks on humans by species not normally prone to attack—mountain lion and deer included—are caused by this disease. How many attacks can be accounted for in this way is not known. Household pets become savage beasts as they approach the terminal stages of the infection. Livestock must be destroyed once the symptoms become apparent, and many otherwise inexplicable accidents with farm animals can probably be traced to rabies.

How do you avoid becoming a victim? Here are a few ground rules:

1. *Do not be a hero* if an oddly-behaving dog shows up in the neighborhood. Get your family, your pets, *and yourself* indoors and call the police. If you even suspect a pet animal of having gotten near a "mad dog," get it to a veterinarian immediately. If you are driving along and an animal suddenly dashes in front of your car and is knocked down, control your natural instincts and don't pick the injured animal up in your exposed hands. By all means, try to help the creature, but throw a blanket or rug around it and don't let its head near your face when you carry it. The animal may have been reacting to a rabies infection when it dashed under your wheels in the first place.

2. If a pet suddenly displays a change in temperament, get it to a vet. If it is unusually cranky, if it reacts too violently to light or noise, don't take chances.

3. If you come across a small wild creature that seems to be sick, or dying, or unusually "tame" or lacking fear of you *do not handle it*. This is particularly true of bats, foxes, and skunks. If a wild animal enters your camp site and acts viciously, avoid any personal contact. Destroy it without exposing yourself to a possible bite, or trap it without handling it. Turn it over to the nearest health authorities. Most important of all, don't touch a wild animal that shows no fear of you, or is wandering about by day and lets you approach it. It is probably diseased, and the disease may be rabies.

4. Be careful in caves, hollow trees, and barns. Do not pick up any bat that seems unable to fly. Avoid *any* area where you note bats crawling around on the floor or ground.

5. If bitten by any wild mammal, *secure the animal*—killing it is the safest course—and take it *at once* to the nearest health authority, hospital, or game warden.

6. If you have reason to suspect a dog that has bitten you or anyone you know, do everything you can to secure or identify the animal, and go to a doctor immediately. (By *secure* is meant trap it in a garage or by some similar technique—do *not* attempt to handle it.) Do not let stories of how unpleasant a course of rabies vaccine is deter you from seeking treatment. It is nothing like the disease itself. Rabies is *not* like most other viral infections that can be treated at home or will pass in time. *If you are exposed to the disease and do not receive professional help, you will die!*

At the beginning of this book we said we would discuss only wild animals, not domestic ones. This chapter is an exception to that rule, for any animal, even a human being, may be a "carrier" of this dread disease—even your lovable dog if it has been so much as scratched by an infected animal. A rabid animal, however small, is the most dangerous animal alive. Unlike snakes, scorpions, spiders, and all other venomous forms, untreated bites of a rabid mammal are *100 per cent fatal.*

# APPENDIX C

# *The Rattlesnakes*

BECAUSE of the special interest in this group of reptiles among residents of the Western Hemisphere, the following tables are provided. Information was obtained from Laurence M. Klauber's two-volume work, *Rattlesnakes: Their Habits, Life Histories, and Influence on Mankind.*

## THE RATTLESNAKES

| Species and Subspecies | Popular Name | Range (Words "parts of" implied) |
|---|---|---|
| 1. *Crotalus adamanteus* | Eastern Diamondback Rattlesnake* | Lowland coastal plains: North Carolina, South Carolina, Georgia, Florida (and some adjacent keys), Alabama, Mississippi, Louisiana |
| 2. *C. atrox* | Western Diamondback | Arkansas, Oklahoma, Missouri (?), Kansas, Oklahoma, Texas (and coastal islands), New Mexico, Arizona, Nevada, California, Baja California, Mexico and islands in Gulf of California |
| 3. *C. basiliscus basiliscus* | Mexican West Coast | Mexico |
| 4. *C. basiliscus oaxacus* | Oaxacan | Mexico—limited range |
| 5. *C. catalinensis* | Santa Catalina Island | Mexican Santa Catalina Island—*not* the California island of that name |
| 6. *C. cerastes cerastes* | Mojave Desert Side-winder† | California, Nevada, Utah, Arizona |
| 7. *C. cerastes cercobombus* | Sonoran Desert Side-winder† | Arizona, Mexico, Tiburon Island |
| 8. *C. cerastes laterorepens* | Colorado Desert Side-winder† | California, Arizona, Baja California, Mexico |
| 9. *C. durissus durissus* | Central American | Mexico, Guatemala, Honduras, El Salvador, Nicaragua, Costa Rica, British Honduras (?) |
| 10. *C. durissus culminatus* | Northwestern Neo-tropical | Mexico |
| 11. *C. durissus terrificus* | South American | Colombia, Venezuela, British Guiana, Surinam, French Guiana, Brazil, Peru, Bolivia, Paraguay, Uruguay, Argentina, Ecuador (?) |

* Unless otherwise noted, the word "Rattlesnake" is part of the preferred popular name.

† Word "Rattlesnake" not included in common or preferred popular name.

THE RATTLESNAKES (*Continued*)

| Species and Subspecies | Popular Name | Range (Words "parts of" implied) |
|---|---|---|
| 12. *C. durissus totonacus* | Totonacan | Mexico |
| 13. *C. durissus tzabcan* | Yucatan Neotropical | Mexico, Guatemala (?), British Honduras (?) |
| 14. *C. durissus vegrandis* | Urucoan | Venezuela |
| 15. *C. enyo enyo* | Lower California | Baja California and west coast Mexican islands |
| 16. *C. enyo cerralvensis* | Cerralvo Island | Cerralvo Island, Mexico, Gulf of California |
| 17. *C. enyo furvus* | Rosario | Baja California |
| 18. *C. exsul* | Cedros Island Diamondback | Cedros Island, Baja California |
| 19. *C. horridus horridus* | Timber | Vermont, New Hampshire, Virginia, West Virginia, Ohio, Kentucky, North and South Carolina, Georgia, Tennessee, Alabama, Indiana, Illinois, Wisconsin, Minnesota, Iowa, Missouri, Nebraska, Kansas, Arkansas, Oklahoma, Texas, New York, Massachusetts, Connecticut, New Jersey, Rhode Island, Pennsylvania.; formerly also Maine and Delaware; Canada (Ontario) |
| 20. *C. horridus atricaudatus* | Canebrake | Virginia, North and South Carolina, Georgia, Florida, Alabama, Mississippi, Kentucky, Tennessee, Louisiana, Arkansas, Missouri, Illinois, Texas |
| 21. *C. intermedius intermedius* | Totalcan Small-Headed | Mexico |
| 22. *C. intermedius omiltemanus* | Omilteman Small-Headed | Mexico |
| 23. *C. lepidus lepidus* | Mottled Rock | New Mexico, Texas, Mexico |
| 24. *C. lepidus klauberi* | Banded Rock | Arizona, New Mexico, Texas, Mexico |
| 25. *C. lepidus morulus* | Tamaulipan Rock | Mexico—limited range |
| 26. *C. mitchelli mitchelli* | San Lucan Speckled | Baja California, Mexico, Gulf and Pacific coast Mexican islands |
| 27. *C. mitchelli muertensis* | El Muerto Island Speckled | El Muerto Island only, off Baja California |
| 28. *C. mitchelli pyrrhus* | Southwestern Speckled | California, Nevada, Arizona, Utah, Baja California, Pacific coast Mexican islands |
| 29. *C. mitchelli stephensi* | Panamint | California, Nevada |
| 30. *C. molossus molossus* | Northern Black-Tailed | Texas, Arizona, New Mexico, Mexico, Gulf of California, Mexico islands |
| 31. *C. molossus estebanensis* | San Esteban Island | San Esteban Island, Gulf of California |

THE RATTLESNAKES *(Continued)*

| Species and Subspecies | Popular Name | Range (Words "parts of" implied) |
|---|---|---|
| 32. *C. molossus nigrescens* | Mexican Black-Tailed | Mexico |
| 33. *C. polystictus* | Mexican Lance-Headed | Mexico |
| 34. *C. pricei pricei* | Arizona Twin-Spotted | Arizona, Mexico |
| 35. *C. pricei miquihuanus* | Miquihuanan Twin-Spotted | Mexico |
| 36. *C. pusillus* | Tancitaran Dusky | Mexico |
| 37. *C. ruber ruber* | Red Diamondback | California, Baja California, Mexico, Gulf of California islands |
| 38. *C. ruber lucasensis* | San Lucan Diamond-back | Baja California, Gulf of California islands |
| 39. *C. scutulatus scutulatus* | Mojave | California, Nevada, Utah, Arizona, New Mexico, Texas, Mexico |
| 40. *C. scutulatus salvini* | Huamantlan | Mexico |
| 41. *C. stejnegeri* | Long-Tailed | Arizona, Mexico |
| 42. *C. tigris* | Tiger | Arizona, Mexico |
| 43. *C. tortugensis* | Tortuga Island Diamondback | Tortuga Island, Gulf of California |
| 44. *C. transversus* | Cross-Banded Mountain | Mexico |
| 45. *C. triseriatus triseriatus* | Central-Plateau Dusky | Mexico |
| 46. *C. triseriatus aquilus* | Queretaran Dusky | Mexico |
| 47. *C. unicolor* | Aruba Island | Aruba Island (coast of Venezuela) |
| 48. *C. viridis viridis* | Prairie | Canada (Alberta, Saskatchewan), Mexico, Montana, Idaho, Wyoming, Colorado, Utah, Arizona, New Mexico, North and South Dakota, Iowa, Nebraska, Kansas, Oklahoma, Texas |
| 49. *C. viridis abyssus* | Grand Canyon | Arizona |
| 50. *C. viridis caliginis* | Coronado Island | South Coronado Island, off Baja California |
| 51. *C. viridis cerberus* | Arizona Black | Arizona, New Mexico |
| 52. *C. viridis decolor* | Midget Faded | Wyoming, Utah, Colorado |
| 53. *C. viridis helleri* | Southern Pacific | California, Baja California, Santa Catalina Island |
| 54. *C. viridis lutosus* | Great Basin | Idaho, Utah, Arizona, Nevada, California, Oregon |
| 55. *C. viridis nuntius* | Arizona Prairie | Arizona, New Mexico |
| 56. *C. viridis oreganus* | Northern Pacific | Canada (British Columbia), California, Washington, Oregon, Idaho |
| 57. *C. willardi amabilis* | | Mexico |
| 58. *C. willardi willardi* | Arizona Ridge-Nosed | Arizona, Mexico |
| 59. *C. willardi meridionalis* | Southern Ridge-Nosed | Mexico |
| 60. *C. willardi silus* | Chihuahuan Ridge-Nosed | Mexico, New Mexico |

THE RATTLESNAKES (*Continued*)

| Species and Subspecies | Popular Name | Range (Words "parts of" implied) |
|---|---|---|
| 61. *Sistrurus catenatus catenatus* | Eastern Massasauga† | New York, Canada (Ontario), Pennsylvania, Michigan, Ohio, Indiana, Illinois, Wisconsin, Minnesota, Iowa, Missouri, Nebraska, Kansas |
| 62. *S. catenatus tergeminus* | Western Massasauga† | Nebraska, Kansas, Colorado, Oklahoma, New Mexico, Arizona, Texas, Mexico |
| 63. *S. miliarius miliarius* | Carolina Pygmy | North and South Carolina, Georgia, Alabama |
| 64. *S. miliarius barbouri* | Southeastern Pygmy | South Carolina, Georgia, Florida, Alabama, Mississippi |
| 65. *S. miliarius streckeri* | Western Pygmy | Mississippi, Louisiana, Tennessee, Missouri, Arkansas, Oklahoma, Texas, Alabama (?) |
| 66. *S. ravus* | Mexican Pygmy | Mexico |

A 67th rattlesnake probably will be recognized as follows:

| | | |
|---|---|---|
| *S. catenatus edwardsi* | | Texas, Colorado, New Mexico, Arizona |

Working from the preceding table, it is worth noting statistically where the rattlesnake is encountered and in what variety. Once again, these figures are not to be taken as an indication of actual population. Some areas are literally infested and others rarely offer even a single specimen. In some cases, only a small corner or pocket of the geographical area indicated has any rattlesnake population at all. A state line or a national boundary is a man-made thing and a rattlesnake in pursuit of prey or shelter is not apt to take much note of so artificial a barrier.

## RATTLESNAKE DISTRIBUTION

Numbers indicate number of presently recognized species and subspecies known to inhabit the area indicated.

### CANADA

| Alberta | British Columbia | Ontario | Saskatchewan |
|---|---|---|---|
| 1 | 1 | 2 | 1 |

### UNITED STATES OF AMERICA

| Alabama | Alaska | Arizona | Arkansas |
|---|---|---|---|
| 5 (Possibly 6) | None | 17 | 4 |
| California | Colorado | Connecticut | Delaware |
| 10 | 3 | 1 | Unlikely, but possibly 1 |
| Florida | Georgia | Hawaii | Idaho |
| 3 | 5 | None | 3 |
| Illinois | Indiana | Iowa | Kansas |
| 3 | 2 | 3 | 5 |

## RATTLESNAKE DISTRIBUTION (*Continued*)

### UNITED STATES OF AMERICA (*Continued*)

| Kentucky | Louisiana | Maine | Maryland |
|---|---|---|---|
| 2 | 3 | Unlikely, but possibly 1 | 1 |
| Massachusetts | Michigan | Minnesota | Mississippi |
| 1 | 1 | 2 | 4 |
| Missouri | Montana | Nebraska | Nevada |
| 4 (Possibly 5) | 1 | 4 | 6 |
| New Hampshire | New Jersey | New Mexico | New York |
| 1 | 1 | 9 | 2 |
| North Carolina | North Dakota | Ohio | Oklahoma |
| 4 | 1 | 2 | 5 |
| Oregon | Pennsylvania | Rhode Island | South Carolina |
| 2 | 2 | 1 | 5 |
| South Dakota | Tennessee | Texas | Utah |
| 1 | 3 | 10 | 6 |
| Vermont | Virginia | Washington | West Virginia |
| 1 | 2 | 1 | 1 |
| Wisconsin | Wyoming | District of Columbia | Canal Zone |
| 2 | 2 | Unlikely, but possibly 1 | Probably none |

### MEXICO

Exclusive of Baja California and adjacent islands—35
Baja California and adjacent islands—18

### CENTRAL AMERICA

| British Honduras | Guatemala | El Salvador | Honduras |
|---|---|---|---|
| 1 | 1 | 1 | 1 |
| Nicaragua | Costa Rica | Panama | Canal Zone |
| 1 | 1 | Probably none | Probably none |

### SOUTH AMERICA

| Colombia | Venezuela | British Guiana | Surinam |
|---|---|---|---|
| 1 | 2 | 1 | 1 |
| French Guiana | Brazil | Ecuador | Peru |
| 1 | 1 | Possibly 1 | 1 |
| Bolivia | Paraguay | Uruguay | Argentina |
| 1 | 1 | 1 | 1 |
| Chile | Aruba Island | | |
| None | 1 | | |

# The Reptile "Hall of Infamy"

THE AUTHOR initially had every intention of compiling a "Reptile Hall of Infamy" to round out this work. The original intention was to prepare this table from statistics and reports of snake "bites" gathered from all over the world. After several abortive attempts, it became obvious that no one man could possibly prepare such a table and expect any single expert to agree with his conclusions.

A second effort was made along different lines. A set of criteria was prepared and dispatched to a number of leading authorities with the request that they use it to prepare individual lists. This too was hopeless. No set of criteria would fit all of the opinions.

Finally, the authorities were asked to prepare a list along any lines they thought best. From these different lists, with these different criteria, a master table—THE REPTILE HALL OF INFAMY—has been prepared. The remarks and observations of the experts are as revealing as their lists. (Reference to these remarks in the table are noted as numbers in parentheses.) The other numbers under the experts' names, and opposite the species listed on the left, refer to the place in the "most dangerous" list assigned to the species by the expert. Number 1 refers to most dangerous, etc. An asterisk under an expert's name (and opposite a species), means that the expert included the snake as belonging on the most dangerous list but that a position on the list was not indicated. The positions and species listed for each expert are meaningless without the footnotes which contain the criteria used. After studying this unique table, the reader is free to decide for himself which is the most dangerous snake in the world.

| Species | Carl Kauffeld (1) | Laurence Klauber (2) | Robert Inger (3) | Clifford Pope (4) | Sherman Minton (5) |
|---|---|---|---|---|---|
| King Cobra (Ophiophagus hannah) (6) | * | 1–1 | * | * | 1–1 |
| Taipan (Oxyuranus scutellatus) | * | 1–2 | * | | 1–2 |
| Mambas (Dendroaspis sp.) (7) | * | 1–3 | | * | 1–3<br>2–8 |
| Common Cobra (Naja naja) (8) | * | 1–6 | | * | 1–9<br>2–1 |
| Javan Krait (Bungarus javanicus) (9) | * | | | | |

| Species | Carl Kauffeld (1) | Laurence Klauber (2) | Robert Inger (3) | Clifford Pope (4) | Sherman Minton (5) |
|---|---|---|---|---|---|
| Tiger Snake (*Notechis scutatus*) |  | 1–5 | * | * | 1–7 |
| Bushmaster (*Lachesis muta*) | * |  |  |  | 1–4 |
| Western Diamondback (Rattlesnake) (10) (*Crotalus atrox*) | * |  |  | * | 1–5 (10) |
| Fer-de-lance (*Bothrops atrox*) | * |  |  | * | 1–6 / 2–2 |
| Tropical Rattlesnake (*Crotalus durissus*) |  | 1–7 |  | * | 1–8 / 2–7 |
| Jararacussu (*Bothrops jararacussu*) |  |  |  |  | 1–10 |
| Saw-scaled Viper (*Echis carinatus*) |  | 1–10 |  |  | 2–3 |
| Russell's Viper (*Vipera russelli*) |  | 1–9 |  | * | 2–4 |
| Puff Adder (*Bitis arietans*) |  | 1–8 |  |  | 2–5 |
| Egyptian Cobra (*Naja haje*) (8) | * |  |  |  | 2–6 |
| Jararaca (*Bothrops jararaca*) |  |  |  | * | 2–9 |
| Indian Krait (11) (*Bungarus caeruleus*) | * |  |  | * (12) | 2–10 |
| Death Adder (*Acanthophis antarcticus*) |  | 1–4 |  |  |  |
| Australian Blacksnake (*Pseudechis porphyiacus*) | * |  |  |  |  |
| Australian Copperhead (*Denisonia superba*) | * |  |  |  |  |
| Gaboon Viper (*Bitis gabonica*) | * |  |  |  |  |
| Eastern Diamond Rattlesnake (*Crotalus adamanteus*) (10) | * |  |  |  |  |
| Ringhals (*Hemachatus haemachatus*) | * |  |  |  |  |

## Notes appending to THE REPTILE HALL OF INFAMY:

(1) As a single criterion, Carl Kauffeld, Curator of Reptiles at New York's Staten Island Zoo, used *"chances for survival,"* what snake you would have the *least* chance of surviving if bitten. He lists five snakes, but did not indicate that they were in order; they are indicated on the chart with an asterisk (*).

(2) Speaking of his two lists, Dr. Laurence M. Klauber says:

. . . based almost exclusively on the literature of herpetology . . . in making selections I have been guided more by the characteristics of the snakes themselves, rather than by the human factors involved. . . . I have given the greatest weight to such criteria as venom quantity, venom toxicity, physiological effects of venom, length of fangs, length and weight of adult snakes, aggressiveness of disposition, abundance of the species, extent of territorial range etc., all of which are natural characteristics inherent in the snakes themselves. . . . In compiling my list, I have considered all snakes at the species level and have introduced no subspecific distinctions. From the standpoint of the human hazard, subspecific differences are usually technical and minor in character.

Speaking of his first list (indicated on the table as 1– ), Dr. Klauber says, "Necessarily it is highly subjective; tomorrow it might be quite different, both in content and order." Speaking of his second list (indicated on the table as *), "Among the candidates that were given consideration but have been relegated to the second ten are these, not here given in any order of relative danger."

(3) Robert F. Inger, Curator of Reptiles at the Chicago Natural History Museum, says of his list:

Your request for an opinion is difficult to comply with because we just don't have enough information. . . . I am willing to give you my impression of the three most dangerous poisonous snakes. By all accounts the three are: . . . This rating is based not upon the number of human fatalities each species is responsible for, or upon the potency of the venom drop by drop. Instead it is based upon an estimate of the chances for survival following a bite.

No order was indicated and his three choices are indicated on the table by an asterisk (*).

(4) Clifford H. Pope says of his list:

Applied to snakes the word dangerous may mean potentially a menace or actually destructive. I assume that you mean the latter and would list the following species: . . . They are not listed in order of dangerousness.

The snakes on his list are indicated on the table by an asterisk (*).

(5) Speaking of his list, Dr. Minton says:

List one is the snakes I consider intrinsically most dangerous—that is, the species I would least care to be locked up in a phone booth with. All are large snakes with a reputation for having an uncertain temper at best. All have large fangs and a good supply of moderately to highly potent venom. Quite a few of them, however, contribute very little to the world mortality for snake bite. . . . List two is the snakes that I estimate, on very inadequate data, are the species that kill the most people. These must obviously have a lethal venom and some inclination to use it, but more importantly they are snakes that have adapted to life with relatively dense human populations living and working under conditions that make snakebite a real hazard. Nearly every one of these snakes has a big geographic range and is plentiful over the greater part of it.

Dr. Minton's two lists are indicated on the table by the respective prefixes, 1– , 2– .

(6) The King Cobra is listed by specific *hannah* but is put into two genera by different experts, *Naja* and *Ophiophagus*. The specialists represented on this chart preferred: *Ophiophagus*—Minton, Kauffeld, Klauber; *Naja*—Inger, Pope.

(7) Speaking of the mambas, Minton says: "The four or more species of mambas confuse even herpetologists, so it is hard to say which one any given account refers to. Those who know the genus best seem agreed that *D. polylepis* is the worst of the lot."

However, Dr. Minton refers to *Dendroaspis* sp. on his list. Clifford Pope refers to *D. polylepis* on his; Kauffeld says: "Mambas, *Dendroaspis* any species, but *angusticeps* and *polylepis* probably tops. . . ."; Klauber says, "Black and/or Green Mamba *Dendroaspis polylepis* and/or *D. angusticeps*."

(8) The names Common Cobra and Indian Cobra are apparently both applied to the species *Naja naja*. Dr. Minton, when speaking of the appearance of the species on his list, says: "I suspect there would be very little choice between this species and any of the big African cobras, e.g., N. haje or N. nigricollis."

(9) Speaking of the Javan Krait, Carl Kauffeld says: ". . . This is an obscure species described by Dr. Felix Kopstein on the basis of a specimen which was responsible for the death of three natives, bitten in succession by the same snake. I am unaware that any specimens but the type have come to light, but it must be a heller!"

(10) Dr. Klauber puts both the Western and the Eastern Diamondback rattlesnakes on his second list; Pope puts just the Western species on his, and Minton says of the Western species holding down fifth position on his first list: "Strictly speaking, I'd put the Eastern Diamondback (*C. adamanteus*) in number 6 or 7 slot. In this list I haven't distinguished between these two closely related rattlesnakes."

(11) Minton refers to the Indian Krait (*B. caeruleus*) on his second list; Pope refers to *B. fasciatus* on his; Klauber refers to *caeruleus* on his. The author has taken the liberty of combining the two on the table as *caeruleus* with this explanation. Kauffeld's *B. javanicus* is apparently a different animal altogether.

What then is the deadliest snake in the world? All five experts named the King Cobra—no other snake was so honored. The two experts who listed their choices in the order they considered most dangerous put the King Cobra in first position. I must concur—the King Cobra, the largest venomous snake in the world, probably by several feet, is the animal I would least like to step on, or, as Dr. Minton put it, "I would least care to be locked up in a phone booth with." It must be remembered, however, that the King Cobra is not necessarily a major contributor to world snake bite mortality. This apparent contradiction arises from the fact that the King Cobra prefers heavily forested and generally remote regions. It does not invade agricultural areas as regularly as do the other cobras, and so many other truly dangerous serpents the world over. If it did, the bite/death ratio would shoot up even higher than it already has. The bite of the King, evidently, is not easy to survive.

# Shark Attacks Off Florida

## MONTHLY DISTRIBUTION OF 19 UNPROVOKED SHARK ATTACKS IN THE COASTAL WATERS OF FLORIDA

| Jan. | Feb. | Mar. | Apr. | May | June | July | Aug. | Sept. | Oct. | Nov. | Dec. |
|---|---|---|---|---|---|---|---|---|---|---|---|
|  |  |  |  | X | X |  |  |  |  |  |  |
|  |  |  |  | X | X |  |  |  |  |  |  |
|  |  |  |  | X | X |  |  |  |  |  |  |
| X |  |  |  | X | X |  | X |  |  |  |  |
| X | X | X | X | X | X | X | X | X |  |  |  |

With the generous consent of the Florida State Board of Conservation, the following table is reproduced from that organization's Educational Series Pamphlet No. 13, "The Florida Shark Story," written by Robert F. Hutton and issued March 30, 1959. It covers known attacks from 1913 to early 1959. Forty-seven reports are dealt with, illustrating the unpredictable and therefore dangerous behavior of these large fishes.

## A LIST OF SHARK-ATTACK REPORTS IN FLORIDA WATERS

| Date | Locality | Type Shark | Remarks | Source of Information |
|---|---|---|---|---|
| 9-21-13 | West Palm Beach | Eight ft. long, Hammerhead | "Man. West Palm Beach. Recovery. "Attacked and so seriously injured that wounds required 200 stitches and seven weeks' hospital treatment. Attacker described as hammerhead shark about eight feet long." | Coppleson (1958) |
| 10-11-16 | Sewell's Point, near Palm Beach | | "J. L. Hanscomb. Sewell's Point, near Palm Beach. Fatal. "Attempted to take large shark in net alive. Right leg severely mangled. Died in hospital after amputation of leg." | Coppleson (1958) |
| 1919 or 1920 | Near Panama City | | Woman swimming had leg bitten off by shark. Apparently recovered. | Mrs. W. Avery, Miami, Florida (Personal contact) |
| 6-19-20 (6:30 P.M.) | ½ mile north of Point of Rock on Manasota Peninsula near the Manasota Beach Club. | Tan color | Swimming about three hundred yards offshore on outside of breaker bar. Water about 3½ feet deep. Headed toward shore. Took all of left knee in mouth. Had leg doubled to kick. "At that time I was 13½ years old. Had 21 stitches taken in outside of thigh, six in muscle to pull it together. Scars on both upper and lower leg also three teeth prints on knee cap. I was in bed for three weeks." | Hayward Sayre Green (victim). Information given to State Conservation Agent, Englewood, Fla. |
| 6-19-20 | Off Englewood Beach | | "Case of Hayward Green. Now a gas station attendant in Englewood who was attacked by an unidentified shark which he estimates was 15 feet long. The attack took place off the Englewood Beach at about 6:00 P.M. on June 19, 1920. Mr. Green was then 13½ years old. The shark grabbed him by the right knee (folded during a kick). Green's leg was severely lacerated but he can walk O.K. now." | Dr. Eugenie Clark, Director, Cape Haze Marine Laboratory, Placida, Fla. |
| Prior to 1921 | Gadsden Point, Tampa Bay | | Five feet, two inches of scars on body. | James Kelley, local fisherman, St. Petersburg. |

## A LIST OF SHARK-ATTACK REPORTS IN FLORIDA WATERS (*Continued*)

| Date | Locality | Type Shark | Remarks | Source of Information |
|---|---|---|---|---|
| 1922 | East of Municipal Pier, St. Petersburg | Rumored to be Barracuda, but wound appeared to be a shark bite. | Victim was Dorothy McClachie; a good swimmer; girl friend along; died from shock and loss of blood. | James Kelley, local fisherman, and John Gough, Spa Beach and Municipal Pier, St. Petersburg. Coppleson (1958) |
| 6-17-22 | Tampa Bay, near St. Petersburg | | "Dorothy McClachie, 18 years old. Tampa Bay, near St. Petersburg, Florida. Lat. 27°46′N. Fatal. "Dorothy McClachie, expert swimmer, with another girl, floating far from shore when she was suddenly struck above inner side of knee. Large piece of flesh torn away. She called, "A shark has bitten my foot off!" Her companion towed her more than half a mile towards shore, but she died from shock, loss of blood." | |
| 6-17-22 | Tampa Bay | | "The death of Miss Dorothy McClachie from bites of an inhabitant of the sea is the first authentic instance of a human being killed in these waters by a fish or shark. Many reports have been current here of persons falling into the water and never being seen again but these tales are difficult or impossible to verify. The only other instance of a man being attacked in the waters, so far as the older bay men can remember, was when George Eaton was struck by some unknown fish while swimming off Gadsden Point between here and Tampa. He went overboard from his boat one hot Sunday afternoon and something slashed his thigh badly, cutting two deep slashes and many smaller ones. Mr. Eaton got back to his boat and the fish did not hit the second time." | The St. Petersburg Independent, June 17, 1922 |
| 7-12-30 | Stuart | | "William Harris, 21 years old. Stuart, Florida. Lat. 27°11′N. Recovery. "Attacked about 159 yards out. Arm lacerated from shoulder to wrist. Swam unaided to shore, where collapsed from loss of blood." | Coppleson (1958) |

| Date | Locality | Type Shark | Remarks | Source of Information |
|---|---|---|---|---|
| 9-21-31 | Palm Beach | Hammerhead about eight ft. long, according to Sam Barrow, lifeguard, who saw the shark. | Victim: Miss Gertrude Holaday. ". . . There were several jagged lacerations of right thigh and calf. The largest, ten inches long, was on the thigh. Here the muscles were torn from the bone but fortunately the large deep-seated blood vessels escaped injury. The cut on the right calf was about five inches long. In addition there were other smaller cuts on the right leg, and on the left leg were found abrasions and lacerations made presumably by the horny shagreen of the shark's skin as he threshed about the girl when she was striving to get away. ". . . The patient was admitted to the hospital September 21 and was discharged on November 11—seven weeks later. On her return home, she was in bed for about a month while she gained more strength, and when she got out she was on crutches for about two months longer. When able to walk alone, she found the leg stiff and she had a slight limp. After a year, however, she had completely recovered, and now is as active as before the hurt. She swims, walks and runs like any normal girl. Unfortunately no photograph was made of the wounds, and when I asked for one to be made of the scars, Miss Holaday wrote that these were so insignificant that they hardly show at all." | Gudger (1937) |
| 1931 | Palm Beach | Hammerhead | "Gertrude Holaday. Palm Beach, Florida. Lat. 26°42'N. Recovery. Sam Barrows, lifeguard at Palm Beach, received a gold medal for bravery for going to rescue of this girl. Girl swimming 150 yards from shore, screamed. Barrows dived in, dragging a line and buoy. Saw what he described as a "hammerhead shark," which after ripping victim's right leg maneuvered to make another attack. The shark followed them to beach, and made three more attacks on girl. Seven weeks in hospital were needed for recovery. | Coppleson (1958) |

## A LIST OF SHARK-ATTACK REPORTS IN FLORIDA WATERS (*Continued*)

| Date | Locality | Type Shark | Remarks | Source of Information |
|---|---|---|---|---|
| 10-20-43 | Englewood | Shark | "Hayward Green, 12 years old. Englewood, Florida. Recovery. 'Swimming alone across bar in water eight to ten feet deep when injured on knee by shark.' (According to our information this attack occurred in 1920.) | Coppleson (1958) |
| 10-26-43 | Baker's Haulover, Miami Beach | 14-foot Leopard Shark | "Fingerprints on a man's hand found with other portions of a body in a shark caught off Baker's Haulover last Tuesday were identified as those of Clyde Kelly Ormond, Jr., Houston, Texas, according to telegram from Federal Bureau of Investigation in Washington . . ." Victim was a member of the Armed Forces on a tanker which collided off Florida coast on October 20. "In addition to man's hand, portions of a forearm, leg and pelvis were found." | Miami Herald Newspaper Library |
| 5-31-44 | Atlantic Beach, near Mayport | | "Mary Ann Shands, 15 years old. Atlantic Beach, near Mayport, Florida. Lat. 30°22'N. Recovery. "Bitten on left calf just above ankle." | Coppleson (1958) |
| Late May or early June, 1944 | Mayport | *Carcharhinus maculipinnis?* Large Black-tipped Shark | "The size of the shark's jaws, as outlined by the wounds, showed that it was only 5½–6½ feet long, and other circumstantial evidence pointed to a *Carcharhinus maculipinnis* as responsble." | Bigelow, H. B. and Schroeder, W. C. (1948) |
| 7-24-47 | 10 miles north of St. Augustine | "Shark bites" | Victim: Ralph R. Rives, Jr., Jacksonville, 20, in serious condition according to Dr. Eugene B. Elder, Flagler Hospital. "The fish took a bite out of Rives' calf as he swam in a canal ten miles north of here. Young Rives thought the fish was a shark because it turned on its back before each of its repeated strikes. Two school-aged companions watched helplessly from shore during the student's struggles with the fish." | Miami Herald Newspaper Library |

| Date | Locality | Type Shark | Remarks | Source of Information |
|---|---|---|---|---|
| 8-4-47 | St. Augustine | | "Ralph Reginald Rives, Jr., St. Augustine, Fla. Lat. 29°52'N. Fatal. "Injured while swimming and rescued. In hospital blood transfusions were given and badly mangled leg was amputated, but died from shock and hemorrhage. (This attack was attributed to barracuda.)" | Coppleson (1958) |
| July, 1950 | Key Largo | Shark | "Warren Rathjen, 21 years. Rock Harbour, Key Largo, Florida. Recovery. "Fishing in muddy water three feet deep. Felt something grip upper part of right thigh. Surfaced, removed by force a 30-inch shark by grasping its tail and twisting it. Wounds, two small semi-lunar scars." | Coppleson (1958) |
| July, 1950 | Rock Harbor, Key Largo | 2½-foot Shark | ". . . The student, Mr. Warren Rathjen, was goggle diving for seaweeds in three feet of water about 50 yards offshore. He was bending over in the rather muddy water when he suddenly felt something clamp itself firmly to the extreme upper portion of the back of his right thigh, immediately below his swimming trunks. He surfaced at once and removed the object, which proved to be a 2½-foot shark, by grasping its tail and twisting. In the excitement the shark was thrown some distance and escaped . . .'" | Phillips, C. and Brady, W. H. (1953) |
| 6-6-50 | 275 miles northeast of Miami | Shark | Pedro Guzman survived a two-engined C-46 transport plane crash. Shark was observed making passes at Guzman as rescue vessel approached. Victim died from shock and loss of blood from five shark bites 34 minutes after being brought aboard rescue vessel. Account is well-illustrated with actual photographs of rescue. | Life (1950) |
| 1952 | Key West | Shark | "Pan American Pilot. Key West. Lat. 24°40'N. Fatal. "Bathing off one of the keys, wearing fluorescent bathing suit, struck in groin by shark or barracuda." | Coppleson (1958) |

## A LIST OF SHARK-ATTACK REPORTS IN FLORIDA WATERS (Continued)

| Date | Locality | Type Shark | Remarks | Source of Information |
|---|---|---|---|---|
| 7-15-53 | Juno Beach | Thought to be a barracuda | Victim: Mrs. D. F. Gunn, 26, a visitor from Longview, Texas. "Authorities said her left leg was almost severed between ankle and knee by a fish believed to have been a barracuda while she was standing in knee-deep water with her husband and another couple. Doctors didn't know if they could save her leg," | Miami Herald Newspaper Library |
| 1953 | Juno Beach, Miami | | "Girl. Juno Beach, Miami, Florida. Lat. 25°40'N. Recovery. "Standing waist-deep in water. Leg ripped from thigh to ankle." | Coppleson (1958) |
| 12-11-55 | ½ mile offshore and nine miles north of Ft. Pierce | Shark | Boat of P. D. Neilly and Charlton Anderson bitten by shark while fishing for pompano. Three big sharks released from net, one bit hole in boat, "as big as your head," stuffed sweater in hole until shore was reached. | Miami Herald Newspaper Library |
| 1955 | Vero Beach | | "Two attacks north of Vero Beach, Florida (Ref. R. North, Scientific American, 1957.)" | Coppleson (1958) |
| 1955–1957 | Ft. Pierce and Vero Beach | Sharks | ". . . this year a friend of mine, bathing at Fort Pierce, Fla., was badly mauled by a five-foot shark in about 2½ feet of water. The same thing occurred last year at Vero Beach. . . ." | Nauth, R. (1957) |
| 8-15-56 | Pismo Beach | Nine-foot Shark | "Douglas Clarke, 10 years old. Pismo Beach, Fla. Recovery. "Shark about nine feet long scraped against boy who was swimming near pier. Severe cuts on right shoulder." | Coppleson (1958) |
| 5-11-57 | Fort Pierce | Four-foot Shark | "3:30 P.M., David Carson. South Beach, Fort Pierce, Fla. Lat. 27°28'N. Recovery. "Floating on back in waist-deep water. Foot seized by a four-foot shark. Threshed loose." | Coppleson (1958) |
| Early 1957 | Seaquarium, Virginia Key, Miami | Bull Shark | Bull shark attacked diver's helmet from above. No body harm. | Jim Kline, Seaquarium (Personal communication) |

| Date | Locality | Type Shark | Remarks | Source of Information |
|---|---|---|---|---|
| February, 1957 | Florida Keys | Probably a large Mako | "The large shark that attacked me in that instance was probably a large Mako and it occurred in Feb. of 1957 as near as I can recall. I had a very similar experience a year later." | Personal communication with R. P. L. Straughan, Coral Reef Exhibits, P. O. Box 23, Coconut Grove 33, Fla. |
| February, 1957 | Florida Keys | Mako? | Shark made several passes at skin diver, but no injury resulted. | Taken from a manuscript by R. P. L. Straughan entitled "Personal Encounters With Sharks" |
| 4-22-57 | Ormond Beach | Shark | "11 A.M., Michael Carpenter, 17 years old. Ormond Beach, Florida. Lat. 29°19'N. Air Temp. 75°. Sea temp. 68°. Recovery (see text). . . . A 17-year-old Californian youth named Carpenter received injuries to his ankle. The lifeguard, Jim Patterson, said the shark had been caught in a pool inshore from a sandbar and was trying to get out when it brushed against Carpenter. Patterson added that it probably would not have attacked had it not collided with the victim." | Coppleson (1958) |
| 1957 | Miami Beach | Barracuda? | "Mrs. Eleanor Nelson, 28 years old. Miami Beach. Recovery. "Injured on left leg and calf of right leg while wading in surf. Barracuda claimed to be responsible." | Coppleson (1958) |
| 4-30-58 | About one mile off Miami Beach | Five-foot Nurse Shark | Victim: Johnny Bowers, 29, 20640 NE 15th Ave., Miami, bitten on thigh when shark's tail released by victim; incident occurred at a depth of about 30 feet; two men in boat released shark from victim's thigh; victim recovered with only teeth marks to show. | Miami Herald Newspaper Library |

## A LIST OF SHARK-ATTACK REPORTS IN FLORIDA WATERS (*Continued*)

| Date | Locality | Type Shark | Remarks | Source of Information |
|---|---|---|---|---|
| June, 1958 | Turtle Beach, Siesta Key | | "Case of Frank Mahala, 17 years old. Attacked in early June of this year by an unidentified creature. The teeth marks indicate it was almost certainly a shark. The attack took place in shallow water at Turtle Beach on Siesta Key. His left leg and foot were severely lacerated." | Dr. Eugenie Clark, Director, Cape Haze Marine Laboratory, Placida, Fla. (Personal communication) |
| 6-26-58 | Sanibel Island | Believed to be a shark | "Name and address of victim. Cockerill, Eric Napier, Sanibel Island, Florida. Extensive lacerations of foot while swimming off Sanibel Island. Kind of fish is not known, but it is believed that this individual was attacked by a shark." | Lee Memorial Hospital, Fort Myers, Fla. (Personal communication) |
| Mid-1958 | Shark Channel, Sequarium, Virginia Key, Miami | Nine-foot Bull Shark (*Carcharhinus leucas*) | ". . . A nine-foot Bull shark cruised by. The net was thrown over him. Suddenly the shark sliced through the nylon net and edged out of it. No panic. The men merely redoubled their efforts to hold the monster.<br>". . . the shark hooked to the left and caught Gray's assistant, Phil Case. Spurting blood, Case lunged toward the ladder. Before he had taken more than one step, the shark swung around and nailed Gray with a 52-stitch gash on his right leg, just below the knee . . ." | St. Petersburg Times (Sunday Magazine) March 1, 1959 |
| July, 1958 | Sarasota Area | Shark | "We also had two emergency room admissions (both men) who were bitten on the foot—one man was sure it was by a shark and the other one thought so." | Memorial Hospital, 1901 Arlington Street, Sarasota, Fla. (Personal communication) |
| 7-10-58 | Vicinity of Key West | | Victim: Angel B. Escartin, 35, 360 SW Fourth Avenue, Miami. Key West coroner said he thought victim was partly eaten alive by a barracuda or shark. | Miami Herald Newspaper Library |

| Date | Locality | Type Shark | Remarks | Source of Information |
|---|---|---|---|---|
| July, 1958 | Siesta Key, Sarasota | Five-foot Nurse Shark | "Case of John Hamlin, age 20. Bitten by a five-foot Nurse Shark in mid-July of this year. He was skin diving in six feet of water at Point of Rocks, Siesta Key, Sarasota. He grabbed the shark by the tail and it bit him just below the left knee. The shark released its grip as soon as Hamlin let go of his tail. The small wound healed quickly but will leave a scar." | Dr. Eugenie Clark, Director, Cape Haze Marine Laboratory, Placida, Fla. |
| 7-27-58 | Longboat Key, Sarasota | Tiger Shark, according to Dr. E. Clark, Ichthyologist, Cape Haze Marine Lab, based on examinations of the wounds. | Victim: 8-year-old Douglas Lawton, Miami Beach; swimming in three feet of water; left leg so badly mangled that it had to be amputated. | Newspaper Accounts (St. Petersburg Times and Tampa Tribune) and personal contact with boy's relatives on day following attack. |
| 7-27-58 | Longboat Key, Sarasota | Tiger Shark | "Following is a short description of the vicious attack: Douglas J. Lawton, age 8. Douglas lives at 1245 NE 201 Terrace, North Miami Beach, Florida. He was visiting, with his parents, on Longboat Key and was attacked in about four feet of water. This occurred at 4:30 P.M. on July 27, 1958.<br><br>"Dr. H. O. Spect dictated the following under Present Illness: 'The patient was viciously attacked by a shark in shallow water off Longboat Key. In fact, he was pulled from the water with the shark still hanging on to his left leg and chewing the while . . .' Dr. J. O. Fergeson performed a high thigh amputation of the left leg and repaired multiple lacerations of the left hand." | Memorial Hospital, 1901 Arlington Street, Sarasota, Fla. (Personal communication) |

## A LIST OF SHARK-ATTACK REPORTS IN FLORIDA WATERS (*Continued*)

| Date | Locality | Type Shark | Remarks | Source of Information |
|---|---|---|---|---|
| 7-27-58 | Florida | Five-foot Shark | "Douglas Lawton, 8 years old. Florida. Recovery. "A five-foot shark's jaws still clamped the boy's leg when rescued." | Coppleson (1958) |
| 10-5-58 | Baker's Haulover, Miami Beach | Two Sharks | Victim: Mr. Lytton Evans, 60, was attacked by two sharks; sharks swam away when help arrived; apparently no damage done. | Miami Herald Newspaper Library |
| March, 1959 first week | Miami Area | Tiger Shark | ". . . my boat was attacked by a large tiger shark. I was just preparing to dive when I noticed a very large shark swimming along the edge of the reef so I started following him in the boat. I stayed over him for perhaps five minutes or more and was attempting to drive him from the area so I could dive. The water was about eight to ten feet deep. This fellow was quite short tempered for after a very few minutes, he stopped swimming away and instead started circling the boat. It was a flat calm day and he could look up and see me clearly. Suddenly, he swam off about 20 or 30 feet and turned extremely fast back to the boat. He hit the boat right in the center and lifted the rear end clean out of the water. I have no doubt he tried to knock me overboard. He was approximately 14 feet long as I compared him with the length of the boat. He swam away after the one assault. After he was gone I went into the water and found that he had ripped away a piece of fiberglass and wood about a foot in diameter. If it had been a light boat he would have gone right through!" | R. P. L. Straughan, Coral Reef Exhibits, P. O. Box 23, Coconut Grove 33, Fla. (Personal communication) |
| Date Unknown | Palm Beach | Shark | "Horton Chase. Palm Beach, Florida. Lat. 26°42'N. Recovery. "Standing waist-deep in water, when shark brushed against leg, leaving bruises and abrasions from hip to ankle." | Coppleson (1958) |

# APPENDIX F

## *The Shark Questionnaire*

THE SMITHSONIAN INSTITUTION is developing a documented file of shark attacks. The following form is issued by the Division of Fishes, Museum of Natural History, United States National Museum, to aid in this work. Perhaps, when thousands of these reports have been compiled and analyzed, some pattern, some predictable combination of time, place, and conditions will emerge that will make the avoidance of these dreadful accidents possible.

The Smithsonian Institution is seeking information for a documented file on shark attacks. Please fill in this form and return to:

Form Approved
Budget Bureau
#105-R004

Division of Fishes
Museum of Natural History
United States National Museum
Smithsonian Institution
Washington 25, D.C., USA

Victim's name and address:      Age_____ Sex_____ Date_____
_____ Depth of attack_____ Time of day_____
_____ Temperature: Water_____ Air_____
_____ ☐ Bright sun ☐ Cloudy
Distance from shore:_____ Water condition: ☐ Clear ☐ Murky
Was victim's body fully clothed: ☐ Yes ☐ No   Color of clothing:_____
Color of exposed skin: ☐ Light ☐ Tan ☐ Dark
Occupation of victim:_____
Locality of attack:_____
_____

Kind of shark:_____ Identified by:_____
Number of sharks involved:_____
Photographs: ☐ Yes ☐ No   Photographer's name:_____
     Address:_____
If hospitalized, name of
Hospital:_____ Victim's recovery: ☐ Yes ☐ No
Address: _____
Name of attending physician:_____
Address:_____
Names and addresses of witnesses:

_____      _____
_____      _____
_____      _____
_____      _____

Description of attack: (Describe behavior of shark and victim, both before and after attack; nature of injury, bleeding, rescue and subsequent treatment; use additional pages if necessary.)

Source of above information:_____
Signature_____ Date_____
Address_____

# APPENDIX G

## Ciguatera—"Fish Poisoning"

FOR MOST of the people on this planet, fish is not a luxury food. Fishes are the sole source of animal protein for many, many millions; and, as earth's population expands, the importance of food from the sea increases each year. Unfortunately, some fish can be dangerously poisonous; but where, and why, are mysteries of significant concern in some parts of the world.

From ancient times, up to the present, whole families or even villages have been suddenly stricken with a debilitating sickness caused by eating poisonous fish. Many lives have been lost. The cause of the ailment has often been traced to fish species which only days before were perfectly safe to eat. On the next island, or in the next village down the coast, the same species may have been eaten on the same fateful day without harm to anyone.

The mysterious workings of fish poisoning still, to a very large degree, elude us. The disease, or rather diseases, are properly labeled (generically) as *ichthyosarcotoxism*—as opposed to *ichthyoacanthotoxism*, which is the subject of Chapter 20 and means "injurious injection of venom" by fish specially equipped for the purpose. Specifically, the ailment is variously referred to as *Ciguatera*, Tetraodon poisoning, Elasmobranch poisoning, Gymnothorax poisoning, Clupeoid poisoning, Scombroid poisoning, or "Hallucinatory" Mullet poisoning, according to the fish involved. The word *ciguatera*, the most commonly-heard name for fish poisoning, comes from the American-Spanish word *cigua*, the name of a certain kind of poisonous sea snail, *Livona pica*. Mollusks, as well as fishes, can be responsible for the condition. It is commonly called, simply, "fish poisoning," but it is not to be confused with *ptomaine poisoning*.

An attack of *Ciguatera* can be likened, symptomatically, to poisoning by curare, muscarine, or aconitine. A definite poisonous substance is involved, and a number of these substances have been isolated. Only in Scombroid poisoning are bacteria involved, the other forms being caused solely by the noxious substance found in the animal's tissues.

Before going on to discuss where fish poisoning occurs and which animals are responsible, it is necessary to have a general impression of what it is like when it strikes. An actual case history can best serve this purpose. *The Indian Journal of Medical Research*, in April, 1956, carried the following case report in an article by S. Jones of the Central Marine Fisheries Research Substation, Calicut, Malabar:

Early morning on 11th February, 1954, one Muthukumaran, a fisherman of about 65 years of age belonging to Pattimacherry brought home the roes of a large sized 'Plachee' fish (*Tetraodontid*) out of which a curry was prepared. His wife, Kuppamma, aged about 50, and an adopted daughter of about 8 years took this curry along with rice at 8 A.M. After taking the food both of them felt drowsy. Muthukumaran,

373

who in the meanwhile was away at work returned at 10 A.M. and took rice with a very small quantity of this roe curry. His wife and child had a second meal at this time and soon after both became unconscious. In the case of the woman it was gradual and it is reported that during the semi-conscious state she told her husband that she was feeling giddy and could not see the house or anything around and that she was feeling as if she was going to Kailas (*the sacred mountain peak in the Himalayas, believed to be the abode of Lord Shiva*). The girl became completely unconscious and died at about 12 noon. In the meanwhile Muthukumaran showed different symptoms. He felt quite restless and vomited several times. Some of the neighbors removed the ailing old couple to the Local Fund Hospital, Porayar. The woman died at 5 P.M. just as she was being carried into the hospital. The Medical Officer observed that the death was due to 'respiratory failure.' Muthukumaran was admitted to the hospital for 'weakness, giddiness and inability to walk.' The diagnosis was 'fish poisoning' and the condition on admission was given as follows: 'A well-built man of 65 years. Not anaemic. Strong. Able to talk. Cannot walk. Slightly restless and thirsty. Pupils dilated. Heart—nil abnormal. Respiration—19. Pulse—80.' The temperature was normal and nothing except coffee was given to the patient on the day of admission. On the next day (12-2-54) he was feeling better and on the third day he appeared normal and was discharged at his own request in the evening.

The report goes on to say that a few years previously, five members of another family were killed in the village of Negapatam by the roe of a *Plachee*. Actually, Muthukumaran and his family were stricken with Tetraodon poisoning. The disease is caused by puffer fishes of the family *Tetraodontidae*, and it kills many people, particularly in Japan, each year. There is a saying in Japan: "Great is the temptation to eat 'Fugo' (Puffer) but greater is the dread of losing life."

The Puffers are Tetraodonts, but not all members of the family are poisonous and not all parts of the poisonous specimens are necessarily dangerous. It is generally accepted that the ovaries, gonads, skin, bile, and liver are most apt to be dangerous. The flesh is sometimes safe to eat, at other times, deadly. Certain other fishes of the order Tetraodontiformes (but not of the family *Tetraodontidae*) may be similarly hazardous as food.

The following table gives a breakdown of fishes of *all* orders known to be directly and edibly poisonous to man—at least part of the time.

## FISHES KNOWN TO HAVE BEEN DANGEROUSLY POISONOUS ON OCCASION

| Type of Poisoning | Representative Fishes Known to Be Involved: (By Genera) | Remarks |
|---|---|---|
| Ciguatera or Tropical Marine Fish Poisoning | Snappers: *Monotaxis, Gnathodentex, Aprion, Lethrinus, Lutjanus.*<br>Parrotfish: *Scarus, Callyodon.*<br>Wrasse: *Coris, Epibulus.*<br>Groupers: *Variola, Julis, Cepthalopholis, Epinephelus, Plectopomus.*<br>Barracuda: *Sphyraena*, plus others.<br>Jacks: *Caranx.*<br>Surgeonfish: *Acanthurus, Ctenochaetus, Zebrasoma.*<br>Ladyfish: *Albula.*<br>Herring: *Clupanodon* (only).<br>Surmullet: *Parupeneus, Upeneus.* | Limited to tropics: reef fishes involved, particularly larger carnivorous species and specimens. Neurological damage and death can result. Recovery can take years. |

| Type of Poisoning | Representative Fishes Known to Be Involved: (By Genera) | Remarks |
|---|---|---|
| | Seabass: *Myceteroperca* (see Groupers above). | |
| | Trunkfish: *Lactoria, Lactophrys.* | |
| | Porgie: *Pagellus, Pagrus.* | |
| | Squaretails: *Tetragonurus.* | |
| | Chinamanfish: *Paradicichthys.* | |
| | Filefish: *Alutera.* | |
| | Triggerfish: *Balistoides, Rhineacanthus, Baliates, Pseudobalistes.* | |
| | Anchovy: *Engraulis* (only). | |
| | Squirrelfish: *Myripristis*, plus others. | |
| | Bonito: *Katsuwonus.* | |
| Tetraodon | Puffers: *Arothron, Sphaeroides, Canthigaster.* | Not limited to tropics. |
| | Triggerfish: *Balistoides, Balistes, Rhineacanthus, Pseudobalistes.* | |
| | Filefish: *Aleutera.* | |
| | Boxfish: *Ostracion.* | |
| | Ocean Sunfish: (Types uncertain). | |
| | Porcupine fish: *Diodon.* | |
| Elasmobranch | Sand sharks: *Carcharhinus.* | Liver particularly dangerous. May be caused by sharks eating poisonous fishes. May be closely related to ciguatera. Most common in tropics, but known far to the north. "Intoxicating." Can be fatal. |
| | White shark: *Carcharodon.* | |
| | Hammerheads: *Sphyrna* (only). | |
| | 7-Gilled: *Heptranchus.* | |
| | 6-Gilled: *Hexanchus.* | |
| | Greenland: *Somniosus.* | |
| | Plus some rays. | |
| Gymnothorax | Moray Eels: (*Gymnothorax*). | Resembles ciguatera, but can be even more severe. Reportedly *at least* 10 per cent fatal. *Moray eels should not be eaten.* |
| Scombroid | Tuna, Skipjack, Bonito, and all other mackerel-like fishes—all of the numerous genera. | *Bacterial:* Strains of *Proteus morganii* involved. Caused by improperly stored fish. Violent allergy-like reactions. Histamine and other substances produced in tissues by bacteria. |
| "Hallucinatory" Mullet | Mullet: *Mugil, Neomyxus.* | Seasonal: Pacific islands—limited range—generally mild. *Not fatal.* |
| | Goatfish: *Mulloidichthys, Upeneus, Parauoeneus.* | |
| | Surgeonfish (Tang): *Acanthurus, Ctenochaetus, Zebrasoma.* | |
| | Rudderfish: *Kyphosus* (plus). | |
| Clupeoid | Herring-like fishes: (*Clupea, Melleta*). Possibly *Sardinella.* | Very little known. Can be extremely serious. Known to be fatal. May be connected with the swarming of non-poisonous marine worm Palolo (?) |

The preceding table is certainly not complete. Indeed, even if it were desirable to give a complete listing here, it would not be possible. Fish and Cobb—in "Noxious Marine Animals of the Central and Western Pacific Ocean"—list 83 species of 19 families as poisonous from that region alone. Of these 83, they list 11 as moderate, 25 as mild, 25 as strong, 4 as variable, 1 as a "?," 1 as *deadly*, and 16 as nonspecifically *poisonous*. A great deal of research and statistical analysis stands between the cross-section given in this chapter and full knowledge.

It is believed by many investigators that "fish-poisoning" is a result of a food chain. Presumably, a fish eats a poisonous plant, mollusk, or other marine form, and is then eaten by man, or by a larger fish which is eventually caught by man, and consumed. *Ciguatera*, particularly, appears to be caused by larger predatory fish. It is quite possible that the original organism that triggers this unfortunate chain reaction is harmless to man, but induces a chemical reaction within the tissues of the ciguatera-causing fish that *is* harmful. It is frequently pointed out that the occurrence of Clupeoid poisoning, occasionally with high mortality, *always* coincides with the swarming of the Palolo worm. The worm itself has been shown to be harmless to man.

Marine biologist Philip Helfrich prepared a report on the study of the possible relationship between radioactivity and toxicity in fishes. The report, published by the United States Atomic Energy Commission, concluded:

The accumulated data show an absence of any correlation between radioactivity (gross beta and gamma activity) and *Ciguatera*-type toxicity in samples of muscle, liver, and gonads from Lutjanid fishes from the Marshall and Line Islands.

As indicated earlier, fishes are not the only poisonous marine forms. A marine annelid *Lumbriconereis heteropoda* produces a poison commonly called *nereistoxin*. This may contribute to the poisoning of man in a food chain. Gastropods of the genus *Neptunes* are toxic, perhaps on a seasonal basis. A number of mussels and clams can produce paralytic intoxication, and can be deadly. Respiratory arrest and cardiovascular collapse are the causes of death in fatal cases. Shellfish poisoning has been frequently connected with "red tides," the swarming of a motile, photosynthetic dinoflagellate, *Gonyaulax catenella*. Certain sea cucumbers are quite dangerously poisonous, and a number of cockles can cause serious disturbances. Shellfish poisoning is generally divided into three self-explanatory types: (1) *gastrointestinal* which *may* be bacterial in origin, (2) *allergic*, probably the result of individual sensitivity, and (3) *paralytic*, frequently regarded as the most serious type, and the form generally associated with dinoflagellates ingested by shellfish.

Halstead reports that certain sea turtles taken in the vicinity of the Philippines, Ceylon, and Indonesia can be dangerously poisonous. He implicates the Green Sea Turtle (*Chelonia mydas*), the Hawksbill Turtle (*Eretmochelys imbricata*) and the Leatherback Turtle (*Dermochelys coriacea*), all of which are eaten with impunity in vast numbers each year. Here, too, a food chain may be involved. Halstead points out that the liver is particularly dangerous.

Polar Bear (*Thalarctos maritimus*) liver and kidneys can cause a serious but seldom fatal poisoning, possibly due to a dangerous level of vitamin A concentration. Some of the seals and sea lions are reportedly dangerous to eat, as are certain whales and dolphins, but substantiating data have not turned up at the time of this writing.

Unlike the other health hazards discussed in this book, poisoning by marine forms requires a specific action on the part of man. Nothing happens to man at the will, discretion, or choice of another creature. It is the positive act of eating that causes the distress. To avoid the distress, man need only avoid the action. It is not really that simple, however, since man can hardly give up eating the abundant food made available to him by the sea. He must utilize seafood, and increasingly so, and extensive research is called for to eliminate the present guesswork.

It is doubtful that these forms of poisoning will ever be completely eliminated. If you, an individual, are in unfamiliar surroundings, particularly in the tropics, the only safeguard, aside from totally avoiding seafood, is a check with local inhabitants as to what is considered safe food and what is not. If you fish and eat your catch, there will always be a measure of hazard, but this can be substantially reduced by the advice of the locals or natives. For the time being, at least, poisoning by marine forms, including fish, is a distinct hazard, and a cause of not infrequent medical emergencies.

[*Note:* Subsequent to the completion of this appendix a note was received about *Ciguatera* research in Cuba about 1930. A list was maintained of all species ever implicated. After ten years, just about every commercial species was on the list, and the list was dropped!]

It has been suggested that this appendix include advice on the treatment of "fish-poisoning." Since the treatment involves taking medicines and other substances, I would hesitate to give such advice. Anyone interested is referred to the bibliography. The Halstead book is valuable, as are others listed therein. Researchers interested in the problem can be found in the listing and should be approached directly. Travel in tropical areas should be preceded by some careful study of this problem.

# Acknowledgments

THIS BOOK is essentially a compendium of the accumulated knowledge of professional observers—the naturalists of the earth and the sea. Since it ranges geographically from clear, cool mountain ranges to steaming coastal swamps, from high savannahs to lowland river banks, and the oceanic depths, relatively little that is reported here arises from my own personal observations in the field. While I like to feel that my own trips afield, begun in rural Massachusetts before I was ten years old, have provided both a tempering of the will to accept without question what other people say, and some crude understanding of the workings of nature, the fact remains that no man could, in one lifetime, cover by personal observation the scope and range attempted herein.

In plain fact, this book is the work of hundreds, and perhaps thousands of men and women. Many of these people are anonymous today, because in our state of advanced technology it is often no longer possible to trace the sources of individual bits of information that make up our larger knowledge. Man's learning is slow and inexorable, and builds bit upon bit, just as the fertile plains in which we plant our wheat are built from bits of mountains that are carried down by the frosts, winds, and waters of time.

Many people, however, have contributed directly to this effort. Some of the most highly skilled and heavily burdened scientists in the world of natural history have responded to my pleas for help with a willingness and to an extent that is nothing short of staggering. People all over the United States and in many distant lands who learned of this project by various means, came forward and volunteered their knowledge, their experience, and their help. However the approach was made, on my initiative or on that of other people, a common desire to set the record straight on the subject of so-called dangerous animals pervaded and controlled all efforts.

Every chapter in this book was checked by at least one renowned specialist in the field involved. Not one of these men could really spare the time, yet not one failed to provide notes, corrections, and, on occasion, a good sound thrashing for making avoidable errors. Interestingly enough, each specialist was the first approached by the author. Not one said no. It must be pointed out that the specialists received a *second* draft of the chapter that was their concern. Every effort was made by the author and the editors to lock all scientific data and information firmly in place, once it had been returned. If errors in technical points are to be found in this book, it is because subsequent editorial adjustment altered unwittingly what the specialist had passed on. These errors, if they exist, are, of course, unknown as we go to press, but are the sole responsibility of the author. The authorities who took the time and trouble to render this invaluable service are, with the author's profound gratitude:

Richard Carrington  
Perry W. Gilbert  
Harris W. Hantman (M.D.)  
Carl Kauffeld  
Laurence M. Klauber  

Alan J. Kohn  
Frank W. Lane  
Victor B. Scheffer  
J. L. B. Smith  
Bruce S. Wright  

The many, many people who corresponded with the author, supplying information, clarification, personal unpublished narratives, photographic material, and just plain enthusiasm and goodwill are also listed in the following pages, and are one and all among the very nicest people in the world! Nearly *two thousand* letters were involved. When I think of what that means in man-hours, freely contributed by others to my project, I must confess to feelings of guilt.

It is almost impossible to single out individuals for special thanks without committing grave crimes of omission, but certain people really must be thanked for extraordinary help. Close friends Sterling Lanier and Ivan Sanderson contributed endless hours of encouragement and help. Carl Kauffeld, Curator of the outstanding Staten Island Zoo, not only advised, guided, made his institution's superb collection of venomous reptiles available for photography, but became a kind of herpetological guilty conscience enforcing constant reevaluation. Bruce S. Wright supplied photographs, data, ideas, and even flew down from New Brunswick, Canada, for a pleasant day at sea.

Wilford L. Miller, of Bismarck, N.D., made his superb file of mountain lion photos (almost surely the best in the world) available without cost. Bill also searched the files at Yellowstone for data useful in compiling portions of this book. His help has been beyond estimate. Professor J. L. B. Smith of Rhodes University, in Grahamstown, South Africa, answered endless questions, supplied photos and data, and generally offered his invaluable support to the project. Victor Scheffer put his unique fund of knowledge of marine mammals at the author's disposal, as well as important photographs. David Fleay, of Australia, supplied data, wrote a newspaper piece publicizing the project to obtain information, and arranged for special photos to be taken in Queensland. C. A. W. Guggisberg supplied a number of his priceless photos of African fauna free of charge. Frank W. Lane supplied prints of cephalopods from his book, *Kingdom of the Octopus.* Margaret Dodd, of the Australian News and Information Bureau in New York, helped most willingly in the search for photographs and out-of-print medical and technical reports. Dr. Harris W. Hantman, Dr. John Hessing, and Dr. Robert Ullian surveyed medical literature and provided reprints of important articles, and their personal advice and help. Dr. Perry W. Gilbert, of Cornell, lent his expert's knowledge of sharks to improving that section of this book, and supplied data and photographs. Kindly Ernest P. Walker, of Washington, D.C., supplied both photographs and advice important to this project. Dr. Laurence M. Klauber was exceptionally kind in helping compile the chapters on venomous reptiles, particularly on the rattlesnakes. Dr. Sherman Minton, Jr., then in Karachi, Pakistan, supplied valuable data on snakes. *Sea Breezes* magazine of Liverpool published my letter asking for help, which brought responses from all over the world. The International Oceanographic Foundation of Miami provided a similar platform in their publication, *Sea Secrets*, with similar results. The National Safety Council and the United States Department of the Interior both supplied important statistical information and attendant data. Both the United States Navy and the Army provided manuals on survival, copies of medical journals and reports, and other helpful material. Special thanks to Lieutenant Colonel Wayne Larrabee for his help. Dr. Christopher Coates, of the New York Aquarium, gave of his valuable time and Dr. James Atz was extremely helpful on several occasions. Eleanor Buckley, of Wyeth Laboratories, supplied very informative material from their files. Jeff Sparks, of the United Nations, made rare, out-of-print material from the library of that organization available for reproduction, and good friends Warren West and Oscar "Ed" Pearson of SATOUR obtained excellent studies of South African fauna and made them available for use. Mr. Michael Lerner kindly permitted reproductions of his photographs of squid, and various officers of the U.S. Fish and Wildlife Service helped in a number of ways. Messrs. Lee Ball, James Barclay, and Peter Ianuzzi joined me in an evening "up to our ears in cobras" to obtain a number of photographs used herein. Lee Ball's work, particularly, proved most valuable. To Keeper "Ziggy" of the Staten Island Zoo went the task of controlling the venomous specimens and keeping them in front of our cameras. Captain Frank Mundus of the *Cricket II* out of Montauk, New York, guided us to several adventures with big sharks and provided valuable information on their behavior. Major Simpson of India, as indicated in the text, was extremely helpful in a number of ways. Chris Bottomley spent uncounted hours providing the excellent line drawings scattered throughout this book. Alice Sorensen spent many dozens of hours on the manuscript and made the book possible.

That, certainly, is but a cross-section of those who deserve special thanks. A complete listing would be impossible here, but a list of individual correspondents follows.

Interestingly, of the hundreds of solicitations that were sent out, a scant two dozen failed to elicit cooperation. Some of these, no doubt, were due to langauge barriers. All in all, the researching of this book was a most instructive process.

Out of necessity, I can do little more than issue a blanket, but heartfelt, "Thank You!" to the hundreds of men and women who helped so willingly, and so extensively, in the preparation of this effort. This book is theirs as much as mine!

# List of Correspondents

J. A. Anderson
  Karachi, Pakistan
Luis A. Arrarte
  Caracas, Venezuela
Christopher Ash
  Edinburgh, Scot.
Dr. James W. Atz
  New York City
Louis Bacigalupi
  South San Gabriel, Calif.
W. J. Baerg
  University of Ark.
Robert L. Beutel
  International Oceanographic Foundation
  Miami, Fla.
Walter L. Boxell
  Washington, D.C.
J. E. Bryant
  Department of Northern Affairs and
  National Resources
  Fort Smith, Can.
Dr. W. Bryden
  The Tasmanian Museum
  Hobart, Tasmania
Eleanor E. Buckley
  Wyeth Laboratories
  Philadelphia, Pa.
California Fish and Game Documents
  Section
  Sacramento, Calif.
C. Marshall Caras
  Boston, Mass.
Richard Carrington
  London, Eng.
Craig J. M. Carter
  West Mystic, Conn.
G. M. Chagnon
  National Museum of Canada
  Ottawa, Ontario, Can.
Daniel M. Cohen
  Fish and Wild Life Service
  U.S. National Museum
  Washington, D.C.

Roger Conant
  Philadelphia Zoological Garden
  Philadelphia, Pa.
Dr. V. M. Coppleson
  Sydney, Austral.
Dr. Robert C. Courter
  Department of Health, Education and
  Welfare
  Public Health Service
  Communicable Disease Center
  Atlanta, Ga.
Carl C. Cutler
  West Mystic, Conn.
David H. Davies
  South African Association for Marine
  Biological Research
  University of Natal
  Durban, Natal, S.A.
Dr. P. J. Deoras
  Department of Entomology
  Haffkine Institute
  Bombay, India
George Dickinson
  Sea Breezes Magazine
  Liverpool, Eng.
Margaret Dodd
  Australian News and Information
  Bureau
  New York City
Jill Donisthorpe
  Nairobi, Kenya
J. B. Fitzgerald
  Yukon Territorial Government
  Canada
Dr. V. Fitzsimons
  Transvaal Museum
  Pretoria
  Republic of South Africa
David Fleay
  Queensland, Austral.
Dr. Edward Ford
  School of Public Health and Tropical
  Medicine
  University of Sydney
  Sydney, Austral.

Gladys R. Gary
University of Colorado Museum
Dr. Perry W. Gilbert
Department of Zoology
Cornell University
Ithaca, N.Y.
Dr. Raymond M. Gilmore
La Jolla, Calif.
Kelvin C. B. Green
Sydney, Austral.
C. A. W. Guggisberg
Nairobi, Kenya
East Africa
Lillian Guralnick
Mortality Statistics Branch
National Vital Statistics Division
Department of Health, Education and
Welfare
Washington, D.C.
W. F. Haast
Miami Serpentarium
Miami, Fla.
Bruce W. Halstead, M.D.
World Life Research Institute
Colton, Calif.
Dr. Paul Hansen
Ministeriet for Grønland
Grønlands Fiskeriundersøgelser
Charlottenlund, Denmark
Harris W. Hantman, M.D.
Flushing, N.Y.
Dr. Philip Helfrich
Hawaii Marine Laboratory
University of Hawaii
Honolulu
Archie Herzoff
Universal–International Pictures
Calif.
John Hessing, M.D.
Jamaica, N.Y.
Randolph Hodges
Florida Conservation Department
Tallahassee, Fla.
S. L. Hopkins
London, Eng.
A. S. Hourston
Fisheries Research Board of Canada
Biological Station
Nanaimo, B.C.
G. F. Humphrey
Division of Fisheries and Oceanography
Commonwealth Scientific and Industrial
Research Organization
Marine Laboratory
Sydney, Austral.

Joan Ingalls
Northridge, Calif.
Dr. Robert F. Inger
Chicago Natural History Museum
Robert M. Ingle
Florida State Board of Conservation
Tallahassee, Fla.
Dr. R. S. Irwin
Glen Innes, N.S.W. Austral.
Hans E. Iversen
Santiago, Chile
Dr. S. Jones
Central Marine Fisheries Research
Station
Ramnad District, South India
Carl Kauffeld
Staten Island Zoo
Staten Island, N.Y.
Elmer Keith
Salmon, Idaho
A. P. King
Office of the Scientific Attaché
Australian Embassy
Washington, D.C.
Dr. Laurence M. Klauber
San Diego, Calif.
Dr. Alan J. Kohn
Department of Zoology
University of Washington
Dr. Labuschagne
South African Parks Board and Kruger
National Park
Pretoria, S.A.
Dr. Charles E. Lane
University of Miami
Frank W. Lane
Ruislip, Middlesex, Eng.
Howard V. Langborgh
Chatham, N.J.
Sterling Lanier
Philadelphia, Pa.
P. G. Law
Australian Antarctic Division
Melbourne, Austral.
Robert W. Lee
San Francisco News-Call Bulletin
San Francisco, Calif.
Michael Lerner
New York City
Howard J. Lewis
National Academy of Sciences
National Research Council
Washington, D.C.

F. C. Lochner
National Physical Research Laboratory
South African Council for Scientific
and Industrial Research
Dr. Leonard B. Loeb
Department of Physics
University of California
Berkeley, Calif.
George Mack
Queensland Museum
Brisbane, Queensland, Austral.
B. J. Marlow
The Australian Museum
Sydney, Austral.
Mary A. McCarthy
Mortality Statistics Branch
National Vital Statistics Division
Clarence J. McCoy, Jr.
University of Colorado Museum
Boulder, Col.
W. F. McCulloch, D.V.M.
Institute of Agricultural Medicine
State University of Iowa
D. F. McMichael
The Australian Museum
Sydney, Austral.
Dr. Don W. Micks
Department of Preventive Medicine
and Public Health
The University of Texas Medical
Branch
Galveston, Tex.
Wilfred L. Miller
Meyer Broadcasting Company
Bismarck, N.D.
Dr. Sherman Minton, Jr.
Basic Medical Science Institute
Indiana University Contract
Karachi, Pakistan
Alexander M. Moore
Parke-Davis and Company
Ann Arbor, Michigan
David A. Munro
Canadian Wildlife Service
Department of Northern Affairs and
Natural Resources
Ottawa, Ont.
B. Nelson
Redlands, Bristol, Eng.
Colonel William Nobel, M.D.
Atlanta, Ga.
J. H. Noldt
Australian Medical Publishing Company Ltd.
Glebe, Sydney, Austral.

Hans Nussbaum
American Association for the Advancement of Science
Washington, D.C.
Ross R. Olney
Skin Diver Magazine
Lynwood, Calif.
Clifford H. Pope
Winnetka, Ill.
Dr. Chaloem Puranananda
Queen Saovabha Memorial Institute
Bangkok, Thailand
David Quinton
Department of Mines, Agriculture and
Resources
St. John's, N.F.
Dr. John E. Randall
University of Puerto Rico
Mayaguez
Dr. Harald A. Rehder
Division of Mollusks
Smithsonian Institution
Washington, D.C.
Dr. H. A. Reid
Snake and Venom Research Institute
Penang, Malaya
P. O. Rhynas
Ontario Department of Lands and
Forests
Toronto, Ont.
Dr. W. D. I. Ride
The Western Museum of Australia
Perth, Austral.
Hugo G. Rodeck
University of Colorado Museum
Boulder, Col.
John D. Rush
Agricultural Finance Branch
Washington, D.C.
Dr. Findlay E. Russell
Laboratory of Neurological Research
Loma Linda University
Los Angeles County Hospital
L. S. Russell
Department of Fisheries
Department of Northern Affairs and
National Resources
Ottawa, Ont.
Ivan Sanderson
New York City
Paul R. Saunders, Ph.D.
University of Southern California
Los Angeles

Victor B. Scheffer
  Fish and Wildlife Service
  Sand Point Naval Air Station
  Seattle, Wash.
Dr. Leonard P. Schultz
  Division of Fishes
  Smithsonian Institution
  Washington, D.C.
Ruth L. Shepherd
  General Biological Supply House, Inc.
  Chicago, Ill.
Major C. H. Simpson
  Kanyakumar District
  South India
Dr. N. Sitaraman
  Nagercoil, South India
B. G. Sivertz
  Northern Administration Branch
  Department of Northern Affairs and
    Natural Resources
  Ottawa, Ont.
F. May Smith
  International Oceanographic Founda-
  Miami, Fla.
J. L. B. Smith, Professor
  Department of Ichthyology
  Rhodes University
  Grahamstown, S.A.
Dr. Ronald V. Southcott
  Hyde Park, Austral.
Jeff Sparks
  United Nations, N.Y.
Stewart Springer
  Bureau of Commercial Fisheries
  U.S. Fish and Wildlife Service
  Washington, D.C.
Dr. Herbert L. Stahnke
  Poisonous Animals Research Labora-
  Arizona State University
William M. Stephens
  Homestead, Fla.
Major Howard G. Stevenson
  U.S. Army Information
  New York City
Lieutenant J. W. Stierman, U.S.N.
  Department of the Navy
  Office of Information
  Washington, D.C.
Dr. Donald P. deSylva
  The Marine Laboratory
  University of Miami

Fred L. Thomas
  National Safety Council
  Chicago, Ill.
Josephine M. Thorpe
  Cornell University Library
G. B. Treadwell
  The Wild Life Protection Society of
    South Africa
James B. Trefethen
  Wildlife Management Institute
  Washington, D.C.
Dr. G. F. Trinca
  Commonwealth Serum Laboratories
  Victoria, Austral.
Walker Van Riper
  Museum of Natural History
  Denver, Col.
Gilbert L. Voss
  Biological Sciences Division
  The Marine Laboratory
  Institute of Marine Science
  University of Miami
Ernest P. Walker
  Washington, D.C.
Dr. H. K. Wallace
  Department of Biology
  University of Florida
  Gainesville
Dr. S. Wiener
  Victoria, Austral.
James Wiles
  International Oceanographic Founda-
    tion
  Miami, Fla.
Henry C. Wolhuter
  Kruger National Park
  Republic of South Africa
Bruce S. Wright
  North Eastern Wildlife Station
  University of New Brunswick
  Fredricton, N.B.
John A. Yntema
  Frederiksted, St. Croix
  U.S. Virgin Islands
Dr. Stanley P. Young
  Department of the Interior
  U.S. Fish and Wildlife Service
  U.S. National Museum
  Washington, D.C.

# Bibliography

THE FOLLOWING bibliography covers *most* of the references used in the preparation of this book. Since a great many references were cited from second and third recountings, some original references are missing. In every case, an effort was made to go to the original source, but it was not always possible to do so.

In a bibliography as large as this must be, it may be difficult for the average reader to find suggested reading for himself should he desire further information. In an effort to make this bibliography serve as a suggested reading list as well, I have made notations in the left-hand margin that reflect my own personal opinion. The notations do not necessarily indicate an evaluation of literary quality—indeed they don't. The books are marked which will be of most interest to the group involved:

| | |
|---|---|
| * | of more than average interest |
| ** | of great interest |
| *** | essential reading in the field |
| G | for general readers |
| S | for specialists |

**GS ABBOT, R. TUCKER (1954). *American Seashells.* D. Van Nostrand Co., New York.

ADAMSON, JOY (1960). *Born Free.* Pantheon Books, New York.

ADAMSON, JOY (1962). *Forever Free.* Harcourt, Brace & World, New York.

AHUJA, M. L., & GURKIRPAL SINGH (1956). "Snakebite in India." *Venoms,* Publication No. 44 of Amer. Assoc. for the Advancement of Science, Washington, D.C.

ALLAM, M. W., D. WEINER, & F. D. W. LUKENS (1956). "Comparison of Cortisone and Antivenin in the Crotaline Envenomation." *Venoms,* Publication No. 44 of Amer. Assoc. for the Advancement of Science, Washington, D.C.

ALLEN, DURWARD L., & L. DAVID MECH (1963). "Wolves versus Moose on Isle Royale." *National Geographic,* vol. 123, no. 2.

*G ALLEN, E. ROSS, & WILFRED T. NEILL (1961). "Alligators and Crocodiles in Florida." Florida Game & Fresh Water Fish Comm., Tallahassee.

*GS ALLEN, GLOVER M. (1939). *Bats.* Harvard Univ. Press, Cambridge, Mass.

ALLINGTON, HERMAN V., & R. R. ALLINGTON (1954). "Insect Bites." *Jour. Amer. Medical Assoc.,* vol. 155, no. 3, pp. 240–247.

385

*G    ALPERS, ANTONY (1960). *Dolphins: The Myth and the Mammal.* Houghton Mifflin Co., Boston.

**S    ALTAMIRANO, MARIO, C. W. COATES, H. GRUNDFEST, & D. NACHMANSOHN (1953). "Mechanisms of Bioelectric Activity in Electric Tissue." *Jour. Genl. Physiology,* vol. 37, no. 1, p. 91.

ALTAMIRANO, MARIO, & C. W. COATES (1957). "Effect of Potassium on Electroplax of Electrophorus Electricity." *Jour. Cellular & Comparative Physiol.,* vol. 49, no. 1.

AMBROSE, MICHAEL S. (1956). "Snakebite in Central America." *Venoms,* Publication No. 44, Amer. Assoc. for the Advancement of Science, Washington, D.C.

***GS American Assoc. for the Advancement of Science (1956). *Venoms,* Publication No. 44, Washington, D.C.

American Med. Assoc. (1960). "Wasp Bite." *Journal,* July, pp. 1512 ff.

American Medical Assoc. (1961a). "Insects and Man." *Journal,* vol. 177, no. 7, August, pp. 505 ff.

American Medical Assoc. (1961b). "Venomous Animals." *Journal,* September, pp. 94 ff.

ANDERSON, KENNETH (1961). *The Call of the Man-Eater.* Chilton Books, Philadelphia.

ANDERSON, LOUIS (1957). "This Happened to Me! Killer Foiled!" *Outdoor Life Magazine,* vol. 119, no. 4, April.

*GS    ARCISZ, W. (1950). "Ciguatera: Tropical Fish Poisoning." U.S. Fish & Wildlife Serv. Special Scientific Report, Fisheries 27, Washington, D.C.

ASANO, MOTOKAZU, & MOSOO ITAH (1960). "Salivary Poison of a Marine Gastropod *Neptunea arthritica bernardi* and the Seasonal Variation of Its Toxicity." *Biochem. & Pharm. of Compounds Derived from Marine Organisms. Annals of the N.Y. Acad. of Science,* vol. 90, art. 3.

**GS ASH, CHRISTOPHER (1962). *Whaler's Eye.* Macmillan Co., New York.

ATTENBOROUGH, DAVID (1958). *Zoo Quest to Guiana.* The Reprint Society, Ltd. (England) by arrangement with Lutterworth Press.

ATZ, JAMES W. (1954). "Most Dangerous to Man? (Piranha)." *Animal Kingdom,* vol. 57, no. 3, May-June.

*GS    ATZ, JAMES W. (1960). "Stonefishes: The World's Most Venomous Fishes." *Animal Kingdom,* vol. 63, no. 5.

*GS    ATZ, JAMES W. (1962). "The Flamboyant Zebra Fish." *Animal Kingdom,* vol. 65, no. 2.

AUSTIN, OLIVER L., JR. (1961). *Birds of the World.* Golden Press, New York.

AYMAR, BRANDT (ed.) (1956). *Treasury of Snake Lore.* Greenberg, New York.

BACKUS, RICHARD H., S. SPRINGER, & E. L. ARNOLD, JR. (1956). "A Contribution to the Natural History of the White-Tip Shark." *Deep-Sea Research.* Vol. 3. Pergamon Press, London.

BACKUS, RICHARD H. (1957). "Notes on Western North Atlantic Sharks." *Copeia*, no. 3, August.

BAERG, W. J. (1933). "The Effects of the Bite of *Latrodectus mactans*." *Jour. Parasitology*, vol. IX, no. 3, March, pp. 161–169.

\*\*GS BAERG, W. J. (1958). *The Tarantula*. Univ. of Kansas Press, Lawrence, Kan.

\*\*GS BAERG, W. J. (1959). "The Black Widow and Five Other Venomous Spiders in the United States." Agric. Experiment Sta. Bul. No. 608, February. Univ. of Arkansas, Fayetteville.

BAERG, W. J. (1961). "Scorpions: Biology and Effect of Their Venom." Agric. Experiment Sta. Bul. 649, August. Univ. of Arkansas, Fayetteville.

BALDAUF, RICHARD J. (1957). "Records of *Ancistrodon piscivorus leucostoma* (Troost)." *Copeia*, no. 3, August.

BALOZET, LUCIEN (1956). "Scorpion Venoms and Antiscorpion Serum." *Venoms*, Publication No. 44, Amer. Assoc. for the Advancement of Science, Washington, D.C.

BANNER, ALBERT H., & H. BOROUGHS (1957). "Observations on Toxins of Poisonous Fishes." *Proceedings of the Soc. of Experimental Biol. Med.*, vol. 98, pp. 776–778.

BANNER, ALBERT H., *et al.* (1960). "Observations on Ciguatera-Type Toxin in Fish." *Biochem. & Pharm. of Compounds Derived from Marine Organisms. Annals, N.Y. Acad. Science*, vol. 90, art. 3.

BANNER, ALBERT H., S. SATOSHI, PHILIP HELFRICH, CHARLES B. ALENDER, & PAUL J. SCHENER (1961). "Bioassay of Ciguatera Toxin." *Nature*, vol. 189, no. 4760, January, pp. 229–230.

BARDACH, JOHN E., HOWARD E. WINN, & DAVID W. MENZEL (1960). "The Role of the Senses in the Feeding of the Nocturnal Reef Predators *Gymnothorax vicinus.*" *Copeia*, no. 2, July.

BARNES, J. H. (1963). "Stingings by Jelly-Fish." *Supp. to the Bul. of the Post Grad. Comm. in Med.*, vol. 18, no. 12, March. Univ. of Sydney, Australia.

BARTLETT, NORMAN (1954). *The Pearl Seekers*. Coward-McCann, New York.

BAUGHMAN, J. L. (1947*a*). "Sharks, Sawfishes and Rays." *Texas Game & Fish*, October.

BAUGHMAN, J. L. (1947*b*). "Sharks." *Texas Game & Fish*, April.

BAUGHMAN, J. L., & S. SPRINGER (1950). "Biological and Economic Notes on the Sharks of the Gulf of Mexico." *American Midland Naturalist*, vol. 44, no. 1, July.

BEEBE, B. F. (1963). *American Lions and Cats*. David McKay Co., New York.

\*G BEEBE, WILLIAM (1918). *Jungle Peace*. Henry Holt & Co., New York.

\*G BEEBE, WILLIAM (1924). *Galapagos: World's End*. G. P. Putnam's Sons, New York.

\*G BEEBE, WILLIAM (1925). *Jungle Days*. G. P. Putnam's Sons, New York.

*G     BEEBE, WILLIAM (1926). *The Arcturus Adventure*. G. P. Putnam's Sons, New York.

*G     BEEBE, WILLIAM (1928). *Beneath Tropic Seas*. G. P. Putnam's Sons, New York.

*G     BEEBE, WILLIAM (1932). *Nonesuch Land of Water*. Harcourt, Brace & Co., New York.

**GS    BEEBE, WILLIAM (1934). *Half Mile Down*. Harcourt, Brace & Co., New York.

*G     BEEBE, WILLIAM (1938). *Zaca Venture*. Harcourt, Brace & Co., New York.

BELL, THOMAS (1839). *A History of British Reptiles*. John Van Voorst, London.

BENNETTS, J. A. W. (1956). "The King of the Mambas." *African Wild Life*, vol. X, no. 1, December.

BENT, WILLIAM H. (1952). *A Field Guide to the Mammals*. Houghton Mifflin Co., Boston.

BEST, E. A. (1961). "Occurrence of the Round Stingray *Uroloplus halleri* Cooper in Humboldt Bay, California." *California Fish & Game*, vol. 47, no. 4, October.

BIGELOW, HENRY B., W. C. SHROEDER, & S. SPRINGER (1953). "New and Little Known Sharks from the Atlantic and from the Gulf of Mexico." *Bul. Mus. Comparative Zoology*, July.

BISHOP, S. C. (1947). *Handbook of Salamanders*. Comstock Pub. Co., New York.

BLAIR, W. F., *et al.* (1957). *Vertebrates of the United States*. McGraw-Hill, New York.

BLOMBERG, ROLF (1956). "Giant Snake Hunt." *Natural History*, vol. 65, no. 4.

BOGEN, EMIL (1932). "Poisonous Spider Bites." *Jour. Amer. Med. Assoc.*, vol. 99, no. 24, December 10.

BOGEN, EMIL (1956). "The Treatment of Spider Bite Poisoning." *Venoms*, A.A.A.S. Publication No. 44.

BOGERT, CHARLES M. (1954). "Snakes That Spit Their Venom." *Animal Kingdom*, vol. 57, no. 3, May-June.

***GS   BOGERT, CHARLES M., & RAFAEL MARTIN DEL CAMPO (1956). "The Gila Monster and Its Allies—The Relationships, Habits and Behavior of the Lizards of the Family Helodermatidae." *Bul. Amer. Mus. Nat. Hist.*, vol. 109, art. 1.

BOLIN, ROLF L. (1954). "Report on a Fatal Attack by a Shark." *Pacific Science*, vol. 8, no. 1, January.

BOQUET, P. (1956). "Effect of Hyaluronidase on the Therapeutic Activity of Antivenoms." *Venoms*, A.A.A.S. Publication No. 44.

BOURLIÈRE, FRANCOIS (1954). *The Natural History of Mammals*. H. M. Parshley translation. Alfred A. Knopf, New York.

BROWN, MARGARET E. (ed.) (1957). *The Physiology of Fishes*, Vol. II, *Behavior*. Academic Press, New York.

BROWN, M. V. (1950). "The Electric Discharge of the Electric Eel." *Electrical Engineering*, March.

BROWN, M. V., & C. W. COATES (1952). "Further Comparisons of Length and Voltage in the Electric Eel *Electrophorus electricus* (Linnaeus)." *Zoologica*, vol. 37, part 4, 12/31.

*G  BRUNNER, JOSEF (1941). *Tracks and Tracking*. Macmillan Co., New York.

BUCHERL, WOLFGANG (1956). "Studies on Dried Venom of *Phoneutria fera* Perty, 1833." *Venoms*, A.A.A.S. Publication No. 44.

BUCHSBAUM, RALPH, & LORUS J. MILNE. *The Lower Animals*. Double-day & Co., New York.

***GS  BUCKLEY, E. E., & N. PORGES (1956). *Venoms*, A.A.A.S. Publication No. 44.

BUE, GERALD T., & M. H. STENLUND (1953). "Recent Records of the Mountain Lion *Felis concolor* in Minnesota." *Jour. Mammalogy*, vol. 34, no. 3, August.

BULLEN, FRANK T. (1904). *Denizens of the Deep*. Fleming H. Revell Co., New York.

BURDEN, W. D. (1945). "Development of a Shark Deterrent." *Air Surg. Bul.*, vol. 2, no. 10, October.

**GS  BURNET, MACFARLANE (1962). *Natural History of Infectious Diseases*. 3d ed. The University Press, Cambridge, Mass.

BURTON, E. MILBY (1935). "Shark Attacks Along the South Carolina Coast." *Scientific Monthly*, vol. 40, pp. 279–283.

BURTON, MAURICE (1956). *Living Fossils*. Readers Union, Thames & Hudson, London.

BURTON, MAURICE (1960). *In Their Element: the Story of Water Mammals*. Abelard-Schuman, London.

BYERS, ROBERT D. (1940). "The California Shark Fishery." *California Fish & Game*, vol. 26, no. 1.

CARAS, ROGER A. (1962). *Antarctica: Land of Frozen Time*. Chilton Books, Philadelphia.

CARITHERS, HUGH A. (1958). "Mammalian Bites of Children." *Jour. Amer. Med. Assoc., Diseases Child.*, vol. 95, February.

CARLSON, FRED A. (1946). *Geography of Latin America*. Prentice-Hall, New York.

CARPER, JEAN (1960). "Snakes Are Safe (But Stick to Cats and Dogs)." *Natl. Safety Council Education*, April.

CARR, ARCHIE, & the Editors of *Life* (1963). *The Reptiles*. Time Inc., New York.

CARRINGTON, RICHARD (1957). "Sea Serpent: Riddle of the Deep." *Natural History*, April.

***G  CARRINGTON, RICHARD (1959). *Elephants: A Short Account of Their Natural History, Evolution, and Influence on Mankind*. Basic Books, New York.

**G  CARSON, RACHEL L. (1954). *The Sea Around Us*. Oxford Univ. Press, New York.

CECIL, RUSSEL L., & ROBT. F. LOEB (ed.) (1959). *A Textbook of Medicine* (10th ed.). W. B. Saunders, Philadelphia.

CHEESMAN, EVELYN (1949). *Six-Legged Snakes in New Guinea.* Geo. G. Harrap & Co., London.

CHRISTENSEN, P. A. (1955). *South African Snake Venoms and Antivenins.* South Afr. Inst. Med. Res.

CLARK, EUGENIE (1959). "Instrumental Conditioning of Lemon Sharks." *Science,* vol. 130, no. 3369, July.

**GS CLARK, EUGENIE (1960). "Four Shark Attacks on the West Coast of Florida, Summer 1958." *Copeia,* no. 1, March.

CLARK, LEONARD (1953). *The Rivers Ran East.* Funk & Wagnalls Co., New York.

CLARKE, ARTHUR C. (1955). *The Coast of Coral.* Harper & Bros., New York.

CLELAND, J. B. (1924). "Injuries and Diseases in Australia Attributable to Animals." *Med. Jour. Austral.,* 2:339.

CLEMENS, W. A., & G. V. WILBY. "Fishes of the Pacific Coast of Canada." Fisheries Research Bd. of Canada, Ottawa (Bul. No. 68, Rev.).

CLENCH, W. J., & Y. KONDO (1943). "The Poison Cone Shell." *Am. Jour. Trop. Med. & Hyg.,* vol. 23, pp. 105–121.

***GS COATES, C. W., R. T. COX, & L. P. GRANATH (1937). "The Electric Discharge of the Electric Eel *Electrophorus electricus* (Linnaeus)." *Zoologica,* vol. 22 (part 1), April.

COATES, C. W., R. T. COX, W. A. ROSENBLITH, & M. V. BROWN (1940). "Propagation of the Electric Impulse along the Organs of the Electric Eel *Electrophorus electricus* (Linnaeus)." *Zoologica,* vol. 25 (part 2), July.

*S COATES, C. W. (1949). "Electric Fishes." *Electrical Engineering,* January 31.

COATES, C. W. (1955). "Three More Gymnotid Eels Found to Be Electrogenic." *Zoologica,* vol. 40 (part 4), December.

COCHRAN, D. M. (1943). "Poisonous Reptiles of the World: A Wartime Handbook." Smithsonian Inst., War Background Studies, No. 10. Washington, D.C.

COCHRAN, D. M. (1954). "Our Snake Friends and Foes." *National Geographic,* vol. 106, no. 3, September.

COGGER, HAROLD G. (1963). "Sea-Snakes." *Supp. to the Bul. of the Post Grad. Comm. in Med.,* vol. 18, no. 12, March. Univ. of Sydney, Australia.

**G COLBY, C. B. (1963). *Fur and Fury.* Duell, Sloan & Pearce, New York.

COLE, ROBERT A. (1960). Bat Rabies, Natl. Safety Council, A New Health and Safety Challenge.

COLLINS, HENRY HILL, JR. (1959). *Complete Field Guide to American Wildlife.* Harper & Bros., New York.

COLMAN, JOHN S. (1950). *The Sea and Its Mysteries.* Wm. Norton & Co., New York.

Commonwealth Serum Laboratories. *Red-Back Spider Antivenene.* Melbourne, Australia.

Commonwealth Serum Laboratories. *Treatment of Snakebite in Australia.* Melbourne.

CONANT, ROGER (1958). *A Field Guide to Reptiles and Amphibians.* Houghton Mifflin Co., Boston.

CONSTANCE, ARTHUR (1958). *The Impenetrable Sea.* Citadel Press, New York.

***GS COON, CARLETON S. (1962). *The Origin of Races.* Alfred A. Knopf, New York.

***GS *Copeia, The Quarterly of the American Society of Ichthyologists and Herpetologists.* Philadelphia.

COPPLESON, V. M. (1950). "A Review of Shark Attacks in Australian Waters Since 1919." *Med. Jour. Austral.*, November.

***GS COPPLESON, V. M. (1962). *Shark Attack.* Angus & Robertson, Sydney and Melbourne.

COPPLESON, V. M. (1963). "Distribution and Pattern of Australian Shark Attacks." *Supp. to the Bul. of the Post Grad. Comm. in Med.*, vol. 18, no. 12, March. Univ. of Sydney, Australia.

COPPELSON, V. M. "Biting and Attack Mechanisms of Sharks," *ibid.*

***GS CORBETT, JIM (1946). *Man-Eaters of Kumaon.* Oxford Univ. Press.

***GS CORBETT, JIM (1948). *The Man-Eating Leopard of Rudraprayag.* Oxford.

***GS CORBETT, JIM (1954). *The Temple Tiger and More Man-Eaters of Kumaon.* Oxford.

CORKILL, NORMAN L. (1956). "Snake Poisoning in the Sudan." *Venoms,* A.A.A.S. Publication No. 44.

COTT, HUGH B. (1938). "Wonder Island of the Amazon Delta." *National Geographic,* vol. 74, no. 5, November.

**G COUSTEAU, JACQUES-YVES (1953). *The Silent World.* Harper & Bros., New York.

COUSTEAU, JACQUES-YVES (1952). "Fish Men Explore a New World Undersea." *National Geographic,* vol. 52, no. 4.

**G COUSTEAU, JACQUES-YVES (with JAMES DUGAN) (1959). *Captain Cousteau's Underwater Treasury.* Harper & Bros., New York.

**G COUSTEAU, JACQUES-YVES (with JAMES DUGAN) (1963). *The Living Sea.* Harper & Row, New York.

COWLES, R. B., & C. M. BOGERT (1935). "Observation on the California Lyre Snake, *Trimorphodon vandenburghi,* Klauber, with Notes on the Effectiveness of Its Venom." *Copeia,* July.

COX, R. T., & C. W. COATES (1937). "Electrical Characteristics of the Electric Eel *Electrophorus electricus.*" *Zoologica,* vol. 22 (part 8), no. 1, April.

COX, R. T., & C. W. COATES (with M. V. BROWN) (1946). "Electrical Characteristics of Electric Tissue." *Annals N.Y. Acad. Science,* vol. 47, art. 4, December.

CRAIG, JOHN D. (1941). *Danger Is My Business*. Garden City Pub. Co., Garden City, N.Y.

CRILEY, B. R. (1956). "Development of a Multivalent Antivenin for the Family Crotalidae." *Venoms*, A.A.A.S. Publication No. 44.

\*\*\*GS    CRISLER, LOIS (1958). *Arctic Wild*. Harper & Bros., New York.

CROMIE, WILLIAM J. (1963). "Killer Whale!" *Readers Digest*, March.

DAIBER, FRANKLIN C. (1960). "A Further Note on the Night Shark *Hypoprion signatus*." *Copeia*, no. 1, March.

DANIEL, J. F. (1934). *The Elasmobranch Fishes*. Univ. of California Press, Berkeley.

DAY, L. R., & H. D. FISHER (1954). "Notes on the Great White Shark, *Carcharodon carcharias*, in Canadian Atlantic Waters." *Copeia*, no. 4, October.

DEAR, L. S. (1955). "Cougar or Mountain Lion Reported in Northwest Ontario." *Canadian Field-Naturalist*, vol. 69, no. 1, January-March.

DEARBORN, NED (1927). "An Old Record of the Mountain Lion in New Hampshire." *Jour. Mammalogy*, vol. 8, no. 4, November.

DEORAS, P. J. (1959). "Snakes: How to Know Them." The Directorate of Publicity, Govt. of Bombay, Bombay, India.

DEORAS, P. J. (1961). "A Study of Scorpions: Their Distribution, Incidence and Control in Maharashtra." *Probe*, no. 2, December.

DEVI, A., A. K. BOSE, & N. K. SARKAR (1956). "Prothrombin-like Property of Russell's Viper Venom." *Venom*, A.A.A.S. Publication No. 44.

DICUS, DONALD R. (1962). "Current Status of Treatment of Poisonous Snakebite." *Postgraduate Med.*, March.

\*\*\*GS    DOBIE, J. FRANK, JR. (1947). *The Voice of the Coyote*. Curtis Publishing Co., New York.

\*G    DODGE, NATT N. (1961). *Poisonous Dwellers of the Desert*. Southwestern Monuments Assoc., Globe, Arizona.

DOUKAN, GILBERT (1957). *The World Beneath the Waves*. George Allen & Unwin, London.

DOYLE, ADRIAN CONAN (1953). *Heaven Has Claws*. Random House, New York.

DUHIG, J. V., & G. JONES (1928). "The Venom Apparatus of the Stone Fish (*Synanceja horrida*)." *Memoirs of the Queensland Museum*, 9:136. Australia.

DYKSTRA, PHILIP (1961). "Is the Bite of the Black Widow Spider Deadly?" *Natl. Safety Council Home Safety Review*, Summer.

\*\*GS    DYSON, JAMES L. (1962). *The World of Ice*. Alfred A. Knopf, New York.

ELLISON, NORMAN (1932). "Shark Fishing—An Australian Industry." *National Geographic*, vol. LXII, no. 3, September.

EMERTON, JAMES H. (1902). *The Common Spiders of the United States*. Ginn & Co., Boston.

ENDEAN, R. (1962). "Stonefish." *Austral. Nat. Hist.*, vol. 14, no. 1.

ENDEAN, R. "A Study of the Distribution, Habitat, Behavior, Venom Apparatus, and Venom of the Stonefish." *Austral. Journal Marine & Freshwater Research*, vol. 12, no. 2.

ENGEL, LEONARD, & the Editors of *Life* (1961). *The Sea*. Time Inc., New York.

ESSEX, H. E. (1945). "Animal Venoms and Their Actions." *Physiol. Rev.*, vol. 45, p. 148.

EVANS, H. M. (1921). "The Poison Organs and Venoms of Venomous Fish." *Brit. Med. Jour.*, 2:690.

EVANS, H. M. (1943). *Sting-fish and Seafarers*. Faber, Ltd., London.

EWERS, B. (1963). "Swimmer's Itch (*Schistosome dermatitis*)." *Supp. to the Bul. of the Post Grad. Comm. in Med.*, vol. 18, no. 12, March. Univ. of Sydney, Australia.

*Explorers Newsletter*. New York Explorers Club, New York. (Various.)

FANSLER, THOMAS (1958). "Are Dog Bites a Home Safety Problem?" *Home Safety Review*, vol. 15, no. 6, June.

FAVILLI, GIOVANNI (1956). "Occurrence of Spreading Factors and Some Properties of Hyaluronidase in Animal Parasites and Venoms." *Venoms*, A.A.A.S. Publication No. 44.

FINLAYSON, M. H. (1956). "Arachnidism in South Africa." *Venoms*, A.A.A.S. Publication No. 44.

***GS FISH, CHARLES J., & M. C. COBB (1954). "Noxious Marine Animals of the Central and Western Pacific Ocean." Research Report No. 36, Fish & Wildlife Serv., U.S. Dept. Int.

FITCH, JOHN E. (1949). "The Great White Shark *Carcharodon carcharias* (Linnaeus) in California Waters During 1948." *California Fish & Game*, vol. 35, no. 2, April.

FLECKER, H. "Injuries Produced by Marine Animals in Tropical Australia." Unpublished remarks made available by Dr. R. S. Irwin of Glen Innes, N.S.W. (Private communication.)

*GS FLECKER, H. (1945). "Injuries by Unknown Agents to Bathers in North Queensland." *Med. Jour. Austral.*, vol. 1, no. 4, January.

*GS FLECKER, H. (1952). "Fatal Stings to North Queensland Bathers." *Med. Jour. Austral.*, January, pp. 35 ff.

*GS FLECKER, H. (1952). "Irukandji Sting to North Queensland Bathers without Production of Weals but with Severe General Symptoms." *Med. Jour. Austral.*, July, pp. 89 ff.

**GS FLECKER, H., & BERNARD C. COTTON (1955). "Fatal Bite from Octopus." *Med. Jour. Austral.*, 2:429.

FLOYD, JIM (1960). "Snakes Can Kill." Florida Game & Fresh Water Fish Comm., Tallahassee.

FOGELBERG, J. M., & F. E. BRINNOCK (1944). "First Partial Report on the Uses of Chemical Materials as Shark Repellents." Naval Res. Lab. Rep. No. P2230, February.

FOGELBERG, J. M., & F. E. BRINNOCK (1944). "Final Report on the Use of Chemical Materials as Shark Repellents." Naval Res. Lab. Rep. No. P2373.

FORD, W. J. A. (1957). "The Treatment of Dog Bites and the Rabies Problem." *Amer. Jour. Surg.*, 93, April.

FOUCHER-CRETEAU, JEAN (1957). *My Adventures Under the Sea.* Frederick Muller, Ltd., London.

FOWLER, H. W. (1908). "Notes on Sharks." *Proc. Acad. Nat. Sci. of Phila.*, April.

FRACHTMAN, H. J., & W. T. McCOLLUM (1945). "Portuguese Man-of-war Stings: A Case Report." *Amer. Jour. Trop. Med.*, vol. XXV, no. 4.

FRYE, O. E., & BILL and LES PIPER (1952). "The Disappearing Panther." Florida Game & Fresh Water Fish Comm., Tallahassee.

FUNK, BEN (1958). "Keeper of the Cobras." *Coronet*, April.

GHEERBRANT, ALAIN (1953). *The Impossible Adventure.* Victor Gollancz Ltd., London.

GHIRETTI, F. (1960). "Toxicity of Octopus Saliva Against Crustacea." *Biochem. & Pharm. of Compounds Derived from Marine Organisms. Annals N.Y. Acad. Science*, vol. 90, art. 3.

**S    GHOSH, B. N., & N. K. SARKAR (1956). "Active Principles of Snake Venoms." *Venoms*, A.A.A.S. Publication No. 44.

GILBERT, PERRY W. (1958). "Conference on Shark Repellents." *Amer. Inst. Biol. Sci.*, Bul. 8(3).

GILBERT, PERRY W. (with HENRY KRITZLER) (1960). "Experimental Shark Pens at the Lerner Marine Laboratory." *Science*, vol. 132, no. 3424, August 12.

**GS    GILBERT, PERRY W. (with LEONARD P. SCHULTZ & STEWART SPRINGER) (1960). "Shark Attacks During 1959." *Science*, vol. 132, no. 3423, August 5.

GILBERT, PERRY W. (1960). "The Shark Research Panel." *AIBS Bul.*, February.

GILBERT, PERRY W. (1962). "About Sharks." *New York Times Magazine*, August 5.

**GS    GILBERT, PERRY W. (1962). "The Behavior of Sharks." *Scientific American*, vol. 207, no. 1, July.

GILLIS, R. G. (1961). "Some Observations on Stonefish." *North Queensland Naturalist*, vol. 29, no. 130.

GILMORE, C. W. (1938). "Fossil Snakes of North America." Geological Society of America, Special Paper No. 9.

GINGRICH, W. C., & J. C. HOHENADEL (1956). "Standardization of Polyvalent Antivenin." *Venoms*, A.A.A.S. Publication No. 44.

GINSBURG, ISAAC (1953). "Western Atlantic Scorpionfish." *Smithsonian Misc. Coll.*, vol. 121, no. 8.

GITHENS, T. H. (1935). "Snake Bite in the United States." *Scientific Monthly*, August.

GITTER, S., C. MOROZ, E. LIWNI, & A. DE VRIES (1961). "Pathogenesis of Snake Venom Intoxication, I. Neurotoxins." *Proc. Staff Meet. Beilinson Hosp. Supp.* No. 10, Tel Aviv.

GOE, D. R., & B. W. HALSTEAD (1955). "A Case of Fish Poisoning from *Caranx Ignobilis* Forskal from Palmyra Island with Comments on the Sensitivity of the Mouse—Injection Technique for Screening of Toxic Fishes." *Copeia*, vol. 3, 238–240.

GORDON, BERNARD L. (1956). "The Amazing Angel Shark." *Sea Frontiers*, vol. 2, no. 2, July.

GORSHENIN, N. (1963). "Shark Meshing in New South Wales." *Supp. to the Bul. of the Post Grad. Comm. in Med.*, vol. 18, no. 12, March. Univ. of Sydney.

GORSKY, BERNARD (1954). *Mediterranean Hunter*. Souvenir Press, Ltd., London.

GRAHAM, D. H. (1954). *A Treasury of New Zealand Fishes*. A. H. & A. W. Reed, Wellington.

GREATHOUSE, TEDFORD L. (1960). "Killer Whale." *Skin Diver*, vol. IX, no. 1, January.

GREGOR, PAUL (1962). *Amazon Fortune Hunter*. Souvenir Press, Ltd., London.

GRIMBLE, SIR ARTHUR (1952). *We Chase the Islands, a Six-Year Adventure in the Gilberts*. Wm. Morrow & Co., New York.

GUDGER, E. W. (1915). "Natural History of the Whale Shark." *Zoologica*, vol. 1, no. 19, March.

GUDGER, E. W. (1930). "Poisonous Fishes and Fish Poisonings with Special Reference to Ciguatera in the West Indies." *Amer. Jour. Trop. Med.*, vol. 10, no. 1.

GUDGER, E. W. (1932). "Cannibalism Among the Sharks and Rays." *Scientific Monthly*, vol. 34, May.

GUDGER, E. W. (1936). "Open Ocean and Coastal Sharks: Do They Attack Man?" *The Collecting Net*, vol. XL, no. 6, August.

GUDGER, E. W. (1937). "Will Sharks Attack Human Beings?" *Natural History*, vol. XL, no. 1.

GUDGER, E. W. (1940). "The alleged pugnacity of the swordfish and the spearfishes as shown by their attacks on vessels." *Memoir Royal Asiatic Soc. Bengal*, vol. 12, no. 2.

GUDGER, E. W. (1943). "Is the Sting Ray's Sting Poisonous? A Historical Resume Showing the Development of Our Knowledge That It Is Poisonous." *Bul. Hist. of Med.*, vol. XIV, no. 4, November.

GUDGER, E. W. (1950). "A Boy Attacked by a Shark, July 25, 1936, in Buzzard's Bay, Massachusetts, with Notes on Attacks by Another Shark Along the New Jersey Coast in 1916." *Amer. Midland Naturalist*, vol. 44, no. 3, November.

***GS GUGGISBERG, C. A. W. (1961). *Simba: The Life of the Lion*. Bailey Bros. and Swinfen, Ltd., London; Chilton Books, Philadelphia (1963).

GUNTER, G. H. (1937). *Adventures of a Trepang Fisher*. Hurst and Blackett, London.

HABEL, K. (1957). "Rabies Prophylaxis in Man." *Pediatrics*, vol. 19, May.

HALEY, N. C. (1948). *Whale Hunt*. Washburn, New York.

HALFORD, GEORGE BRITTON (1894). *Thoughts, Observations, and Experiments on the Action of Snake Venom on the Blood*. Stillwell & Co., Melbourne.

HALSTEAD, B. W., *et al.* (1956). "Stonefish Stings and the Venom Apparatus of *Synanceja horrida* (Linnaeus)." *Trans. Amer. Microsc. Soc.*, vol. 75, no. 4.

HALSTEAD, B. W. (1956). "Current Status of Research on Pacific Poisonous Fishes and Ichthyosarcotoxism." *Venoms*, A.A.A.S. Publication No. 44.

HALSTEAD, B. W. (1957). "Weever Stings and Their Medical Management." *U.S. Armed Forces Med. Jour.*, vol. 8, 1441–4151.

***GS HALSTEAD, B. W. (1959). *Dangerous Marine Animals*. Cornell Maritime Press, Cambridge, Md.

HANSEN, T. J. (1963). "Sea-Wasp Syndrome or Acute Nematocyst Poisoning." *Supp. to the Bul. of the Post Grad. Comm. in Med.*, vol. 18, no. 12, March. Univ. of Sydney.

***GS HARDY, SIR ALISTER (1959). *The Open Sea—Its Natural History*. Part II, *Fish and Fisheries*. Collins, London.

HARMON, R. W., & C. B. POLLARD (1948). *Bibliography of Animal Venoms*. Univ. of Florida Press, Gainesville.

HASHIMATO, Y. (1956). "A Note on the Poison of a Barracuda *Sphyraena picuda*." *Bul. Japan. Soc. Sci. Fisheries*, vol. 21, no. 11.

**GS HASKINS, CARYL P. (1943). *The Amazon: The Life History of a Mighty River*. Doubleday, Doran & Co., New York.

HASS, HANS (1952). *Manta, Under the Red Sea with Spear and Camera*. Rand McNally & Co., Chicago.

HASS, HANS (1959). *We Come from the Sea*. Doubleday & Co., New York.

HELFRICH, PHILIP (1960). "A Study of the Possible Relationship Between Radioactivity and Toxicity in Fishes from the Central Pacific." U.S. Atomic Energy Comm., Tech. Info. Serv. TID-5748, May.

HELFRICH, PHILIP (1961). "Fish Poisoning in the Tropical Pacific." Pamphlet prepared in conjunction with survey by the Natl. Inst. Health, Honolulu, June.

HEMINGWAY, L., & J. C. DEVLIN (1961). "Watch Out for Sharks." *Readers Digest*, July.

HERALD, EARL S. (1951). "The Relative Abundance of Sharks and Bat Stingrays in San Francisco Bay." *California Fish and Game*, vol. 37, no. 3, July.

HERALD, EARL S. (1961). *Living Fishes of the World*. Doubleday & Co., Garden City, New York.

HERMITTE, L. C. P. (1946). "Venomous Marine Mollusks of the Genus *Conus.*" *Trans. Royal Society Trop. Med. Hyg.*, vol. 39, 485–512.

HESSE, DONALD W., *et al.* (1960). "Marine Biotoxins. I, Ciguatera Poison: Some Biological and Chemical Aspects." *Biochem. and Pharm. of Compounds Derived from Marine Organisms, Annals N.Y. Acad. Science*, vol. 90, art. 3.

**G    HEUVELMANS, BERNARD (1955). *On the Track of Unknown Animals.* Hill and Wang, New York.

*G    HEYERDAHL, THOR (1950). *Kon-Tiki.* Rand McNally & Co., Chicago.

HIBBERN, FRANK C. (1948). *Hunting American Lions.* Thomas Y. Crowell Co., New York.

HILL, RALPH N. (1956). *Window in the Sea.* Rinehart & Co., New York.

HILL, RALPH N. (1956). "Victory Over the Shark." *Natural History*, vol. LXV, no. 7, September.

HIYAMA, Y. (1943). "Report of an Investigation of Poisonous Fishes of the South Seas." U.S. Fish & Wildlife Serv. Spec. Sci. Report No. 25 (Van Campen translation).

**GS    HOLZWORTH, JOHN M. (1930). *The Wild Grizzlies of Alaska.* G. P. Putnam's Sons, New York.

*G    HORNADAY, W. T. (1904). *The American Natural History.* Charles Scribner's Sons, New York.

HUMBERT, ARTHUR C. (1898). "Photographing a Wounded African Buffalo." *Harper's New Monthly Magazine*, April.

HUTNER, S. H., *et al.* (1958). "Poisonous Tides." *Scientific American*, August.

***GS    HUTTON, ROBERT F. (1959). "The Florida Shark Story." Educational Series No. 13, State of Florida Board of Conservation.

IKEHARA, ISAAC (1959). Progress Report: Shark Research Control Program April 1 to August 27, 1959. State of Hawaii Bd. of Comm. of Agric. and Forestry, Div. of Fish and Game.

**G    INNES, WILLIAM T. (1954). *Exotic Aquarium Fishes* (7th ed.). Innes Publishing Co., Philadelphia.

IRWIN, R. S. (1952). "Funnel-Web Spider Bite." *Med. Jour. Austral.*, September, p. 342.

*    ISEMONGER, R. M. (1962). *Snakes of Africa.* Thomas Nelson & Sons, Johannesburg.

JACOBS, WERNER (1962). "Floaters of the Sea." *Natural History*, vol. LXXI, no. 7, August.

JACQUES, H. E. (1964). *How to Know the Insects.* Wm. C. Brown Co., Dubuque, Ia.

JACQUES, R. (1956). "The Hyaluronidase Content of Animal Venoms." *Venoms*, A.A.A.S. Publication No. 44.

JAEGER, ELLSWORTH (1948). *Tracks and Trailcraft.* Macmillan Co., New York.

JENSEN, H., & U. WESTPHAL (1956). "Chemical Structure and Inter-relationship of Toad Poisons." *Venoms,* A.A.A.S. Publication No. 44.

JOHNSON, MURRAY L., & L. K. COUCH (1954). "Determination of the Abundance of Cougar." *Jour. Mammalogy,* vol. 35, no. 2, May.

JONES, S. (1956). "Some Deaths Due to Fish Poisoning (Ichthyosarcotoxism) in India." *Indian Jour. Med. Res.,* vol. 44, April.

KAILIN, ELOISE (1962). "Insect Sting Registry." Letter in *Medical Tribune,* June 11.

KAISER, E. (1956). "Enzymatic Activity of Spider Venoms." *Venoms,* A.A.A.S. Publication No. 44.

KASTON, B. J., & ELIZABETH (1953). *How to Know the Spiders.* Wm. C. Brown Co., Dubuque, Ia.

KATHAN, R. H., G. S. HUBER, & R. S. LEOPOLD (1956). "Evolution of the Tourniquet-Incision and Suction Treatment of Snake Bite." Naval. Med. Field Res. Lab., NM 005 052.08, Spec. Rep. Vol. VII.

KEEGAN, HUGH L. (1956). "Antivenins Available for Treatment of Envenomation by Poisonous Snakes, Scorpions, and Spiders." *Venoms,* A.A.A.S. Publication No. 44.

**GS KEEGAN, HUGH L. (1960). "Some Venomous and Noxious Animals of the Far East." Med. Gen. Lab. (406) U.S. Army Med. Command, Japan.

***GS KEEGAN, HUGH L. (with W. V. MACFARLANE) (1963). *Venomous and Poisonous Animals and Noxious Plants of the Pacific Region.* Pergamon Press, New York.

**GS KEELE, C. A. (1963). "Venoms and the Causes of Pain." *New Scientist,* no. 327, February.

KEITH, ELMER (1948). *Big Game Hunting.* Little, Brown & Co., Boston.

KEMP, ROBERT (1956). "The Devilfish." *Texas Game & Fish,* May.

KENT, MELVIN, & H. L. STAHNKE (1939). "Effect and Treatment of Arizona Scorpion Stings." *Southwestern Med.,* vol. 4, no. 39.

KENYON, KARL W. (1959). "A 15-foot Maneater from San Miguel Island, California." *California Fish & Game,* vol. 45, no. 1, January.

*GS KINLOCH, ALEXANDER A. A. (1892). *Large Game Shooting in Thibet, the Himalayas, Northern and Central India.* Thacker, Spink & Co., Calcutta.

**S KLAUBER, LAURENCE M. (1956). "Some Factors Affecting the Gravity of Rattlesnake Bite." *Venoms,* A.A.A.S. Publication No. 44.

***GS KLAUBER, LAURENCE M. (1956). *Rattlesnakes: Their Habits, Life Histories, and Influence on Mankind.* 2 vols. Univ. of California Press.

KLEIN, W. E., & R. H. BRADSHAW (1951). "Portuguese Man-of-War Sting." *U.S. Armed Forces Med. Jour.,* (3).

KLOTS, ALEXANDER B., & ELSIE B. *Living Insects of the World.* Doubleday & Co., Garden City, New York.

*G    KOBLER, JOHN (1957). "The Terrible Threat of Nerve Gas." *Saturday Evening Post,* vol. 230, no. 4, July.

**GS   KOHN, ALAN J. (1958). "Recent Cases of Human Injury Due to Venomous Marine Snails of the Genus *Conus.*" *Hawaii Med. Jour.,* vol. 17, July-August.

KOHN, ALAN J., *et al.* (1960). "Preliminary Studies on the Venom of the Marine Snail *Conus.*" *Biochem. & Pharm. of Compounds Derived from Marine Organisms, Annals N.Y. Acad. Science,* vol. 90, art. 3.

KOSZALKA, M. F. (1949). "A Case of Hemoglobineuria in Bee Sting." *Bul. U.S. Army Med. Dept.,* 9.212, 3/49. As abstracted by Natl. Safety Counc.

KROEBER, THEODORA (1961). *Ishi in Two Worlds: a Biography of the Last Wild Indian in North America.* Univ. of California Press, Berkeley.

KULKARNI, M. E., and S. S. RAO (1956). "Antigenic Composition of the Venoms of Poisonous Snakes in India." *Venoms,* A.A.A.S. Publication No. 44.

LAFARGE, OLIVER (1956). *A Picture History of the American Indian.* Crown Publishers, New York.

LANE, CHARLES E. (1963). "The Deadly Fisher." *National Geographic,* vol. 123, no. 3, March.

***GS  LANE, FRANK W. (1960). *Kingdom of the Octopus.* Sheridan House, New York.

DE LATIL, PIERRE (1954). *The Underwater Naturalist.* Jarrolds Ltd., London.

*S    LEAKE, CHAUNCEY D. (1956). "Development of Knowledge About Venoms." *Venoms,* A.A.A.S. Publication No. 44.

LEE, R. K. C., & H. Q. PANG (1945). "An Outbreak of Fish Poisoning in Honolulu, Hawaii." *Hawaii Med. Jour.,* vol. 4, no. 1.

LEE, R. K. C., & H. Q. PANG (1945). "Ichthyotoxism—Fish Poisoning." *Amer. Jour. Trop. Med.,* vol. 25, no. 3.

LEOPOLD, A. STARKER. *The Desert* ("Life Nature Library.") Time Inc., New York.

LETT, WILLIAM P. (1890). *The Wolf.* (*The Big Game of North America,* ed. G. O. Shields.) Rand McNally & Co.

LIGHT, S. F. (1914). "Another Dangerous Jellyfish in Philippine Waters." *Philippine Jour. Sci.,* 9B (3).

LLANO, G. A. (1957). "Sharks vs. Men." *Scientific American,* 196 (6).

LLANO, G. A. (1957). "Airmen Against the Sea." Arctic, Desert, Tropic Info. Cent. Res. Study Inst.

LOCKWOOD, R. A. (1963). "Fatal Case of Sting by Box Jellyfish." *Supp. to the Bul. of the Post Grad. Comm. in Med.,* vol. 18, no. 12, March. Univ. of Sydney.

LOVERIDGE, ARTHUR (1931). "On Two Amphibious Snakes of the Central African Lake Region." *Bul. Antivenin Inst. of America,* vol. 5.

LUDWIG, EMIL (1937). *The Nile: The Life-Story of a River.* The Viking Press, New York.

LUMIERE, CORNEL (1956). *Beneath the Seven Seas.* Hutchinson & Co., London.

LYDEKKER, R. *Marsupials.* John F. Shaw & Co., London.

***GS McCORMICK, HAROLD W., TOM ALLEN, & WILLIAM YOUNG (1963). *Shadows in the Sea.* Chilton Books, Philadelphia.

McDONALD, WILLIAM A. (1958). "The Deadly Glossinia." *Natural History,* October.

McMICHAEL, DONALD F. (1963). "Dangerous Marine Molluscs." *Supp. to the Bul. of the Post Grad. Comm. in Med.,* vol. 18, no. 12, March. Univ. of Sydney.

McNEIL, F. A., & E. C. POPE (1943). "A Venomous Medusa from Australian Waters." *Austral. Jour. of Sci.,* vol. 5.

McNEIL, F. A. (1963). "Stinging Coral and So-called Stinging Sea-weed." *Supp. to the Bul. of the Post Grad. Comm. in Med.,* vol. 18, no. 12, March. Univ. of Sydney.

**GS MARAIS, EUGENE N. (1939). *My Friends the Baboons.* Methuen & Co., London.

MARDEN, LUIS (1944). "A Land of Lakes and Volcanoes." *National Geographic,* vol. 86, no. 2, August.

MARTIN, W. B. (1946). "Clinical Experience with Snake Bites on Okinawa." *Bul. U.S. Army Med. Dept.,* 5 (1).

MASTER, R. W. P., & S. SPINWASO RAIO (1961). "Identification of Enzymes and Toxins in Venoms of Indian Cobra and Russell's Viper After Starch Gel Electrophoresis." *Jour. Biol. Chem.,* vol. 236, no. 7, July.

***GS MATTHIESSEN, PETER (1959). *Wildlife in America.* The Viking Press, New York.

MATTHIESSEN, PETER (1961). *The Cloud Forest.* The Viking Press, New York.

MAXWELL, GAVIN (1952). *Harpoon at a Venture.* Rupert Hart-Davis, London.

MAYER, A. G. (1910). *Medusae of the World.* 3 vols. Carnegie Inst., Publ. No. 109, Washington.

MAYER, CHARLES (1921). *Trapping Wild Animals in Malay Jungles.* Duffield & Co., New York.

Medical News Letter:
"Venomous Fish Stings." Vol. 34, no. 1.
"Spiders." Vol. 34, no. 1.
"Bats—Public Health Importance and Control." Vol. 34, no. 1.
"Early Treatment of Snake Bite." Vol. 36, no. 2.
"Repeated Poisonous Snake Bites in Man." Vol. 33, no. 9.

MERRIAM, T. W., JR. (1962). "Snake Bite Survey." Abstracted in *Naval Res. Rev.,* July, from *Naval Med. Field Res. Lab. Rep.,* Camp Lejeune, N.C.

MICKS, DON W. (1952). "Clinical Effects of the Sting of the 'Puss Caterpillar' (*Megalopyge opercularis* S and A) on Man." *Tex. Rep. on Biol. and Med.*, vol. 10, no. 2, summer.

MICKS, DON W. (with VICTOR C. COLMA) (1952). "Nasal Myiasis of Man Due to the Screwworm Fly (*Caitroga americana* C and P)." *Tex. Rep. on Biol. and Med.*, vol. 10, no. 4, winter.

**GS MICKS, DON W. (1960). "Insects and Other Arthropods of Medical Importance in Texas." *Tex. Rep. on Biol. and Med.*, vol. 18, no. 4, winter.

MICKS, DON W. (1962). "An Outbreak of Dermatitis Due to the Grain Itch Mite *Pyemotes ventricosus* Newport." *Tex. Rep. of Biol. and Med.*, vol. 20, no. 2, summer.

MILLER, CHARLES (1950). *Cannibal Caravan.* Museum Press Ltd.. London.

**GS MILLER, D. G., JR. (1956). "Massive Anaphylaxis from Insect Stings." *Venoms,* A.A.A.S. Publication No. 44.

*G MILLER, WILFORD L. (1959). *Wildlife in North Dakota.* Bismarck Tribune Co., Bismarck, N.D.

MILLS, ERNEST M. (1959). "Rats—let's get rid of them." U.S. Dept. of the Int., Fish & Wildlife Serv., Bureau of Sport Fisheries & Wildlife, Circular No. 22.

MILNE, LOUIS J., & MARGERY (1962). *The Mountains.* ("Life Nature Library.") Time Inc., New York.

MINTON, SHERMAN A., JR. (1956). "Some Properties of North American Pit Viper Venoms and Their Correlation with Phylogeny." *Venoms,* A.A.A.S. Publication No. 44.

**GS MINTON, SHERMAN A., JR. (1957). "Snakebite." *Scientific American,* vol. 196, no. 1, January.

MIVART, ST. GEORGE (1890). *Dogs, Jackals, Wolves and Foxes.* London.

MONKMAN, NOEL (1958). *From Queensland to the Great Barrier Reef.* Doubleday & Co., Garden City, New York.

MOORE, ROBERT ALLAN (1945). *A Textbook of Pathology.* W. B. Saunders Co., Philadelphia.

MORGAN, F. G. (1956). "The Australian Taipan *Oxyuranus scutellatus* (Peters)." *Venoms,* A.A.A.S. Publication No. 44.

MORGAN, ROBERT (1956). *World Sea Fisheries.* Methuen & Co., London.

MUELLER, HARRY LOUIS (1959). "Further Experience with Severe Allergic Reactions to Insect Stings." *New England Jour. of Med.,* August.

MUELLER, HARRY LOUIS (1960). "Yellow Jacket Sting." *Jour. Amer. Med. Assoc.,* vol. 173, no. 10, July.

MUELLER, HARRY LOUIS (1960). "Serious Allergic Reactions to Insect Stings." *Amer. Jour. Nursing,* August.

MURPHY, R. C., & J. T. NICHOLS (1916). "The Shark Situation in the Waters About New York." *Brooklyn Museum Quart.,* vol. 3, no. 4.

Murtha, Edmund F. (1960). "Pharmacological Study of Poisons from Shellfish and Puffer Fish." *Biochem. and Pharm. of Compounds Derived from Marine Organisms, Annals N.Y. Acad. of Science,* vol. 90, art. 3.

Nachmansohn, David (1950). "Electric Currents in Nerve Tissue and Electric Organs." *Electrical Engineering,* March.

*National Geographic Magazine,* vol. XXXII, no. 4, October, 1917. ("Our Flag Number.")

*National Geographic Magazine* (1960). "Wild Animals of North America."

National Safety Council (1948). "Domestic Animals." Safety Educ. Data Sheet No. 26.

———— (1949). "Poisonous Reptiles." Safety Educ. Data Sheet No. 35.

———— (1949). "Animals in the Classroom." Safety Educ. Data Sheet No. 37.

———— (1958). "Black Widow Spiders May Be Dangerous." *Home Safety Review,* vol. 15, no. 2.

———— (1958). "Tick Bites." NSC Data Sheet D-228.

———— (1958). "If You Can't Avoid Snakes." *Natl. Safety News,* May.

———— (1959). "Fight Flies—Safely." *Safety Newsletter.*

———— (1959). "Wild Pets." *Home Safety Review,* winter.

———— (1960). "Bites and Stings Can Have Serious Effects." *NSC Safety Newsletter,* August (Textile Section).

———— (1960). "Bee-ware of Wasps." *NSC Bulletin Board,* May.

———— (1960). "Bites and Stings." *NSC Natl. Safety News,* April.

———— (1960). "Beware: Rabies in the Wild." *Home Safety Review,* fall.

———— (1961). "Don't Invite Snakebite." *NSC Home Safety Review,* spring.

———— (1961). "Caterpillar Is Health Menace." *Safety Newsletter* (Occupational Health Section).

———— (1961). "Bats Can Carry Rabies." *NSC Newsletter,* June (Occupational Health Nursing Section).

———— (1962). "Poisonous Snakes." *NSC Natl. Safety News,* March.

————. "Black Widow Spiders." NSC Data Sheet No. 258 (Revised).

Nichols, John T. (1921). "What Sharks Really Eat." *Natural History,* vol. 21, no. 3.

Nichols, John T. (with Paul Bartsch) (1946). *Fishes and Shells of the Pacific World.* Macmillan Co., New York.

Norman, J. R. (1948). *A History of Fishes.* Frederick A. Stokes Co., New York.

O'Connor, P. Fitzgerald (1953). *Shark-O!* Secker & Warburg, London.

Old, E. H. (1908). "A Report of Several Cases with Unusual Symptoms Caused by Contact with Some Unknown Variety of Jellyfish *(Scyphozoa).*" *Philippine Jour. of Sci.,* Vol. 3.

*G    Oliver, James A. (1952). "The Prevention and Treatment of Snakebite." N.Y. Zoological Soc., New York.

**G  OLIVER, JAMES A. (1955). *North American Amphibians and Reptiles.* D. Van Nostrand Co., New York.

**G  OLIVER, JAMES A. (1958). *Snakes in Fact and Fiction.* Macmillan Co., New York.

O'ROURKE, FERGUS J. (1956). "The Toxicity of Black Widow Spider Venom." *Venoms,* A.A.A.S. Publication No. 44.

*Outdoor California* (1962). "Skindivers Hitch Ride with Sharks." The Resources Agency of Calif.–Dept. of Fish & Game, vol. 23, no. 5, May.

PACKARD, VANCE (1950). *Animal I.Q.* The Dial Press, New York.

PACY, J. R. (1963). "Stingray, Blackfish and Catfish Injuries." *Supp. to the Bul. of the Post Grad. Comm. in Med.,* vol. 18, no. 12, March. Univ. of Sydney.

PARKE-DAVIS (1962). "Camp Medicine." *Therapeutic Notes,* vol. 69, June.

PARRISH, H. M. (1959). "Deaths from Bites and Stings of Venomous Animals and Insects in the United States." *A.M.A. Arch. Int. Med.,* 104, August.

PARRISH, H. M. (with F. B. CLARK, D. BROBST, & J. F. MOCK) (1959). "Epidemiology of Dog Bites." *Public Health Reports,* Public Health Serv., U.S. Dept. of Health, Education & Welfare, vol. 74, no. 10, October.

PARROTT, ARTHUR W. (1958). *Big Game Fishes and Sharks of New Zealand.* Hodder & Stoughton Ltd., London.

***GS  PATTERSON, J. H. (1926). *The Man Eaters of Tsavo.* Macmillan Co., London.

PEARSON, OLIVER P. (1956). "A Toxic Substance from the Salivary Glands of a Mammal (Short-Tailed Shrew)." *Venoms,* A.A.A.S. Publication No. 44.

PERCIVAL, ARTHUR BLAYNEY (1924). *A Game Ranger's Note Book.* Geo. H. Doran Co., New York.

PERLMUTTER, ALFRED (1961). *Guide to Marine Fishes.* N.Y. Univ. Press, New York.

PERRY, W. A. (1890). "The Cougar." (*The Big Game of North America,* ed. G. O. Shields) Rand McNally & Co., New York.

PHILLIPS, CRAIG, & W. H. BRADY (1953). "Sea Pests: Poisonous and Harmful Sea Life of Florida and the West Indies." Spec. Public. Marine Lab., Univ. of Miami.

PHELPS, R. (1963). "Experiences with Stonefish Stingings in New Guinea." *Supp. to the Bul. of the Post Grad. Comm. in Med.,* vol. 18, no. 12, March. Univ. of Sydney.

PIKE, GORDON C. (1954). "The Killer Whale." *Western Fisheries,* vol. 48, no. 1.

PILLSBURY, R. W. (1957). "Avoidance of Poisonous Eggs of the Marine Fish *Scorpaenichthys marmoratus* by Predators." *Copeia,* No. 3, August.

PINCHER, CHAPMAN (1948). *A Study of Fish.* Duell, Sloan & Pearce, New York.

PLATT, RUTHERFORD (1949). "Shells Take You Over World Horizons." *National Geographic*, vol. XCVI, no. 1, July.

POLLARD, C. B. (1956). "Venom Research: A Challenge to the Various Sciences." *Venoms*, A.A.A.S. Publication No. 44.

POPE, CLIFFORD H. (1946). *Snakes of the Northeastern United States.* New York Zoo. Soc., New York.

*G     POPE, CLIFFORD H. (1955). *The Reptile World.* Alfred A. Knopf, New York.

**GS    POPE, CLIFFORD H. (1961). *The Giant Snakes.* Alfred A. Knopf, New York.

POPE, CLIFFORD H. (1962). "The Six Giants." *Natural History*, vol. LXXI, no. 6, June-July.

POPE, ELIZABETH C. (1963). "Some Noxious Marine Invertebrates from Australian Seas." *Supp. to the Bul. of the Post Grad. Comm. in Med.*, vol. 18, no. 12, March. Univ. of Sydney.

PORTER, J. HAMPDEN (1894). *Wild Beasts.* Chas. Scribner's Sons, New York.

DEL POZO, E. C. (1956). "Mechanism of Pharmacological Actions of Scorpion Venoms." *Venoms*, A.A.A.S. Publication No. 44.

*Principles of Internal Medicine* (1950). Harrison, T. R., *et al.*, eds. Blakiston Co., New York.

PURANANANDA, CHALOEM (1956). "Treatment of Snakebite Cases in Bangkok." *Venoms*, A.A.A.S. Publication No. 44.

RADCLIFFE, LEWIS (1914). "The Sharks and Rays of Beaufort, North Carolina." *Bul. U.S. Bur. Fisheries*, pp. 239–284.

**GS    RANDALL, JOHN E. (1958). "Review of Ciguatera (Fish Poisoning)." *Bul. Marine Science Gulf & Caribbean*, vol. 8, no. 3.

RANDALL, JOHN E. (1960). "The Living Javelin." *Sea Frontiers*, vol. 6, no. 4, November.

RANDALL, JOHN E. (1961). "Let a Sleeping Shark Lie." *Sea Frontiers*, vol. 7, no. 3, August.

RANDALL, JOHN E. (1961). "Ciguatera: Tropical Fish Poisoning." *Sea Frontiers*, vol. 7, no. 3, August.

RANDEL, H. W., & G. B. DOAN (1956). "Caterpillar Urticaria in the Panama Canal Zone: Report of Five Cases." *Venoms*, A.A.A.S. Publication No. 44.

RAO, SHANTA S., & S. S. RAO (1956). "Proteases of Cobra (*Na ja na ja*) venom." *Venoms*, A.A.A.S. Publication No. 44.

RATCLIFF, J. D. (1943). "Sharks." *Colliers*, vol. 112, no. 6.

REED, ALLEN C. (1953). "Arizona's Venom Man." *Arizona Highways*, vol. 24, no. 2, February.

REID, H. A. (1956). "Three Fatal Cases of Sea Snakebite." *Venoms*, A.A.A.S. Publication No. 44.

**GS    REID, H. A. (1959). "Sea-Snake Bite and Poisoning." *The Practitioner*, vol. 183, pp. 530.

REID, H. A. (with K. E. CHAN & P. C. THEAN) (1963). "Prolonged Coagulation Defect (Defibrination Syndrome) in Malayan Viper Bite." *The Lancet*, March 23.

REID, H. A. (with P. C. THEAN, K. E. CHAN, & A. R. BAHAROM) (1963). "Clinical Effects of Bites by Malayan Viper (*Ancistrodon rhodostoma*)." *The Lancet*, March 23.

RIEGEL, B., *et al.* (1949). "Paralytic Shellfish Poison." *Jour. Biol. Chem.* 177:7.

RODAHL, KAARE (1953). *North: The Nature and Drama of the Polar World*. Harper & Bros., New York.

ROEDEL, PHIL M., & W. E. RIPLEY (1950). "California Sharks and Rays." State of Calif. Dept. of Nat. Res., Div. of Fish & Game, Bur. of Mar. Fish, Fish Bul. No. 75.

ROOSEVELT, THEODORE (1893). *The Wilderness Hunter*. G. P. Putnam's Sons, New York.

ROOSEVELT, THEODORE (1905). "A Colorado Bear Hunt." *Scribner's Magazine*, vol. 38, no. 4, October.

ROOSEVELT, THEODORE (1905). "A Wolf Hunt in Oklahoma." *Scribner's Magazine*, vol. 38, no. 5, November.

ROOSEVELT, THEODORE (1910). *African Game Trails*. Charles Scribner's Sons, New York.

ROOSEVELT, THEODORE (1914). *Through the Brazilian Jungle*. G. P. Putnam's Sons, New York.

ROSENBLATT, RICHARD H., & W. J. BALDWIN (1958). "A Review of the Eastern Pacific Sharks of the Genus *Cardrarkinus* with a Redescription of *C. malpeloensis* (Fowler) and California Records of *C. remotus* (Dumeril)." *California Fish & Game*, vol. 44, no. 2, April.

ROUGHLY, T. C. (1954). *Wonders of the Great Barrier Reef*. Angus & Robertson, London.

ROULE, LOUIS (1935). *Fishes, Their Ways of Life*. George Routledge & Sons, London.

*S    RUSSELL, FINDLAY E. (1953). "Stingray Injuries." *Amer. Jour. Med. Sci.*, 226:611.

RUSSELL, FINDLAY E. (with A. VAN HARREVELD) (1956). "Cardiovascular Effects of the Venom of the Round Stingray, *Urobatis halleri*." *Venoms*, A.A.A.S. Publication No. 44.

RUSSELL, FINDLAY E. (with R. D. LEWIS) (1956). "Evaluation of the Current Status of Therapy for Stingray Injuries." *Ibid.*

RUSSELL, FINDLAY E. (with W. C. BARRITT & M. D. FAIRCHILD) (1957). "Electrocardiographic Patterns Evoked by Venom of the Stingray." *Proc. Soc. Experimental Biol. Med.*, 96:634.

RUSSELL, FINDLAY E. (with T. C. POWERS, L. W. KANG, A. M. WARNER, & T. C. COLKET, III) (1958). "Studies on the Mechanism of Death from Stingray Venom." *Amer. Jour. Med. Sci.*, 235:566.

RUSSELL, FINDLAY E. (1959). "Stingray Injuries." Public Health Reports, U.S. Dept. of Health, Educ. & Welfare, vol. 74, no. 10, October.

RUSSELL, FINDLAY E. (with J. A. EMERY) (1960). "Venom of the Weevers *Trachinus draco* and *T. vipera*." *Biochem. & Pharm. of Compounds Derived from Marine Organisms, Annals N.Y. Acad. Science*, vol. 90, art. 3.

RUSSELL, FINDLAY E. (1960). "Rattlesnake Bites in Southern California." *Amer. Jour. Med. Sci.*, 239:51.

RUSSELL, FINDLAY E. (1962). "Muscle Relaxants in Black Widow Spider (*Lactrodectus mactans*) Poisoning." *Amer. Jour. Med. Sci.*, 243:2.

ST. CLAIR, GORDON P. (1956). "Snake Bite Manual." National Safety Council, Chicago.

SANDERSON, G. P. (1896). *Thirteen Years Among the Wild Beasts of India*. W. H. Allen & Co., London.

**G   SANDERSON, IVAN T. (1955). *Living Mammals of the World*. Hanover House, Garden City, New York.

**G   SANDERSON, IVAN T. (1956). *Follow the Whale*. Cassell & Co., London.

*G   SANDERSON, IVAN T. (1957). *The Monkey Kingdom*. Hanover House, Garden City, New York.

***G   SANDERSON, IVAN T. (1962). *The Dynasty of Abu: a History and Natural History of the Elephants and Their Relatives, Past and Present*. Alfred A. Knopf, New York.

SAUNDERS, PAUL R. (1959). "Venom of the Stonefish *Synanceja verrucosa*." *Science*, vol. 129, no. 3344, January.

SAUNDERS, PAUL R. (1959). "Venom of the Stonefish *Synanceja horrida* (Linnaeus)." *Arch. Int. Pharmacodyn*, vol. 123, nos. 1–2.

*S   SAUNDERS, PAUL R. (with P. B. TAYLOR) (1959). "Venom of the Lionfish *Pterois volitans*." *Amer. Jour. Physiol.*, vol. 197, pp. 437 ff.

*S   SAUNDERS, PAUL R. (1959). "Venom of the Scorpionfishes." *Proc. of the Western Pharm. Soc.*, vol. 2, no. 4.

SAUNDERS, PAUL R. (with SOLOMON E. LIFTON) (1960). "Sting by a Venomous Lionfish." *U.S. Armed Forces Med. Jour.*, vol. 11, no. 2.

SAUNDERS, PAUL R. (1960). "Pharmacological and Chemical Studies of the Venom of the Stonefish (Genus *Synanceja*) and Other Scorpionfishes." *Biochem. & Pharm. of Compounds Derived from Marine Organisms, Annals N.Y. Acad. Science*, vol. 90, art. 3.

SAUNDERS, PAUL R. (with L. TOKES) (1961). "Purification and Properties of the Lethal Fraction of the Venom of the Stonefish *Synanceja horrida* (Linnaeus)." *Biochem. Biophys. Acta.*, vol. 52, pp. 527 ff.

***GS   SCHALLER, GEORGE B. (1963). *The Mountain Gorilla: Ecology and Behavior*. Univ. of Chicago Press, Chicago.

SCHANTZ, EDWARD J. (1960). "Biochemical Studies on Paralytic Shellfish Poisons." *Biochem. & Pharm. of Compounds Derived from Marine Organisms, Annals N.Y. Acad. Science*, vol. 90, art. 3.

***GS SCHEFFER, VICTOR B. (1958). *Seals, Sea Lions and Walruses.* Stanford Univ. Press, Stanford, Calif.

*GS SCHMIDT, KARL P. (1957). "Anent the Dangerous Bushmaster." *Copeia,* no. 3, August 26.

SCHMIDT, KARL P. (with ROBERT F. INGER) (1957). *Living Reptiles of the World.* Hanover House, Garden City, New York.

SCHNURRENBERGER, PAUL R., & JACK H. RUSSELL (1961). "A Rabies Control Program in Ohio." *Public Health Reports,* vol. 76, no. 4, April.

*School Health* (1961). "Rabies—a Present Day Problem," May.

SCHULTZ, LEONARD P. (with E. M. STERN) (1948). *The Ways of Fishes.* D. Van Nostrand Co., New York.

**GS SCHULTZ, LEONARD P. (with PERRY W. GILBERT & STEWART SPRINGER) (1961). "Shark Attacks." *Science,* vol. 134, no. 3472, July 14.

SCOTT, JACK DENTON (1962). "Prince of Cats—the Lethal Leopard." *Readers Digest,* July. (Condensed from *Rod and Gun,* June, 1962.)

* SCOTT, ROBERT FALCON (1913). *Scott's Last Expedition.* Smith, Elder & Co., London.

*Sea Secrets,* International Oceanographic Foundation. Various issues of this monthly question-and-answer bulletin.

SETON, ERNEST THOMPSON (1904). "The Whitetailed (Virginia) Deer and Its Kin." *Scribner's Monthly,* vol. 40.

**G SETON, ERNEST THOMPSON (1929). *Lives of Game Animals,* Vol. II, Part I, *Bears,* etc. Chas. Scribner's Sons, New York.

SETON, ERNEST THOMPSON (1937). *Great Historic Animals—Mainly about Wolves.* Chas. Scribner's Sons, New York.

SEVERIN, JURT (1953). "The Land-Locked Man-Eaters." *True Magazine,* July.

SHANNON, FREDERICK A. (1956). "Comments on the Treatment of Reptile Poisoning." *Venoms,* A.A.A.S. Publication No. 44.

SHIELDS, G. O. (ed.) (1890). *The Big Game of North America.* Rand, McNally & Co., Chicago.

SIEMEL, SASHA (1952). "The Jungle Was My Home." *National Geographic,* vol. 102, no. 5, November.

SLAUGHTER, SCOTT G. (as told to WM. M. STEPHENS) (1962). "My War with Sharks." *Saturday Evening Post,* vol. 235, no. 26.

***GS SLIJPER, E. J. (1962). *Whales: the Biology of the Cetaceans.* Basic Books, New York.

SMITH, EMIL J., JR. (1960). "Seals and Sea Lions." *Skin Diver,* vol. 9, no. 1, January.

SMITH, F. G. WALTON (1961). "Sea Monsters in the Telling." *Sea Frontiers,* vol. 7, no. 2, May.

SMITH, HUGH M. (1916). "Sharks—Man-Eaters and Others." *Amer. Mus. Jour.,* vol. 16, no. 6, October.

SMITH, J. L. B. (1953). *The Sea Fishes of Southern Africa.* Central News Agency, Capetown.

**GS SMITH, J. L. B. (1957). "Two Rapid Fatalities from Stonefish Stabs." *Copeia*, no. 3, August 26.

SMITH, J. L. B. (1957). "The Fishes of the Family *Scorpaenidae* in the Western Indian Ocean." Part II. *Ichth. Bul.* No. 5, Rhodes Univ.

SMITH, J. L. B. (1960). "Are Whales a Serious Danger to Small Boats?" *Skin Diver*, vol. 9, no. 1, January.

SMYTHE, R. H. (1961). *Animal Vision, What Animals See.* Herbert Jenkins, London.

SOMMER, H., R. P. MONMER, B. RIEGEL, *et al.* (1948). "Paralytic Shellfish Poison." *Jour. Am. Chem. Soc.*, vol. 70, 1015.

SONNEBORN, DUANE G. (1946). "Poisonous Snake (Habu) Bites." *U.S. Naval Med. Bul.*, vol. 46, no. 1, January.

SOUTHCOTT, R. V. (1952). "Fatal Stings to North Queensland Bathers." *Med. Jour. Austral.*, No. 1.

SOUTHCOTT, R. V. (1956). "Studies on Australian Cubomedusae, Including a New Genus and Species Apparently Harmful to Man." *Austral. Jour. Mar. & Freshwater Res.*, vol. 7, no. 2.

**S SOUTHCOTT, R. V. (1959). "Tropical Jellyfish and Other Marine Stingings." *Military Med.*, vol. 124, no. 8, August.

SOUTHCOTT, R. V. (1960). "Venomous Jellyfish." *Good Health*, January. South Australia.

SOUTHCOTT, R. V. (1962). "Jellyfish and Medicine." *A.M.S.S. Rev.*, May.

SOUTHCOTT, R. V. (1963). "Fatal and Other Stingings by Sea-Wasps." *Supp. to the Bul. of the Post Grad. Comm. in Med.*, vol. 18, no. 12, March. Univ. of Sydney.

**S SPECTOR, WILLIAM S. (1955). *Handbook of Toxicology.* W. B. Saunders Co., Philadelphia.

SPRINGER, STEWART (1943). "Sharks and Their Behavior." *Coord. Res. & Devel., U.S.N. Emerg. Rescue Equip. Sect.*, October.

STACKPOLE, EDOUARD A. (1953). *The Sea-Hunters: the Great Age of Whaling.* J. B. Lippincott Co., Philadelphia.

**GS STAHNKE, HERBERT L. (1953). "The L-C Treatment of Venomous Bites or Stings." *Arizona Highways*, vol. 29, no. 2, February. (Reprinted from the *Amer. Jour. Trop. Med. & Hyg.*)

STAHNKE, HERBERT L. (1956). "Scorpions." Poisonous Animals Research Laboratory, Tempe, Ariz.

***GS STAHNKE, HERBERT L. (1958). "The Treatment of Venomous Bites and Stings." Poisonous Animals Research Laboratory, Tempe, Ariz.

STANIC, M. (1956). "Allergenic Properties of Venom Hypersensitiveness in Man and Animals." *Venoms*, A.A.A.S. Publication No. 44.

STANKIK, V. J. (1960). "Introducing Poisonous Snakes." Spring Books, London.

STEBBINS, R. C. (1954). *Amphibians and Reptiles of Western North America.* McGraw-Hill, New York.

\*\*GS  STEFANSSON, VILHJALMUR (1925). *The Friendly Arctic: the Story of Five Years in Polar Regions.* Macmillan Co., New York.

STEINITZ, H. (1959). "Observations on *Pterois volitans* (L) and Its Venom." *Copeia,* no. 2, July.

STICKEL, WILLIAM H. (1952). "Venomous Snakes of the United States and Treatment of Their Bites." U.S. Dept. of the Int., Wildlife Leaflet No. 339, June, Washington, D.C.

STIGAND, C. H. (1913). *Hunting the Elephant in Africa.* Macmillan Co., New York.

STIMSON, A. C., & H. T. ENGLEHARDT (1960). "Snake Bite Needn't Be Fatal." *Natl. Safety News,* May, Natl. Safety Counc.

STOKOE, W. J. (compiler) (1938). *The Observer's Book of Wild Animals of the British Isles.* (Revised by Maurice Burton, 1958.) Frederick Warne & Co., London.

STUART, MONTGOMERY A., & T. D. SLAGLE (1943). "Jellyfish Stings, Suggested Treatment, and Report on Two Cases." *U.S. Naval Med. Bul.,* vol. 41, no. 2, March.

SULKIN, S. E., & M. J. GREVE (1954). "Human Rabies Caused by Bat Bite." *Texas Jour. Med.* 50, August.

\*\*GS  SWAROOP, S., & B. GRAB (1954). "Snakebite Mortality in the World." *Bul. World Health Organization,* vol. 10, no. 1.

SWAROOP, S., & B. GRAB (1956). "The Snakebite Mortality Problem in the World." *Venoms,* A.A.A.S. Publication No. 44.

TALLIEZ, PHILIPPE (1954). *To Hidden Depths.* William Kimber, London.

\*\*\*S  TAYLOR, F. H., & R. E. MURRAY (1946). "Spiders, Ticks and Mites Including the Species Harmful to Man in Australia and New Guinea." Commonwealth of Australia, Dept. of Health, School of Pub. Health & Trop. Med., Serv. Publication No. 6.

\*\*GS  THOMPSON, J. R., & STEWART SPRINGER (1961). "Sharks, Skates, Rays and Chimaeras." Fish & Wildlife Cir. No. 119, Bur. Commercial Fisheries, Fish & Wildlife Serv., U.S. Dept. Int.

\*\*\*GS  THORP, R. W., & W. D. WOODSON (1945). *The Black Widow: America's Most Poisonous Spider.* Univ. of N.C. Press, Chapel Hill.

THORTON, THOMAS (1806). *A Sporting Tour Through Various Parts of France in the Year 1802.* Series of letters published in London.

TINKHAM, ERNEST R. (1956). "Bite Symptoms of the Red-Legged Widow Spider (*Latrodectus bishopi*)." *Venoms,* A.A.A.S. Publication No. 44.

TINKHAM, ERNEST R. (1956). "The Deadly Nature of Gila Monster Venom." *Ibid.*

TOWNSEND, CHARLES H. (1919). "Making Use of the Shark." *Bul. N.Y. Zoo. Soc.,* vol. 23, no. 6. November.

TOWNSEND, CHARLES H. (1930). "Twentieth Century Whaling." *Bul. N.Y. Zoo. Soc.,* vol. 24, no. 6, Nov.-Dec.

TRAVIS, WILLIAM (1961). *Shark for Sale.* George Allen & Unwin, London.

TRETHEWIE, E. R. (1956). "Pharmacological Effects of Australian Snake Venoms." *Venoms*, A.A.A.S. Publication No. 44.

**GS TROUGHTON, ELLIS (1947). *Furred Animals of Australia*. Chas. Scribner's Sons, New York.

TUCKER, DENYS W., & C. T. NEENHAM (1957). "The Blue Shark *Prionace glauca* (L) Breeds in British Seas." *Ann. & Mag. Nat. Hist.*, ser. 12, vol. 10, September, London.

TUVE, RICHARD L. (1947). "The Technology of the U.S. Navy 'Shark Chaser.' " *U.S. Naval Inst. Proc.*, vol. 73, no. 5, May.

TYLER, ALBERT (1956). "An Auto-antivenin in the Gila Monster and Its Relation to a Concept of Natural Antibodies." *Venoms*, A.A.A.S. Publication No. 44.

TYSON, E. B. (1957). "Reaction to Tropical Jellyfish Sting." *Military Med.*, 120:216.

U.S. Govt., Dept. of the Air Force (1952). "Survival," Air Force Man. No. 64–5.

U.S. Govt., Dept. of the Army Field Man. (1957). "Military Sanitation," FM 21-10 AF, 160-46.

U.S. Govt., Dept. of the Army Field Man. (1957). "Survival," FM 21-76.

U.S. Govt., Dept. of the Army Field Man. "Jungle Operations," FM 31-30.

U.S. Dept. of Health, Education & Welfare (1955). "Practical Problems in Rabies Control." *Pub. Health Reports*, vol. 70, no. 6, June.

U.S. Govt., Dept. Int., Fish & Wildlife Serv. (Various years). Annual Reports for: Bur. Comm. Fisheries; Bur. Sport Fish & Wildlife; Branch of Wildlife Res.

U.S. Govt., Dept. Int. (1961). "Hints on Bobcat Trapping." Fish & Wildlife Cir. No. 1.

U.S. Govt. (1944). "Final Report on the Use of Chemical Materials as Shark Repellents." NRL Rep. No. P-2379, Naval Res. Lab. Anacostia Station, Washington, D.C.

U.S. Govt. (1958). "United States Navy Diving Manual." Navships 25–253 (Pt. 3) Change No. 1.

U.S. Govt. (1959). "Shark Sense." Aviation Training Div., Off. Ch. Nav. Op. (NAVAER OO-80Q-14).

U.S. Govt. (1961). "United States Navy Diving Manual." Navships 250–538.

VAN DENSEN, HOBART M., & R. F. PETERSON (1958). "Chiroptera of New Guinea." *Natural History*, October.

VENTERS, H. D., *et al.* (1954). "Rabies in Bats in Florida." *Amer. Jour. Pub. Health*, 44, January.

VERRILL, A. H. (1948). *Strange Fish and Their Stories*. L. C. Page & Co., Boston.

*Veterinary Public Health Newsletter* (1958). "Rabies—Animal Bites in Small Children." April 15.

Von Fraenkel, P. H., & E. S. Krick (1945). "Fish Poisoning by Barracuda in the Marianas." *U.S. Naval Med. Bul.* 44:430.

Voss, Gilbert L. (1959). "Hunting Sea Monsters." *Sea Frontiers*, vol. 5, no. 3, August.

deVries, A., J. Rechnic, & S. Gitter (1961). "Pathogenesis of Snake Venom Intoxication, II, Coagulation Factors and Hemorrhagins." *Proc. Staff Meet. Beilinson Hosp. Supp.* No. 10, Tel Aviv.

deVries, A., E. Condrea, & S. Gitter (1961). "Pathogenesis of Snake Venom Intoxication, III, Hemolysis." *Proc. Staff Meet. Beilinson Hosp. Supp.* No. 10, Tel Aviv.

Wade, H. W. (1928). "Post Mortem Findings in Acute Jellyfish Poisoning." *Amer. Jour. Trop. Med.*, vol. 8.

Waknis, Vijaya N., R. W. P. Master, & S. S. Rao (1961). "Use of Ion-Exchangers in the Separation of Proteins of Cobra Venoms." *Proc. Symposium on Proteins*, August. C.F.T.T.I., Mysore.

Walford, L. A. (1944). "Observations on the Shark Fishery in the Central Part of the Gulf of Calif." *Fishery Market News*, vol. 6, no. 6, June.

Waterman, Stanton A. (1962). "Dr. Gilbert vs. the Shark." *Skin Diver*, vol. 11, no. 7, July.

Webster, David K. (1963). *Myth and Maneater.* W. W. Norton & Co., New York.

Wehrle, L. P. (1939). "Observations on Three Species of Triatoma." *Bul. Brooklyn Ento. Soc.*, vol. 24, no. 3, June.

Wells, A. L. (1958). *The Observer's Book of Sea Fishes.* Frederick Warne & Co., London.

Wendt, Herbert (1959). *Out of Noah's Ark.* (Bullock trans.) Houghton Mifflin Co., Boston.

*What's New* (1957). "Bat Rabies." No. 202.

**GS Whitley, G. P. (1940). *The Fishes of Australia:* Part I, *The Sharks, Rays, Devil-Fish, and Other Primitive Fishes of Australia and New Zealand.* Sydney & Melbourne Pub. Co.

**GS Whitley, G. P. (1943). "Poisonous and Harmful Fishes." Commonwealth of Australia, Counc. for Sci. & Ind. Res., Bul. No. 159, Melbourne.

Whitley, G. P. (with G. H. Payne) (1947). "Testing a Shark Repellent." *Austral. Zool.*, vol. 2, no. 2.

Whitley, G. P. (1950). "Butterfly Cod." *Austral. Mus. Mag.*, vol. 10.

Whitley, G. P. (1951). "Shark Attacks in Western Australia." *West. Austral. Naturalist*, vol. 2, no. 8, April.

Whitley, G. P. (1963). "The Identity of Man-Killing Sharks." *Supp. to the Bul. of the Post Grad. Comm. in Med.*, vol. 18, no. 12, March. Univ. of Sydney.

Whitley, G. P. (1963). "Stonefish." *Ibid.*

Whitley, G. P. (1963). "Dangerous Australian Fishes." *Ibid.*

WIEMAN, H. L. (1938). *General Zoology*. McGraw-Hill Company, New York.

WIENER, SAUL (1956). "The Australian Red Back Spider (*Latrodectus hasselti*), I. Preparation of Antiserum by the Use of Venom Absorbed on Aluminum Phosphate." *Med. Jour. Austral.*, May.

WIENER, SAUL (1957). "The Sydney Funnel-Web Spider (*Atrax polustus*), I, Collection of Venom and Its Toxicity." *Med. Jour. Austral.*, September.

WIENER, SAUL (1958). "Stone-Fish Sting and Its Treatment." *Med. Jour. Austral.*, August.

WIENER, SAUL (1959). "The Production and Assay of Stone-fish Antivenene." *Med. Jour. Austral.*, November.

WIENER, SAUL (1959). "Observations on the Venom of the Stone-fish (*Synanceja trachynis*)." *Med. Jour. Austral.*, May.

**S    WIENER, SAUL (1963). "Stone-fish Venom." *Supp. to the Bul. of the Post Grad. Comm. in Med.*, vol. 18, no. 12, March. Univ. of Sydney.

**S    WIENER, SAUL (1963). "Stonefish Stingings: Venom and Treatment." *Ibid.*

WILES, JAMES (1962). "Wanted: Shark Hunters." *Sea Frontiers*, vol. 8, no. 2, May.

WILSON, G. S., & A. A. MILES (1946). *Topley and Wilson's Principles of Bacteriology and Immunity*. Williams and Wilkins Co., Baltimore.

WISE, H. D. (1937). *Tigers of the Sea*. Derrydale Press, New York.

WOLF, BILL (1953). "The Most Vicious Animal." *Sports Afield*, December.

WOOLLEN, ARTHUR (1953). "Trapping the Cougar." *American Woodsman*, February.

Works Projects Administration Writers Program (1940). *American Wild Life*. Wm. H. Wise & Co., New York.

WRIGHT, BRUCE S. (1948). "Releasers of Attack Behavior Pattern in Shark and Barracuda." *Jour. Wildlife Management*, vol. 12, no. 2, April.

WRIGHT, BRUCE S. (1948). "Survival of the Northeastern Panther (*Felis concolor*)." *Jour. Mammalogy*, vol. 29, no. 3, August.

WRIGHT, BRUCE S. (1953). "Further Notes on the Panther of the Northeast." *Canadian Field-Naturalist*, vol. 67, no. 1, January-March.

***GS    WRIGHT, BRUCE S. (1959). *The Ghost of North America: The Story of the Eastern Panther*. Vantage Press, New York.

WRIGHT, BRUCE S. (1961). "The Latest Specimen of the Eastern Puma." *Jour. Mammalogy*, vol. 42, no. 2, May.

**GS    WRIGHT, BRUCE S. (1962). *Wildlife Sketches, Near and Far*. Brunswick Press, Fredericton, N.B., Canada.

WRIGHT, BRUCE S. (1962). "Notes on North Atlantic Whales." *Canadian Field-Naturalist*, vol. 76, no. 1.

*G    Wyeth Laboratories (1961). "Antivenin (*Crotalidae*) Polyvalent," New York.

*G    WYKES, ALAN (1961). *Snake Man.* Simon and Schuster, New York.

WYLIE, EVAN MCLEOD (1959). "Caution—Stingers at Work!" *Readers Digest*, June.

YLLA (1958). *Animals in India.* Hamish Hamilton, New York.

YLLA. *Animals in Africa.* Harper & Bros., New York.

YONGE, C. M. (1931). *A Year on the Great Barrier Reef.* G. P. Putnam's Sons, New York.

YOUNG, STANLEY P. (1941, rev. 1955). "Hints on Coyote and Wolf Trapping." U.S. Dept. of the Int., Fish & Wildlife Serv., Cir. No. 2.

YOUNG, STANLEY P. (1945). "Mountain Lion Trapping." U.S. Dept. of the Int., Fish & Wildlife Serv., Cir. No. 6.

**GS    YOUNG, STANLEY P. (1946). *The Wolf in North American History.* Caxton Printers, Caldwell, Idaho.

***GS    YOUNG, STANLEY P. (with EDWARD A. GOLDMAN) (1944). *The Wolves of North America.* American Wildlife Management Inst., Washington, D.C.

***GS    YOUNG, STANLEY P. (with EDWARD A. GOLDMAN) (1946). *The Puma— Mysterious American Cat.* American Wildlife Management Inst., Washington, D.C.

**GS    YOUNG, WILLIAM E., & H. S. MAZET (1934). *Shark! Shark! The Thirty-Year Odyssey of a Pioneer Shark Hunter.* Gotham House, New York.

ZAHL, PAUL A. (1952). "Man-of-War Fleet Attacks Bimini." *National Geographic*, February.

ZAHL, PAUL A. (1957). "On Australia's Coral Ramparts." *National Geographic*, vol. 111, no. 1, January.

ZERN, E. (ed.) (1952). *Zane Grey's Adventures in Fishing.* Harper & Bros., New York.

ZIM, HERBERT S., & HOBART M. SMITH (1953). *Reptiles and Amphibians.* Simon & Schuster, New York.

ZIM, HERBERT S., & DONALD F. HOFFMEISTER (1955). *Mammals.* Simon & Schuster, New York.

ZIM, HERBERT S., & HURST H. SHOEMAKER (1956). *Fishes.* Simon & Schuster, New York.

# Index

415

# ROGER A. CARAS

is a delightful and rather remarkable person; he has a knack of doing what the rest of us have always wanted to do, but never dared. He has driven cabs, sold books, trained dogs, cleaned cages in a zoo, acted on TV, MCed in nightclubs, worked in a credit office, dug up ancient Indians, collected art, and produced documentary albums. He helped put himself through college by lecturing on film history, and he studied zoology at Northeastern University. He also served two hitches in the Army and was one of the first tourists in Antarctica, having been invited there by the USN. This trip, which included New Zealand and the Phoenix and Fiji Islands, resulted in his previous book: *Antarctica: Land of Frozen Time.*